Stephen Scheding wrote *A Small Unsigned Painting* over a period of almost five years. During that time he also wrote and illustrated three childrens' books: *Uncle Mick's Magic Trick (for getting rid of monsters)* in 1995; *Ten Thousand Sheep (get driven home)* in 1997; and *King Gilbert (the indolent)*, to be published in 1998.

Stephen lives in Sydney with his wife and their son.

A Small Unsigned Painting

STEPHEN SCHEDING

V
VINTAGE

This project has been assisted by the Commonwealth Government through the Australia Council, its art funding and advisory board.

A Vintage Book
published by
Random House Australia Pty Ltd
20 Alfred Street, Milsons Point, NSW 2061
http://www.randomhouse.com.au

Sydney New York Toronto
London Auckland Johannesburg
and agencies throughout the world

First published by Random House Australia in 1998

National Library of Australia
Cataloguing-in-Publication Data

Scheding, Stephen, 1946–.
A small unsigned painting.

ISBN 0 09 183647 6.

I. Title.

A823.3

Cover design by Yolande Gray
Typeset by Asset Typesetting Pty Ltd, Sydney
Printed by Griffin Press Pty Ltd, Adelaide

10 9 8 7 6 5 4 3 2 1

for Sophia

ACKNOWLEDGEMENTS

I have received more than generous support for this book from all those involved. While writing it I was constantly amazed by strangers rallying to support my quest no matter how bizarre they may have thought it was. I would like to thank the dozens of people who are referred to by name in the book and the many who helped who aren't mentioned—especially all my friends who listened so patiently and reflectively throughout my journey.

Invaluable support was received from staff at Joel's, Sotheby's, Christie's, the Mitchell Library, the Art Gallery of NSW, Telecom (now Telstra), the Department of Imaging, Westmead Hospital, the Documents Examination Unit, NSW Police Service, the NSW Department of Education and Training from which I took leave to write, and the other institutions referred to throughout the book.

In particular I must thank the families of Lloyd Rees and Embrey Crawford as well as Frank McDonald, my mentor way back in the 1960s. Without their help there would be no book.

ILLUSTRATIONS

All images by Lloyd Rees are reproduced courtesy of Alan and Jan Rees; the Shepparton Art Gallery gave permission to reproduce Margaret Preston's *Edward's Beach, Balmoral*; the Art Gallery of NSW gave permission to reproduce John Banks' *The Road to the Beach*, Roland Wakelin's *Synchromy in Orange Major* (copyright courtesy of Judith Murray), Lloyd Rees's *Old Boats Wollstonecraft Bay* and a detail of the de Maistre room; the reproduction of Roy de Maistre's *Flowerpiece* is courtesy of Sotheby's (copyright of de Maistre's work courtesy of Mrs Belinda Price and Mrs Caroline Walker, England); the Australian War Memorial gave permission to reproduce Will Dyson's lithograph *Compensation*; King Street in the 1920s (photograph by W. J. Hall) is reproduced courtesy of the Mitchell Library from a glass negative located by Alan Davies, Curator of Photographs, State Library of NSW; and the photograph of the painting of John Banks by Lawson Balfour is reproduced courtesy of the Banks' family. The *Sydney Morning Herald* article is reproduced courtesy of the *Sydney Morning Herald* and Susan Wyndham. Lloyd Rees's *Old Barn* is in the Manly Art Gallery and his *Villa Medici, Rome,* is in the New England Regional Gallery. Paintings and drawings illustrated but not listed above are in private collections and were photographed variously by 3 Stroke (Catherine Stack, John O'Malley), and Christopher Shain. Sources for black and white photographs not referred to above are given in the captions.

CONTENTS

PREFACE

A few years ago, after twenty-five years of collecting Australian paintings, I decided to put virtually my entire collection, consisting of about 100 works, up for auction at Sotheby's in Sydney.[1] At the time I had been diagnosed as an incurable collector. Collecting had become an addiction. My particular narcotic was collecting and researching paintings by lesser-known Australian artists.

The images I collected tended to be on the quirky, 'cerebral' side. I was particularly interested in artists working in Sydney between the wars who appeared to be covertly expressing the 'modern', psychological spirit of the times while working stylistically within a realist tradition imposed by the current, conservative forces. The collection was also atypical in that it included more female artists than male artists. The art historian and critic Joanna Mendelssohn once kindly wrote in a *Sydney Morning Herald* review of a small exhibition I had organised, that 'one of the pleasures of observing Stephen Scheding over the years is his ability to winkle out quality works by artists who are usually seen as mere footnotes in the canon of art history'.[2]

If this sounds somewhat altruistic on my part, I

must also point out that such works had been relatively inexpensive to purchase. While collecting art is often associated with wealth and glamour, my collection had been put together using a fairly ordinary income. And, whenever I was faced with a choice between a brand new car and art, the latter always seemed to win and I would stick with my ancient, dilapidating station wagon.

The reason for my decision to off-load the collection was that my life had become rather crowded. I was also working full-time as a psychologist, as well as writing occasional articles on art and illustrating on a freelance basis. I needed more time to complete projects which had been on the back burner for years. Something in my life had to go.

So, I decided I would no longer collect paintings. I would rid myself and be free of this collecting disease by going cold turkey.

For about eighteen months after the Sotheby's auction, I was liberated from that morbid, obsessional behaviour common to addicts. I even thought I was cured. The psychologist had healed himself. I continued to look at paintings but without being overwhelmed by an uncontrollable urge to own one of them. Hence, I no longer had the compulsion to immerse myself in time-consuming research.

And then, I saw a small, unsigned painting ...

Friday, 16 April, 1993

I first see the painting hanging amongst a thousand
others at the viewing of a Joel's auction in the
Malvern Town Hall, Melbourne. I am on a holiday
from Sydney with my wife, a film director. She has a
meeting related to her latest project and, trustingly,
has left me to my own devices.

The Joel's painting auctions had been, in my
manic-collective days, my favourite painting auctions.
They are agreeably down-market from Sotheby's and
Christie's auctions which are often held at the same
time. Joel's is a buyers' market rather than a sellers'
market. Out of the thousand paintings at a Joel's
auction there is a good chance that a collector might
make at least one discovery: a painting which might
be incorrectly catalogued by the auctioneer and
worth much more than estimated, at least in
aesthetic terms.

My first real find at Joel's[1] had been a small oil
on canvas which had been incorrectly catalogued as
being by an A. M. Moore.[2] But on inspecting the
reverse of the picture, I found a faint, pencilled title
followed by the inscription 'E. M. M.' This turned

out to be the initials of Eva M. Mofflin. The only reference to Mofflin in the literature is as a student of the National Gallery School in Melbourne in 1882—but fellow students of that year included Arthur Streeton, Phillips Fox, Rupert Bunny, Frederick McCubbin, Emily Meston, Josephine Muntz-Adams and May Vale.

This brilliant little work by Mofflin, titled *St Kilda from the Red Bluff*, appears to be in a style precursory to Australian impressionism. It was probably painted on an outing with the other, now famous, members of her class who had formed a sketching club in the early 1880s. This information can be deduced from the frame which is original and has a patent stamp on it. The frame appears to have been designed so that the small stretched canvas could be removed and taken on an outing, and later replaced in the frame when the artist returned. Original frames, as well as their inscriptions, can tell all sorts of tales.

If there were a few hundred known works by Mofflin of the quality of *St Kilda* her story would be vastly different but virtually no other works by her are known. Eva's story will probably end here. Her fate seems to be an extreme example of what happened to gifted female artists. She is likely to remain a footnote in Australian art history.

Meanwhile, back at Joel's on the 16th of April, when I come to lot 692, I stop. It is a small oil painting crammed in amongst a nineteenth century portrait, a limp watercolour landscape, a late-modern, cubist-inspired cityscape and an Aboriginal dot painting. It is not signed. I check the catalogue and find that it is described as 'Australian School, *Beachside Villas*, oil on board, 14 by 29 centimetres' and estimated at $100 to $200.

My first response, which comes with an exhilarating rush, is: *early Lloyd Rees*. But this couldn't be right. I haven't seen enough early Reeses. How could I know? When I think about it for a moment, I seem to recall that his early, 'immature' work *varies* too much in style to be able to easily pick an unsigned one ... And yet ...

I tell myself to relax and stay calm. I repeat to myself that there is no law which says I *must* have this painting. I am no longer a collector. I have given that away. Today I am just looking. One 'drink' could plunge me again into the dark world of research-oholism. On the other hand the painting is estimated at only $100 to $200 ...

The painting is of a house on the foreshore of a bay or harbour. In front of the house is a red boatshed. In front of the boatshed is an ambiguous shape, possibly a boat or a ramp. The house is partly obscured by foliage on the right of the painting. On the left, a tall tree emerges from shrubs and wavers against the sky above the horizon line which is exactly halfway up the painting. A headland can be seen on the extreme left. My initial 'flash' that it might be an early Lloyd Rees, perhaps early 1920s, is probably on the basis of the thickly but confidently modelled oil paint, the quiet mood and the rather intimate nature of the subject. Rees's love of quiet spots around Sydney Harbour is well documented. The fact that it is small is also a good sign as most of Rees's oil landscapes prior to 1940 were similar in scale. There is also something about the shape of the side of the house which has triggered something in me—perhaps some resemblance to an early Rees drawing seen long ago but now buried in my subconscious.

However, the 'flash' must also be questioned in the light of the fact that Rees's oils from the early 1920s are extremely rare. He is known to have painted over early work and few examples appear to have survived. Later in the decade, he virtually

abandoned oil painting altogether in favour of drawing before returning to oils in the mid-1930s. The
problem is I have not actually seen enough 1920s
oils by Rees.

I do know that his early oils were often experimental and not always well received by his colleagues. He once overheard his fellow artists talking
about his work and learnt some home truths that he
described as 'pungent'.[3] During the 1920s his oils
were not considered professional enough to be
included in the Society of Artists exhibitions. Even
when he was elected a member of the Society in
1932, at a time when he was working exclusively on
drawing, he heard the President remark 'I hope he
doesn't submit his paintings.'[4]

Could this boatshed painting be an early, explor-
atory work in which Rees's better-known features are
just beginning to emerge?

Why have I jumped to the conclusion that it is
Sydney Harbour and not, say, a Melbourne subject?
If it was painted by Rees in the 1920s then it has to
be a Sydney painting because that's where he was
living. And this is a Melbourne auction with a
predominance of work by Melbourne artists!

Well, the topography, or what can be seen of it,
looks like Sydney. The buildings appear to be Feder-
ation in style. I recall the hand-coloured linocuts of
Margaret Preston of the 1920s which feature such
buildings with their distinctive red roofs[5] around
Middle Harbour and the shoreline of Sydney
Harbour itself. Also, I grew up on the Lower North
Shore in the 1950s and sailed small boats on the
Harbour before many waterfront Federation houses
were demolished.

And then, very generally speaking, Sydney

painting differs from Melbourne painting. This is possibly caused in part by differences in the weather. For example, Streeton's Melbourne paintings of the 1880s often seem mellower and hazier than the sharper, clearer Sydney harbourscapes of the mid-1890s, painted after he had become acquainted with Sydney light during several sojourns here. But the character of the light is not the only difference in the art of the two cities. In Melbourne, people (artists included) tend to stay indoors more, around warm fires or over long dinners, conversing, reflecting and introspecting through long, squally winters. Melbourne art as a result tends to be more cognitive, more intellectualised, and often angrier. In Sydney we spend more time outdoors, enjoying the sun and the Harbour. Sydney art tends to be more sensual. In fact, an interesting variation of this is Rees's famous *The Road to Berry*, 1947, a dark painting in which the contours of the landscape suggest the female form.[6]

As I think about this theory, I wonder whether it is too far fetched. As I stare at the boatshed painting it brazenly mocks my doubt: the tree on the left becomes a phallic symbol and the doorway to the boatshed becomes its counterpart ...

I turn my attention to the frame around this potentially potent little painting. It seems contemporaneous with the painting and appears to be from the 1920s. I have seen many similar frames on traditional paintings. Many of these have had the label of the framer S. A. Parker on the reverse. Indeed such frames are often referred to generically in the trade as 'Parker frames'.

I discreetly remove the painting from the wall and inspect the back. It looks like the painting has been in this frame for a very long time without ever having been removed, confirming that it is almost certainly the original frame. But it does not have

S. A. Parker's nor any other framer's label affixed. If
the painting did show signs of having been removed
from its frame, it might have meant that someone, in
recent times, had had a go at attributing it and probably failed. For a researcher, this painting is in a
virginal state.

It is stuck in the frame by rusted nails and green-
coloured tape. There is an old pencilled inscription
which reads '*Suburban Scene*, 8930' (a framer's stock
number? Or previous auctioneer's or gallery owner's
record?) and the name 'Booth' or 'Book' or 'Boon'.
There is also a sticker with a serrated edge, the type
used for numbering paintings in art exhibitions
decades ago. The number on the sticker is 22.

There is a length of brass picture-hanging wire
that has been bunched and tangled up, so as to hide
it behind the painting. This wire looks original since
its strands have been stressed and have started to
separate in places. The bunching of the wire may
have been done hurriedly when the painting was
hung in the auction room. But from the numerous
old kinks in the wire, I can see that the functional
length of the wire has changed several times over the
years. Originally the painting would have hung from
a picture rail. From the full length of the wire I can
deduce that it would have hung about half a metre
below the picture rail in a Victorian or Federation
house.

As part of the tangle, there is also, a shorter and
newer length of wire with a loop at each end. The
addition of this piece of wire may have coincided
with a move by the owner to a house or an apartment which didn't have picture rails. Then the painting would simply have been hung, perhaps, from a
nail in a wall. None of the wire has been put there by
Joel's staff who use eyehooks screwed into the top
centre of the frames to hang the paintings onto their
auction screens.

This tangle of wire seems to indicate a tangled past: many owners or a number of changes of address. Either of which may make it difficult to accurately establish the provenance or history of the painting.

There is nothing at all on the back of the painting which immediately identifies the artist.

I replace the painting on the wall and look at it again. The frame, apart from the surface dirt, is in surprisingly good condition. Usually frames with these gesso or plaster mouldings become chipped over the years, but this frame has not. Perhaps it has not had so many changes of address, or else it has been transported with tenderness.

The surface of the painting is extremely grubby—a good sign, because together with some fine, barely detectable age-cracks, it rules out any sort of 'fake' theory. To make completely sure I tap the surface lightly with my fingernails. The sound this makes is a sharp click. Oil paint takes years to become perfectly dry and, eventually, as resilient as enamel. If an oil painting has been painted recently, the sound is softer and duller. Another way of telling if an oil painting is recent or old is to try to stick a pin into an out-of-the-way edge of the paint. If the pin sinks in, it is new paint. If it cannot penetrate the surface because it is too brittle then it is usually quite old. But I do not have to stick in a pin. I can tell that the painting is decades old—the same period as its original frame.

Working out the artist of an unsigned painting often involves listing all the possible artists and eliminating them. So who else could have painted the boatshed painting? The actual auction is not until the 21st. I have a few days in which to think about it. I will

come back to the auction viewing tomorrow for
another look.

Saturday, 17 April

I sense that the artist has devoted time to recording
what appears to be a private and intimate place.

While the paint has been carefully built up and
modelled, the artist has still taken some inspired
risks. The line of blue in the centre, suggesting the
bay or Harbour in the background, may at first appear
too high, and yet it sets up an intriguing ambiguity
which holds our interest as we consider the swelling
of this stretch of water (is it threatening to 'over-
flow'?) and then the possibilities of the harbourscape
in the distance beyond. In fact, it is probably this
deftly applied line of blue, a line which will always
appear unsettled, that has initially led me to suspect
that the painter is one with an above average gift.
There is a gentle curve to the horizon, suggesting
the world beyond, perhaps even hinting at a theme
of universality of experience—a theme which I think
helps give Rees's 1930s and '40s 'curvilinear' oils
their greatness.

The painting of the trees on the left is deft. The
foliage is difficult to hold in focus, indicating a
decent breeze. The sky, too, seems agitated. In fact,
the more I look, the more I sense anxiety in this
painting. This is an unusual quality for an Australian
landscape of this period: they are usually more manly.
Perhaps this is a clue. Is the painting by an artist with
a nervous disposition? (Rees?)

At the water's edge there is an initial sense of
sunny, sheltered calm. But then again, this foreshore
is not necessarily enticing. There is the suggestion of
seaweed and the rocks appear slippery, uneven and
unlikely to provide a firm purchase. For me, an

approach/avoidance sensation is established. I am intrigued by the house and boatshed and feel I would like to explore them, but the artist seems to suggest that physical access will not be easy. On the periphery of the image, the painterly treatment of the sky and trees and foreshore and water (is the tide rising or ebbing?) seems to set up an uneasy resonance, a tension perhaps, as my gaze wanders around the painting trying to locate the focal point once more.

The focal point is, of course, the door to the boatshed. The eye comes to rest there, and it plays a key role in my enjoyment of the painting. It evokes a sense of mystery or of anticipation. Human activity is implied but in another time frame. I remember being struck by something that the art historian Renee Free wrote about this in relation to Rees. Something about his intensely meditative method of painting and the way it suggests the passage of time.[1]

The composition and balance of the picture are fairly precise. The verticals created by the trees, fence posts, chimney, windows and door, are set at right angles to the horizon, roofs, water, rocks and railings thus emphasising the solidity of the subject and locking in the timelessness of the experience of exploring such a scene. But this grid composition is not typical of Lloyd Rees's best-known landscapes where the whole feel is of roundedness, as if the landscape has been moulded and baked. Can I see any of this in the boatshed painting? Is it an early work, and the slightly curved horizon a sign of things to come? On the other hand, I seem to recall that a series of drawings by Rees of Sydney University published around 1920 have static, grid-like compositions.

Stylistically, there is nothing overtly avant-garde about the picture. The style seems to be loosely related to the Salon style which was dominant in Australia around the First World War. This style is considered conservative today but was the height of fashion around 1920 and regarded by many then as 'modern'. But not 'modern' in the sense we use the term today where it is reserved for more distinctly experimental styles. There is no evidence of the artist of the boatshed painting holding a particular aesthetic theory although, perhaps, there may be some awareness of the painterly techniques of Dattilo-Rubbo and his students—a style with which Rees was familiar. Rubbo's students included Grace Cossington Smith, Tempe Manning and Roland Wakelin from 1915 to 1919. Most art historians associate these artists, along with Roy de Maistre, with the 'coming of modernism' in Sydney.

I will think more about whether the boatshed painting is 'traditional' or 'modernist' in style, but at this stage I am impressed by the feeling that it is the individual honesty of this picture which distinguishes it. Goodness knows what other qualities will emerge when it has an expert clean. That is, if I can buy it.

I make the decision. I'm going to bid!

Tuesday, 20 April

I have taken photographs and returned to Sydney. Back to my day job, and to do some research in the attic late at night before the sale tomorrow.

I ask myself: am I talking myself into the Rees theory? Am I suffering from a case of pathological wish-fulfilment? I have always loved his work and regard him as one of the best painters to have worked in this country. I am aware that I have been seduced to an extent by the Great Romantic Artist story which surrounds him, but nevertheless, I still harbour a desperate desire to own one of his works. Even if I could afford one, it would be hard to choose:

one of the large, divinely detailed Sydney Harbour drawings from the early 1930s? A Werri landscape of the 1940s? A bush and rock painting of the 1960s? Or a Turneresque Sydney Harbour painting of the 1980s? Each new phase built on earlier ones so that when he came to paint the later masterpieces, which almost appear to be poured or tossed onto their canvases, they came as a result of years of obsessive, painstaking craftsmanship directed at the single goal of capturing the essence and character—the soul—of the Australian landscape. And, ultimately perhaps, creating a metaphor for the Australian psyche?

It is not hard to be impressed by the prodigious feat of someone persevering with a focused, personal vision through the ups and downs of a life. And Rees lived to ninety-three, painting nearly blind almost until the end.

But where did it begin? Is lot 692 a part of the beginning?

I search through publications on Rees including Renee Free's excellent 1972 monograph.[1] This includes a fairly extensive but not exhaustive catalogue raisonné of Rees's work. The illustrations of the few known 1920s oil paintings are mostly small black and white illustrations. There is however a large, colour illustration of *An Old Barn, Parramatta, 1924.* It appears to be typical of Rees's paintings of the mid-1920s. A similar modelling of paint is evidenced in places. However, the lines are generally sharper, the light contrasts greater, and it appears to be more detailed and, technically, more accomplished than the boatshed painting. From 1925, Rees strengthens these qualities. If the boatshed painting *is* by Rees then I think it must be earlier than 1924. And since

Rees was painting overseas in 1923, it may be earlier than 1923.

Switching to my collection of auction catalogues I find that an oil painting, *The White Horse*, 19 by 16.5 centimetres (sold at Sotheby's, March 1988), has outlines which are less linear than the mid-1920s Parramatta paintings. I suspect that it is earlier. As with the boatshed painting there is a distinctive technique where one area of paint meets another. In the boatshed painting, where the white/blue of the sky meets the green of the trees on the left, it actually overlays it, which seems to add spontaneity and life to the subject through an interplay of the transparent and opaque areas.

Also sold at Sotheby's (October 1985) is *Near Old Cremorne Wharf, Mosman Bay*. A catalogue note states that the back of the frame is 'inscribed in pencil by Dr Rees, with a description of the location of the painting, dating it to circa 1918'. The illustration of this oil shows it to be decidedly different in style to Rees's work a few years later, being composed of an all-over dabbing of large, squarish brushstrokes. This is evidence that Rees's early style was changing significantly in the relatively short period from 1918 to the early 1920s—that is, during the time when the boatshed painting may have been done.

While I am looking at dozens of images by Rees, I am still thinking of who else might have painted it and I am still stumped.

My wife, Sophia, has stayed on in Melbourne and is prepared to slip off to Joel's and bid for me. I attempt to explain to her why I want the painting so badly. She sighs over the phone, feigning (I think) stoic resignation to my lapse. I insist on instructing her about how to bid, vaguely mumbling an out-rageously high upper limit. She begins to sound seriously anxious. I reassure her that her presence in the auction room as a dark mystery woman will probably confuse other bidders and the painting will be knocked down to her for next to nothing.

My final piece of helpful advice is: 'If the auc-tioneer doesn't see you bidding, create a huge scene.' Sophia signs off with a phrase that I have become familiar with over the past fifteen years: 'Stephen, what *does* go on in your head half the time?'

I am in Sophia's hands.

Wednesday, 21 April

When I look at the photographs again I am nowhere near as sure that the painting is by Rees. But I do know that it is a work of some quality and still feel that I have seen others similar. I continue browsing through my library and wait for Sophia to call.

The first Australian art book that I ever bought was Bernard Smith's *Australian Painting*.[1] Published in 1962 it is still one of the best general texts on Australian art. I bought my copy in a second-hand bookshop in the late 1960s when I found myself suddenly working for an art gallery and needed to do a bit of cramming. Later, in 1968, I was reinvig-orated when I read Robert Hughes's *The Art of Australia*.

Over the years, as I have become more immers-ed in Australian art, my library has grown and now a computer is needed to keep track of information. There are over 2500 references on disk which are

mainly books or monographs on individual artists,
newspaper or magazine articles and the more
extensive catalogues put out by public or commercial
galleries. This number does not include the general
reference books on Australian art, history and related
fields. To find information in these books I use an
incredibly helpful publication titled *Australian
Artists' Index—A biographical index of Australian
artists, craft workers, photographers and architects*
compiled by Jan McDonald.[2] This is the Australian
art researcher's bible.

In all of the vast documentation on Australian
art there is very little reference to the sort of exercise
in which I am now engaged. Art students, historians,
critics and biographers only tend to write and
theorise about artworks where the attributions are
not in question. Since 1971, over 230 Fourth Year
Fine Arts students at the Power Institute of Fine Art
have written approximately 1300 essays and theses[3]
and of these only a couple of titles appear to be
about authenticating or attributing a work of art.[4]

In 1984, the Saleroom Correspondent for the
Australian Financial Review, Terry Ingram, did a
devilish thing.[5] He reported the progress of someone
taking a painting, which Terry considered problematic, around the major Australian public galleries for
appraisal. The subject of the painting bore a relationship with Tom Roberts's *The Flower Sellers* circa
1895. This famous Roberts painting had been stolen
in 1976 from the Manly Art Gallery but recovered
by police in 1982. Now, the problematic painting
had been made to look older than it was—in fact
Terry Ingram felt that it had a certain stylistic and
technical affinity with the signed work of the
contemporary painter Bill Blundell who had
admitted previously to painting what he called
'innuendos': works in the style of the Australian
impressionists of the 1890s. At any rate, the painting

was of recent origin. In other words, it was a recent fake, almost certainly designed to deceive.

The appraisals of this painting by staff at the public galleries varied considerably. One curator thought that it was painted between 1890 and 1910 and possibly by Ethel Carrick Fox or Charles Conder or even Charles Tindall: the painting had an inscription on the reverse which appeared to refer to 'the Tindall estate' (although this was almost certainly bogus). Another thought it was the work of a student of the 1890s Heidelberg School but not necessarily contemporaneous. Others thought that it was an early copy (1920s to 1940s) of the Roberts painting and yet another opinion was that it was a turn-of-the-century European work. The story is probably a little unfair on the galleries since the painting may have been examined by inexperienced staff. One could, of course, cite examples of truly brilliant scholarship by curators.[6] But nevertheless, the story serves to show what a tricky area this is.

Incidentally, the thieves who stole Roberts's *The Flower Seller* from the Manly Art Gallery in 1976 also stole the gallery's *An Old Barn, Parramatta*, the oil painted by Lloyd Rees in 1924. The stolen Rees eventually found its way into the hands of the Melbourne art dealer Dr Joseph Brown who didn't realise it was stolen. A newspaper report of the incident stated that although the painting was signed 'Rees', Dr Brown was not sure from the style that it *was* by Rees.[7] He contacted the artist who told him the whole story and the painting was returned to the Manly Art Gallery. The fact that Dr Brown, an experienced dealer, was not able to definitely identify a Rees painting of the 1920s even though it was signed emphasises the difficulty of the task at hand.

However, some art experts in Australia have a true gift for accurately attributing unsigned paintings. In the 1970s I showed Daniel Thomas, the doyen of

Australian art curators, a large unsigned watercolour
painting of figures on the deck of a ship in rough
seas. Daniel immediately suggested the possibility of
the artist being Henry Silkstone Hopwood.

At that time Daniel was a curator at the Art
Gallery of NSW. (Later he went to the National
Gallery of Australia before becoming Director of the
Art Gallery of South Australia.) In the bowels of the
Art Gallery of NSW was a shipboard painting by
Hopwood titled *Dinner in the Fo'c'sl*. It was at that
time the only signed Australian work known by
Hopwood, an Englishman who spent only a couple
of years in Australia. In the 1970s his work was
mainly known through titles in the Art Society of
NSW exhibitions and because he is recorded in the
literature as having had some influence on the Australian impressionists in Sydney in the early 1890s.
Daniel's attribution was based on almost instant-
aneously eliminating other possibilities and an almost
prescient knowledge of Hopwood's work. Over the
years a few other Hopwoods have appeared on the
market and on stylistic grounds the attribution
stands even more firmly.

But even at this professional level there is
dispute. In 1988 the art historian Nancy Underhill
questioned the attribution of a painting claimed to
be an 1820s history painting by Augustus Earle.
Trajan Inconsolable after the Battle of Ctesiphon was
being shown in 'The Great Australian Art Exhibition' organised for the Bicentennial by Daniel
Thomas and Ron Radford.[8] How could Augustus
Earle have improved so much, demanded Underhill,
from the time he painted the more primitive *Mrs
Piper and her Children*, supposedly only a couple of
years before?

Late in the afternoon Sophia's call comes through. I realise my palms are sweaty as I pick up the receiver.

Sophia tells me she has bid successfully and acquired the boatshed painting for $340 plus the 10% buyer's commission. She bid passionately if not expertly. I tell her she's fabulous.

Thursday, 22 April

Four-year-old son, Sam, and I collect Sophia and the painting from the airport. The painting is gift-wrapped.

On the way home I ask her what she makes of the painting. She knows a bit about Rees—in fact, she had brought to our relationship her own, sensibly small, collection of artworks which included an etching by Lloyd Rees.

'Well, I'm open-minded,' she says. Then she adds cryptically: 'I'm very interested to see what *you* make of it.'

Much later in the evening I unwrap the painting up in the attic. Then, with razor blade and pliers, I carefully take the painting out of its frame and examine it afresh.

Plenty of authentic dust has accumulated under the old, green tape—which appears to be book-binding tape. It is a couple of centimetres wide and has a texture designed to simulate leather. I have not seen such tape holding an oil painting in its frame. Almost invariably, oils of this period are held in their frames with brown tape or glued brown paper and cardboard.

With the painting out of the frame, I see that the edges of the painting which have been obscured by the lip of the frame are much brighter in colour. That is, the edges have not faded from long-term exposure to sun nor been darkened by yellowing varnish.

The painting is definitely not of recent origin. The inside lip of the frame has traces of paint which indicate that the painting was originally placed in the frame while the surface of the painting was still wet which confirms that the frame is the original one. There are no nail holes or other signs to indicate that this frame ever held another painting. Therefore, any information revealed by the framing and inscriptions must relate to this painting.

No inscriptions nor a signature are immediately revealed on the surface of the painting—although the paint is thick and scumbled and it gives lots of promises. But the painting is also dirty. I will have to wait until it is cleaned before being absolutely sure that it is not signed.

What else does close inspection reveal? Well, the windows of the house may be a good clue. The four vertical lines are actually incised in the plywood surface or support, as a guide before adding the paint. Combined with the fact that there is very little paint on the actual windows it also adds depth (and consequently mystery) to them. This incising is a very uncommon device and one which could be looked out for in the work of all possible artists. It is perhaps more likely to have been used by a younger artist developing skills or one who was striving for geometric, architectural correctness of certain features. (Rees in both cases?) Could it be that the artist was more adept at drawing lines on paper and resorted to incising lines while struggling with the less familiar medium of oil paint? (Around 1920 Rees would have been doing far more drawing than painting.)

Something I hadn't noticed before is that the fence posts and railings are out of proportion to the boatshed and house. Their scale works in compositional terms, providing balance to the weight of the buildings—which may be why it took me so long to spot the problem—but, in reality, the railings would be higher than the boatshed door. Perhaps this fact is also indicative of a younger artist at work—one focusing on composition and surface rather than on representing the subject exactly. Or could it be that the cream lines are not fence posts and railings at all, but the outlines of mossy or ivy-clad stone walls designed as windbreaks to protect this waterfront property? This would make sense in architectural as well as compositional terms, but it would mean that the artist has fallen a little short of accurately depicting walls.

And another thing. Whether these structures are walls or posts with railings, the one on the left of the painting seems to generate an optical illusion. The base of the right-hand vertical ends hazily. If we imagine it ending behind greenery on the waterfront rock then the structure runs almost parallel with the front of the boatshed. If we perceive the vertical as ending higher, then the structure might run parallel to the side of the boatshed. Perhaps this adds to the sense of movement, even agitation, around the focal point of the perfectly still doorway of the boatshed.

I also note that there are no curtains in the windows. I have the sense that if the house is occupied, it might be by young men. Or is the painting by an artist who simply did not consider curtains important? A male artist! (Or is that being sexist?) Of course the house could be deserted. Although who would desert a waterfront property on Sydney Harbour? A casualty of the First World War?

The fact that the support of the painting is plywood is not entirely favourable to the Rees theory as he preferred to work on canvas throughout his career. But he is recorded as using plywood to paint on, for example, his *Geraniums* of 1936;[1] and certainly he painted directly onto wooden board in the 1920s, for example, his *Autumn Mist, Parramatta* of 1925.[2] Also, some of his works on canvas painted in the 1920s like *Old Boats, Wollstonecraft Bay,* circa 1920 and *Balmoral,* 1927, were laid down on plywood.[3] Many of the Sydney modernists painted directly on to plywood at this time. Wakelin, de Maistre, Adelaide Perry and Aletta Lewis seemed to use it almost exclusively for their oils between 1926 and 1929. It not only provided a suitable surface but, in a way, also symbolised modernism since it owed its fairly recent existence to mass production.

Rees often preferred to work over existing paint, and the thickness of the paint in the boatshed painting suggests that it may have been built up in this way. It is fairly confidently painted and some of the rhythms which are established seem to be the result of paint below the surface. Rees's friend Roland Wakelin once quoted another friend as saying 'I wish he wouldn't work on them after rigor mortis has set in' when Rees began to paint oils again after his abstinence from circa 1928 to 1934. Wakelin claimed that he did not use this quote derogatively 'but rather in admiration of a painter who will stick at a problem month after month in order to solve it'.[4]

I idly wonder what an X-ray photograph would reveal.

Two elements that are more possible clues are the massing of shapes up to the top of the painting and over to one side of it, and the cypress-like tree to the left. I find examples of Rees's oils from this period which employ the compositional device of massing shapes to one side, which creates intimacy in the foreground. *Afternoon Sunshine, Sydney Harbour*[5] is similar in this respect as are, to a lesser extent, *The White Horse*,[6] *An Old Barn, Parramatta, 1924* and *Coolangatta, 1919*.[7]

The cypress-like tree is often used by Rees, especially in his early drawings and those done in Italy in 1923. His interest in depicting tall trees dates from at least 1915.[8] In the Italian drawings and oils, which are often of cathedrals, the height of these trees reaching upwards as they do lends an air of spirituality to the subject. In other words, trees for Rees are not always a purely compositional thing.

The idea of trees in art being given symbolic meaning probably has its roots in the Garden of Eden with the Tree of Life and the Tree of Knowledge of Good and Evil. Trees may infer the fall and redemption of humankind, rebirth and regeneration following suffering, and so on.[9]

Now, the tree on the left of the boatshed painting is a dominant feature and I am forced to ask whether there might be more to it than just balancing the composition. It reaches upwards but seems to have overtones of disharmony or fragmentation rather than an uplifting spirituality. In fact, the shape is something like a shell exploding, an image which was probably common in illustrations in newspapers during the First World War. I recall a well-known black and white lithograph by the distinguished war cartoonist and illustrator Will Dyson, titled *Compensation*.[10] It shows a digger chatting up a young, smiling French woman. Between them in the background is a tree. But I remember that when I first looked at this image I thought that the tree was a shell exploding. When I locate a reproduction of this lithograph in my library I find that this ambiguous shape is similar to the tree in the boat-shed painting.

I do not think that Dyson, whom Rees knew, is

a candidate as the artist of the boatshed painting—he was almost exclusively a graphic artist. But is it possible that the boatshed painting, painted soon after the Great War, may be communicating something of the psychological effects of the war on life and relationships? Symbolised by the 'watchful' house perhaps?

Could the tree in the boatshed painting be expressing not only the fragmentation of life but the hope of regeneration following the suffering of war?

Does the boatshed itself represent a way of launching a new life?

What of the colours? They appear to be muddier than those normally associated with Rees's known, early work—although it is likely that cleaning will produce a brighter picture.

I track down Rees's description of his first glimpse of Sydney in December 1917 through the porthole of the ship which brought him from Brisbane:

> ... opal-blue water, a band of golden sand [Manly], another of olive-green trees; above them a skyline of coral-pink shimmering against the limpid air.[11]

All of these colours are employed in the boatshed painting.

Norman Carter, who had been a friend of Rees's since the 1920s, wrote in 1938:

> [His] work is not directly painted as a result of momentary impression. It is not topographical in the guide book character of so much landscape

work that is produced. 'Knocking off' sketches is
not a habit of Lloyd Rees. His work is the result
of a deep impression which developed by mature
consideration. The fact that he rarely paints burn-
ing sunlight in open spaces with a slap-dash technique, does not justify the assertion that he is not
typically Australian. The chief claim is that he is
'himself' in his work. He seeks the secluded spot,
a pool in a forest, a quiet inlet of the upper
harbour and patterns of sunlight on rocks and
grass.[12]

Does the boatshed painting foreshadow these
qualities?

I continue to come across references to the
intensity which Lloyd Rees put into his work
throughout his career. I have the impression that he
focused so obsessively on the process of painting that
the finished work takes on a life of its own, somewhat
separate from the landscape on which it was based.
Ironically, this may have been a quality of his early
oils with which his fellow artists had problems. Basil
Burdett, another of Rees's friends, wrote in a 1924
article that Rees has 'a tendency to over-emphasise
intriguing detail at the expense of greater unity'.[13]
Rees's passion for the painting process is apparent in
a magazine article where he is quoted at the age of
eighty-five as saying 'my prayer, if I had one, would
be to work, work, work, and if the inevitable
happens, I hope it happens when I am working'.[14]

I imagine I can see an obsession at work in the
boatshed painting. But does it belong to Lloyd Rees?
And if not, then whose obsession is it?

If Rees was alive today, would the task of
identifying the painter of the boatshed painting be
any easier? Artists are not always infallible at this for
two reasons, their memories or their vanities. The
latter would not have applied to Rees who was the

most humble of people despite his genius but he has admitted to memory lapses. When writing about *Balmoral, 1927* (in, ironically, *An Artist Remembers*) he says 'the small painting entitled *Balmoral* is something of a mystery to me. I had not the vaguest idea of doing it …'[15]

My next step is to contact Rees's family. While an artist's family may not necessarily be recognised experts on the artist's work, they may have lived with it throughout their lives. They can have a highly attuned sense of the authenticity of any works shown to them, a sense which has developed almost through a process of osmosis. They can intuitively sniff out what does not fit into the artist's oeuvre, what would be discordant on the family walls. I am also aware that the Rees family are in the process of creating a catalogue raisonné, which may have a great deal of information not otherwise available.

But before I meet the family and show them the boatshed painting, I would like to be more fully prepared … be armed with as many clues as possible … eliminate as many suspects as I can …

Friday, 23 April

If the frame of the boatshed painting is a 1920s frame, and the painting was put into the frame while still wet, this means that the painting is 1920s as well. Is it a purely traditional painting of the period, or could it be by an artist who was associated with the emerging modernist movement in Sydney in the 1920s? How exactly does Lloyd Rees fit in? In the early 1920s was Rees's work traditional or modern—and just how trite is this dichotomy?

Who are the other suspects who might have painted the boatshed painting?

What were the 1920s like in Sydney? Were they really 'roaring' as the title of Jack Lindsay's book implies?[1] Or does 'The Terrible Twenties' better describe it? The latter is Humphrey McQueen's chapter heading in his *Social Sketches of Australia*[2] where he says that the 1920s are often looked on by historians as 'unproductive and dull'. McQueen agrees that there were barren patches, 'most of all in the creative arts'. But could that be right?

There certainly must have been great anguish following the deaths of around 60,000 Australian men in the 1914–1918 war.[3] Many survivors themselves suffered the loss of arms, legs or sight— not to mention mates. Then there was the influenza pandemic following the war which killed 12,000 people in Australia by the end of 1919 and over 20 million world-wide. And then there was the conscription debate which bitterly divided many families, as well as the community, during the war and for long afterwards.

The 1920s also seem to be the moment in history when marriages began to end because of the decision of a partner and not simply because of the death of a partner.

The effects of all this could not be glossed over for ever. I have a secret, crazy theory that in a global, psychological sense the onset of the Great Depression in the late 1920s gave inevitable form to natural emotions that may have been denied. There was an unfulfilled need to grieve in the 1920s and, in the end, it was easier to grieve about loss of jobs and money.

Virtually all the published accounts of art in Sydney in the 1920s are retrospective. The most comprehensive recording of most aspects of the period, is probably William Moore's two volume

Story of Australian Art. It is chronologically the
closest to the period, having been published in 1934.
In this history, information about artists now
regarded as traditional tends to swamp information
about the so-called modern movement. A fair
reflection of the state of the arts at the time.

Moore records that the origin of the modern
movement began when ...

> Wakelin, Roi de Mestre [sic], and Grace
> Cossington Smith [and Tempe Manning and Neil
> Gren], all students [influenced by the painter and
> teacher Dattilo-Rubbo at the time] began to
> understand something about modern art from
> Norah Simpson, who brought out [from
> England] some reproductions in 1913.[4]

Later art historians have often seized upon this and
plotted their time-lines of the modernist, or at least
post-impressionist, period from this date. (Interestingly, in almost all histories following Moore's, the
modernists swamp the traditionalists.) But Dattilo-
Rubbo was using 'divisionist' brushstrokes[5] dating
from his overseas trip in 1907[6] and Norah Simpson
was simply one of the catalysts for the accelerated
introduction of these Post-Impressionist techniques
and their application to domestic subjects as well as
to landscape.

These divisionist brushstrokes of Rubbo and his
students caused a ruckus when their oils were
exhibited annually with the Royal Art Society from
1915 to 1919. In 1916, when the R. A. S. Hanging
Committee refused to hang a work by Wakelin,
Rubbo challenged Charles Tindall, a member of the
Committee, to a duel with pistols, swords or
fisticuffs.[7]

An even greater ruckus was caused when the
paintings of Wakelin and Roy de Maistre were shown

at their 'Colour in Art' exhibition at Gayfield Shaw's Art Salon, Penzance Chambers, 29 Elizabeth Street, Sydney which opened on 8 August, 1919, and included abstract paintings as well as landscapes. The exhibition arose out of an interest in the relationship between colour and music. It also followed upon de Maistre's professional involvement with Dr C. G. Moffitt at Kenmore Hospital. Moffitt had engaged de Maistre to help devise colour schemes as a form of therapy for shell-shocked soldiers and 'nerve cases'. The 'Colour in Art' exhibition also included 'a series of colour schemes for interiors; the perspective drawings were done by Lloyd Rees, Wakelin's roommate at the Smith and Julius firm of commercial art'.[8]

When Rees arrived in Sydney from Brisbane in 1917 he first lived at Balmoral for a few months, then in Woollahra and then, in 1918, he moved to Waverton, very near Roland and Mrs Wakelin, who became lifelong friends of his. During 1918 and 1919 Rees was a frequent visitor to the Wakelins' home and first saw what he later described as 'the first essays in Cubist and Abstract painting ever done in Australia'.[9] There he met de Maistre who was also a violinist in the Verbruggen Orchestra. (Adrian Verbruggen was Director of the Conservatorium of Music.) Rees later wrote: 'It soon became evident that the Wakelin/de Maistre collaboration would sooner or later have to find public expression.'[10] Which it did, in the famous 1919 exhibition. In *Roy de Maistre—The Australian Years 1894–1930* Heather Johnson writes that 'Lloyd Rees remembers the opening as the biggest and most exciting opening ever for an art exhibition in Sydney, attended by almost 700 people'.[11] While Rees was impressed with the experiments of de Maistre and Wakelin, his own paintings never followed their overtly modernist directions.

Of the landscapes exhibited in the 1919 exhibition only three appear to have survived today: two de Maistres and one Wakelin. They are of harbourside buildings around Berry's Bay near where Wakelin was living at this time. These works pulsate with modernist colour: pinks, purples, oranges, yellows ... and are therefore very different in mood to the boatshed painting. And yet there is an architectural similarity in the 'blocky' waterfront buildings.

While I think 'Modern' painting is about more than just painterly techniques, the term 'traditional' is perhaps less contentious. In the Australian context it has often been used denigratingly and even interchanged with the phrase 'gum tree painting'. In terms of the 1920s it probably means painting which was part of a fairly long-established tradition, such as Salon or Academic painting or even impressionism since, by then, impressionism was some fifty years old (at which point it is sometimes referred to as neo-impressionism to distinguish it from the 'real McCoy').

Almost all professional Australian artists had travelled to Europe after about 1900 and most aspired to exhibit with the Paris Salon and the Royal Academy in London. The accepted style of these institutions was dominant in Europe through to the 1920s and 1930s despite the rise of the more avant-garde forms of modernism. In Australia in the 1920s, the Salon style was generally considered modern. It was epitomised by works which were languid, romantic, sensual, and tasteful.[12] The boatshed painting shows an awareness of this style in terms of its sensuality, although it also seems to be underpinned by deeper, psychological impulses.

The term 'modern' meant different things to those using it in the early 1920s as opposed to those writing retrospective histories of the period today. Nancy Underhill, in *Making Australian Art 1916–1949*, puts it more strongly:

> The majority of present-day art historians have gone off with Don Quixote to search for the definition of Modernism in painting and have yet to return ... That search for categorical definitions must self-destruct because terms such as conservative or modern only firmed as Howard Ashton, Lionel Lindsay, Norman Lindsay, Frank and Margel Hinder, Paul Haefliger, Bernard Smith, John and Sunday Reed [all critics or commentators on the arts] ... tried to position themselves. They all wanted a 'them and us'.[13]

While Underhill nominates a prime mover for her version of modernism in Australian art, namely the publisher and patron Sydney Ure Smith, her main point seems to be that it is misleading to think of art in Sydney in the 1920s merely in terms of 'modern' painting versus 'conservative' or 'traditional' painting. It's not that simple. In 1916, in the middle of the Great War, the first number of Ure Smith's now-famous magazine *Art in Australia* (1916–1942) carried a full-page advertisement for electricity. The heading exhorted the reader to 'Be Modern'. The ad was appealing to the Australian society's desire to be up to date, to be seen as modern. It was attempting to tap into a mood that must have been afoot. The modern movement was being driven home not only by certain artists and struggling art students but, to an extent, by high-profile business interests. Lloyd Rees was to work for Ure Smith around 1920.

Syd Ure Smith's other great magazine was *The Home* (1920–1942). In the 1920s it became an

icon of fashion, employing artists, photographers
and designers now associated with the modern
movement. There is a wonderful paradox in the
title—the magazine in fact tended to eschew household hints, recipes and other domestic detritus and
its goal seemed to be to take women out of the
home.

One reason for this emphasis may have been due
to the fact that Syd, the magazine's proprietor, did
not have a domestic life. Around 1918 he had left his
wife, the artist Viola Quaife, to 'live in sin' with
Ethel Bickley. Following Ethel's death in 1923 he
became involved with the beautiful and much
younger Hera Roberts, a relationship that lasted
until Syd's death in 1949. Incidentally, Hera created
over fifty covers for *The Home* magazine. But, not
long after Syd's death, she succumbed to depression
and committed suicide.[14]

Interestingly, the fate of her original artwork is
not known. It's possible that her suicide may have
been seen as a 'social disgrace' and the artwork
destroyed by her family in an attempt to obliterate
the memory. Or perhaps it remains hidden in an attic
somewhere. Viola Quaife, Syd's rejected wife,
painted watercolours of superb delicacy and design.
Perhaps because she lost the support of the powerful
Syd—almost a prerequisite for an artist to become
established at the time—she now has no place in any
recorded history of Australian art.

Paul Johnson begins his 800-page populist
history *Modern Times*[15] with the sentence: 'The
modern world began on 29 May 1919 when photographs of a solar eclipse, taken on the island of
Principe off West Africa and at Sobral in Brazil,
confirmed the truth of a new theory of the universe.'
This was Einstein's theory of relativity, which,
according to Johnson, became confused throughout
the world with reletavism: the idea that all

judgements are relative. The idea of certainty went out the window and was replaced, claims Johnson, with a universal sense of unease. What Johnson doesn't mention is that prior to 1919 Einstein had been conducting a secret affair with his cousin Elsa while attempting to control the behaviour of his wife using contracts which read like scientific formulae ('A. You will see to it that (1) my clothes are kept in order; (2) That I am served three regular meals a day in my room', etc).[16] The marriage broke down and Einstein married Elsa on Saint Valentine's Day, 1919. Mrs Einstein no doubt formulated her own theory of relative-ity.

Susan Sontag in her book *Illness as Metaphor*[17] has described how epidemic diseases have been used as metaphors for social disorder[18] and indeed a pamphlet published in Australia in 1919 was titled *The Two Plagues: Infuenza and Bolshevism*.[19] This was, of course, written while the influenza pandemic was raging and just two years after the Russian Revolution which spread the bolshevik 'plague'. Humphrey McQueen in *The Black Swan of Trespass— The Emergence of Modernist Painting in Australia to 1944* cites Sigmund Freud as one of the 'prime movers' for modernism in Australia. And he quotes the 'conservative' Norman Lindsay as saying 'We were all badly infected by Freudianism in the twenties'.[20] He also refers to the 'traditionalist' Hans Heysen's 1934 comments that to laud Picasso and Matisse, was 'utterly foolish'. On the other hand, when he was in Europe, Heysen had been 'very agreeably surprised' by the art of Cezanne, Van Gogh, Seurat and especially Gauguin. Other apparent contradictions abound when trying to get a handle on modernist attitudes or attitudes to modernism in Australia.

Mary Eagle in her book *Australian Modern Painting—Between the Wars 1914–1939*[21] has, as her prime mover, an event rather than a person. Her first chapter is titled 'War'. It opens this way:

> The end of the first world war brought the expectation of widespread change. As well as causing the deaths of millions of people it severed the old way of life. 'Modernism' became the term for a host of new, untried ideas, too many to list but including bolshevism, Freudian Psychology and a new focus on the subconscious, atomic theory, electricity, the automobile and aeroplane, the 'movies', new commercial and advertising practices and the 'new woman'—all of which permeated Australian life and changed it after the war. Thus, the appearance of a modern style in Australian art postwar was a more complicated phenomenon than the isolated discovery of an avant-garde who created it, fought for it and won against the odds. Rather, its advent was accepted in advance by older members of Australian society as part of the widespread change—accepted grudgingly of course, almost as part of the price to be paid for a horrific war. The modern way of life was debated in parliament, preached about from pulpits, editorialised in newspapers and discussed in agony columns. When people argued against modern painting they gave vent to their general fear.

While the boatshed painting is certainly not avant-garde in style, I feel it does reveal an influence of the 'complicated phenomenon' referred to above.

But what else is there about the Sydney art scene in the 1920s which might put the boatshed painting in context?

The Smith and Julius commercial art studio (run by Sydney Ure Smith and Harry Julius) has been described by Rees as being the centre of the Sydney art world in the 1920s. According to Nancy Underhill, Lloyd Rees 'left the most extensive personal account of the Studio's heyday'.[22] Rees worked there from about 1919 until 1923 when he travelled abroad. In *Peaks and Valleys* Rees writes:

> As life at Smith and Julius unfolded, I became aware of my amazing good fortune in being linked with such a place. As well as [Percy] Leason, my colleagues were such distinguished artists as Roland Wakelin, James Muir Auld and Alec Sass, and visitors to the studio included Roy de Maistre, Hans Heysen, Max Meldrum, Arthur Streeton, the Lindsay Brothers and many others. Besides the annual exhibitions of the Society of Artists, we had the almost daily interest of John Young's framing workshop in Little George Street, the nearest thing to the Paris cafe atmosphere in Sydney
> Ure Smith's link with the Society of Artists ... made Smith and Julius, at 24 Bond Street, a focal point for virtually all the important artists in the country.[23]

One of the assignments for the Smith and Julius Studio in the early 1920s was presented by the advertising man George Patterson. Apparently in response to a perceived market resistance to the colour of the Ford motor car—you could have any colour providing it was black—Patterson induced Smith and the artists George Lambert, Thea Proctor, Margaret Preston and John D. Moore to advise Ford on car colours.[24] Contemporary art became integrated into publishing, advertising and life in general. Hence Underhill's thesis.

In *Small Treasures of a Lifetime*, Rees gives a brief history of the early years of the Society of Artists, presided over by Ure Smith, adding: 'In my own case the early success of my early drawings [exhibited in the Society's 1917 exhibition] was not maintained—I did not achieve Society membership for another fifteen years ... One [oil painting] did get into the 1918 exhibition on a casting vote, I believe, but the hanging committee at first refused to hang it.'[25] A discussion had taken place in the offices of Smith and Julius which Rees overheard and learned those 'pungent' home truths.[26] But Rees also cites another reason for the initial rejection: before the exhibition, the painting had developed what is called a 'bloom'. He writes: '... in those days I painted in heavy impasto with copious encrustations of deep blues, reds and yellows.' This technique, he claimed, had caused the blooming or cloudy surface to appear. Before submitting the painting, he had been advised by Percy Leason to rub a cut potato into it in order to remove the bloom. This worked for a while, but by the time the hanging committee saw it, 'every crack and cranny of the painting was a river of white, granulated potato juice'.

When checking the Society's catalogue for 1918, there is in fact no reference to Rees exhibiting that year. He did exhibit two oil paintings in 1919, *Farmhouse* and *Sketch for the Farmhouse,* and it is probably one of these that got the potato treatment. Rees's memory seems to be out by a year which means I may have to continue to double-check little details such as this as my research progresses. (Incidentally, from 1921 to 1928, Rees switched his allegiance to the Royal Art Society.) But the really interesting bit of information from the potato story is that Rees records using 'deep blues, reds and yellows'. These are the main pigments, as well as dark green, that are in the boatshed painting. And the paint is fairly heavily 'encrusted'.

The purpose of my potted history is not only to place Rees, but to look at all the other likely suspects. It seems worth looking at artists who exhibited around 1920 since the boatshed painting is, I believe, of an exhibitable quality. In fact, it has on the reverse a sticker which is probably its exhibition sticker (number 22). Admittedly, what the painting lacks is an exhibition label which it almost certainly should have had if it had been exhibited at the Society of Artists or the Royal Art Society. Nevertheless, an artist exhibiting at one of these societies may also have exhibited at a private art gallery which did not use a label. Hardly any artists exhibited privately who did not also exhibit with the two societies. Therefore running through the society exhibitors is an expedient way of covering all possible exhibiting artists.

Other Sydney artists who exhibited oil paintings at the Society of Artists around 1920 included Albert Collins, John D. Moore, Herbert Gallop, Grace Crowley (now considered a modernist but she did paint traditional landscapes before going to Europe), Alice Creswick, Elioth Gruner, Percy Leason, Robert Campbell and Norman Lloyd—but none of these artists stands out as a distinct possibility: most of them employed the square brushstroke technique without rubbing over the strokes as Rees, for example, is known to have done. Then there are Fred Leist and Percy Lindsay but both are unlikely on stylistic grounds. Norman Carter may be a possible suspect and so too Muir Auld, whose work was admired by Rees in the early 1920s, but I don't have strong feelings about either of them. Like most of the other society exhibitors, they had been painting professionally for up to twenty years. And to me the boatshed painting does not have that look of maturity.

The other art society operating in Sydney at the

time was the Royal Art Society, which was established in 1880. The R. A. S. exhibitors at this time tended to be of the more 'traditional' school. This is of course a simplification because Rubbo and his students first exhibited there. And the 'conservatives'—Hans Heysen, Howard Ashton and Norman and Lionel Lindsay—exhibited with the Society of Artists. But Rees's description of the R. A. S. remains generally correct: 'their exhibitions … retained unity.'[27] The R. A. S. included artists such as James R. Jackson (his views were usually expansive), Henry Hanke, Lance Solomon, Fullwood (painting in a neo-impressionist style in the 1920s), Robert Johnson (square brushstrokes), Penleigh Boyd (shiny if not slick surfaces), Alfred Coffey (usually extremely clean and fresh), J. S. Watkins (vaguely possible), Ernest Buckmaster (surfaces even more so than Penleigh Boyd's), Will Ashton (too systematically neo-impressionist), Charles Bryant, John Salvana, Lance Solomon, Erik Langker (all square brushstrokers), Josef Wolinski, G. Lyall Trindall (oils tend to be chocolate boxy), Lawson Balfour (too much abstract flourishing) and John Banks. Banks was taught and strongly influenced by Balfour and both are really too decorative to be considered as suspects. In fact, none of the above artists really leap out as a definite possibility as the painter of the boatshed painting.

Across the acres of traditional landscape painting strode the flamboyant and enigmatic George Lambert. Lambert, with his close friend, the artist Thea Proctor, supported modernist art and was instrumental in the organisation of the 1926 Contemporary Group exhibition at the Grosvenor Galleries which brought together Wakelin, de

Maistre, Adelaide Perry, Aletta Lewis, Frank Weitzel, Kenneth Macqueen and Joseph Connor. It was the second major group expression of modern art. The decade ended with the return of Grace Crowley, Ann Dangar and Dorrit Black from France who further stimulated the modern movement.

The other main art school in Sydney at the time, apart from Dattilo-Rubbo's, was run by the dominating conservative Julian Ashton—although this description of him is really too rigid because it does not allow for the graduation of a number of modernist painters from his classes. Ashton's great strength was that he insisted upon painters learning their craft, and he tended to focus more on the crime of bad painting than on the crime of modernism. Nevertheless, Lloyd Rees describes Ashton's conniptions at the opening of the 1919 Wakelin/de Maistre exhibition where he at last burst out: 'Mr de Mestre, what I want to know is—*is it beautiful*?' To which de Maistre perkily replied: '*I* think so, Mr Ashton.'[28]

The schools of Rubbo and Ashton trained literally hundreds of artists in Sydney.[29] However, it is possible that the artist of the boatshed painting received minimal or no tuition. This could explain the unusual technique of scoring the surface to position the windows. It is not a technique that would be taught at an art school. It may explain how the style of the painting (or rather, perhaps, the lack of it) does not quite fit with either of the main schools in Sydney, nor for that matter with the styles of influential individuals such as Max Meldrum or Roy de Maistre. Lloyd Rees spent one year at the Brisbane Technical College Art School. In reading his account in *Peaks and Valleys* one gets the impression that Rees's emphasis was on drawing and watercolour, but he does record doing some oils during his period of training.

It is interesting to note the predominance of male artists around 1920, especially those exhibiting with the two male-dominated Societies. Interesting because the majority of students who went through the art schools over the previous forty years were female.[30] The profiles of some professional women artists did emerge as the decade became more prosperous but only to be swamped again in the hard times of the 1930s. Grace Cossington Smith was active around 1920; Ethel Stephens enjoyed a reputation on her return from Paris in about 1922; Margaret Preston and Thea Proctor were becoming more prominent from about 1925. But does the boatshed painting look like it was done by a male or a female? My guess is that it is a masculine painting. And this is not only because there are no curtains. For this reason I decide not to look too closely at the exhibitors in the Society of Women Painters nor the Society of Arts and Crafts where female artists often predominated.

But am I right in thinking that a male artist painted the boatshed painting?

And what of the rest of the art scene?

There was a handful of private art galleries operating in Sydney around 1920. There were Gayfield Shaw's Fine Arts Gallery (in 1917 known as The Art Salon), Farmer's Gallery and Basil Burdett's New Art Salon. Lloyd Rees is recorded as having exhibited at each of these galleries in the early 1920s. A Miss Bouffler sold pictures from the Hotel Australia bookstall around 1918 and advertised work by Lloyd Rees.[31] Given the date, these were probably drawings. Miss Bouffler is not recorded as having given Rees a solo exhibition. Similarly, The Artists' Gallery on the corner of Pitt and Bridge Streets also

listed Lloyd Rees as one of its artists.[32] In their
advertising, he is grouped with artists known
primarily for etchings, so his work offered by The
Artists' Gallery was probably black and white.

Both Swain's and Tyrrell's, as well as selling art
materials, also held art exhibitions—though mainly
of prints. The etcher, Squire Morgan, also sold
prints.

A. W. Albers, Sydney's first successful picture
dealer, who specialised almost exclusively in watercolours, operated around 1920 but is not known to
have sold works by Rees, nor it seems did Miss C. V.
Skewes who ran the Salon of Fine Arts in Castlereagh
Street at the same time. The Macquarie Galleries and
the Grosvenor Galleries were established in the mid-
1920s, as was Rubery Bennett's gallery. The latter
tended to show the more traditional artists while the
Macquarie and Grosvenor supported the younger
modernists. Anthony Hordern and Sons Art Gallery
flourished from 1912 through to 1961.[33]

Will it be possible to link the sticker numbered
'22' to any of the galleries which exhibited Rees
paintings? The New Art Salon, at which Rees
exhibited in 1922, may be worth following up in
particular since its director, Basil Burdett, is referred
to in Rees's autobiographies as also being a close
friend.

Burdett is, in fact, a key personality of the
period. He and Lloyd Rees were mates from Brisbane,
when Burdett worked as a journalist on the *Daily
Mail* before enlisting in the war. (Rees did not enlist
for medical reasons.) Burdett rejoined Rees in
Sydney, sharing a flat with him in Waverton in 1920
to early 1922, and then in 1922 boarded with Rees
at a house named 'Bondo' in Parramatta.

Burdett ran his New Art Salon from about
March 1922[34] to 1924. The address of this gallery
was initially at Vickery's Chambers in Pitt Street but

moved in about July to 219 George Street.[35] He opened the illustrious Macquarie Galleries with John Young in March 1925. In 1931 he left for Europe, a move which heralded the end of his partnership with Young. Burdett returned to Sydney later in 1931 because his wife, Edith, was demanding a divorce. Following the messy divorce, Burdett, distraught, went to Melbourne 'where he joined the *Herald* as a journalist'.[36] In *Early Sydney Moderns* Jean Campbell describes Burdett in 1923 as '… a sensitive and fiery character, with quick intellect and highly developed interest in the arts'.[37]

In a 1980 article on Burdett in *Art in Australia*, Jan Minchin writes that 'those who knew Basil Burdett agree that he was provocative, argumentative and at times aloof, even with his friends'.[38] She then quotes Lloyd Rees as saying 'But … he is still a "presence" in my life—such was his dominating personality.' One gets the impression that Lloyd was a little in awe of Basil. In an article in *Art and Australia* in 1975[39] Rees describes Burdett as 'direct' and goes on to say that 'at heart I believe he was very gentle even to the point of sentimentality but his terrible experiences as a stretcher-bearer in World War One called for a protective armour, as it were, against the hard facts of life. His love of art was deep and found expression in fine writing.'

In the early 1930s Basil was befriended in Melbourne by the writers Vance and Nettie Palmer. Nettie Palmer wrote that 'he knows more about painting than any man in the country … But he can't make a significant stroke with a brush.' She went on to add that he was not likely to find fulfilment in music or writing either. He was, she felt, a 'hopelessly unhappy being'. Her hope was that he would use 'his keen intelligence and perception as a critic and entrepreneur'. This was perceptive of Nettie. Apart from his involvement in Macquarie Galleries, it is the 1939 Melbourne Herald Exhibition of French and British Contemporary Art organised and brought to Australia by Burdett that he is remembered for today. His art criticism is still mostly buried in periodicals, but what has emerged shows him to have outstanding powers of perception.

In *Rebels and Precursors* Richard Haese quotes one of Burdett's closest friends, Daryl Lindsay, describing Burdett as 'the strangest mixture of afflictions and inferiority complexes that ever was'. Haese claims that his emotionalism was compounded for Lindsay by another flaw: 'a certain weakness of character that I don't like.' Haese continues: 'That "weakness" was homosexuality, which Daryl Lindsay abhorred to the same degree as his brother Norman.'[40] Burdett died in a plane crash in the Second World War during the evacuation of Singapore.

What about framers in the 1920s? Who framed who? Could a framer other than S. A. Parker have produced the frame on the boatshed painting? There are about sixty framers listed in Sydney in the Sands' Directory in the mid-1920s. Thirty-four were in the suburbs and twenty-four in the city. Of the latter, there were ten in George Street alone. From the paintings of this period of which I have seen with framing labels, it would seem that the professional artists used mainly Parker, Styles and Horace Fleming. John Young did not frame professionally after he established the Macquarie Galleries in 1925. Prior to this he had mainly framed works on paper. Young's business was taken over by Fleming. Of course, I will have to check out whether framers such as John Young and George Styles ever kept stock frames or used frames similar to Parker, but my feeling at this stage is that it was Parker who specialised in (monopolised?) these gilt frames for oil paintings.

Who were the patrons and other buyers who might have purchased paintings in the 1920s? And where were the meeting places, and who were the friends and identities who may have known the artists and acquired paintings directly from them, as gifts or swaps, rather than through galleries?

Will it be any help knowing any of this?

Saturday, 24 April

I have long been friendly with Renee and Keith Free. Renee curated the Rees retrospective exhibition in 1969, wrote the definitive book on Lloyd Rees—a milestone in Australian art book publishing—and collaborated with Rees on a number of other books. I therefore knew, before I even bid on the boatshed painting, that it was possible Renee might be able to help me with research if I purchased it, and, perhaps, even introduce me to the Rees family.

I had met Keith Free in about 1969 in Newell's auction rooms in Neutral Bay. In those days developers were pulling down Federation houses in Neutral Bay, Cremorne and Mosman and replacing them with high-rise apartment blocks. Furniture and paintings from deceased estates were finding their way into Newell's. History was being dispersed. And it was a time when few people seemed to appreciate its value. I was a university student working part-time as a researcher in a private art gallery and had picked up a few ideas.

One day I found myself bidding for a large

1920s mural painting by Norman Carter which was leaning against a wall in the auction room, stacked rudely behind a wardrobe. I bid up to fifty dollars (which I did not actually have, but it was a great painting) before it was knocked down for fifty-five dollars to a tall, shy-looking chap who eventually approached me and asked me if I was interested in the 1920s. Because he had just deprived me of owning my first masterpiece, I responded coldly. This shy chap, I found out later, was Keith.

The following week, I came across a small, colonial portrait of a boy writing by candlelight which I felt was by the convict artist Thomas Bock. On the day of the sale I positioned myself behind a pillar, out of sight of the shy chap. The bidding started at one dollar and went up in ones until it reached five dollars at which point I called out 'ten!' I like to think that this boldness fazed Keith out but whatever it was, I ended up with the portrait. This time I approached *him*. I resisted the temptation of asking him if he was interested in the *eighteen* twenties and, instead, suggested going for a beer.

After a few drinks the conversation turned to the fact that we seemed to be the only two people who knew what was going on. While we did not decide to form a ring—it is illegal to agree not to bid against each other in the auction room and then to sort out ownership later—we agreed to more or less declare our interest in future lots and to see how it worked out.

It worked out pretty well. Newell's auctions continued for about a decade, at the end of which the diminishing treasures were being picked over by many others. But those early days. Those were the days.

I call Renee and Keith and ask them if I could show them the boatshed painting. I tell them I am exploring the possibility of it being by Lloyd Rees. They invite me over. They are, initially, appropriately non-committal as they thoroughly examine the painting. Keith feels the grid composition is not typical but can also point to similarities with Rees's work. Renee is more reserved but kindly offers to phone Rees's son and daughter-in-law.

Jan and Alan Rees agree to see us and the painting straight away. We drive over to where they are living in the house in which Lloyd painted so many of his pictures. At least that will be a treat even if the response to the boatshed painting is negative. This thought is designed to rationalise any near-future disappointment. I must say I hadn't expected things to be happening quite so fast. Perhaps there was more enjoyment in not knowing. To travel hopefully is a better thing than to arrive, etc.

We take the painting onto the Reeses' veranda, lay it on a table in the sunlight and Alan says 'Oh, yes!'

A while later he says, 'Well, if someone showed me that and said it was by Dad I wouldn't dispute it.' He moves his fingers above the paint surface, as if holding a paintbrush, mimicking the brushstrokes. He brings out a painting titled *The Hill Top, Old Cremorne, 1918* and points out some similarities in relation to the brushstrokes. At this point Renee breaks in and comments on the differences. 'In *The Hill Top*', she says, 'the artist has a system going. The short, vigorous brushstrokes are used all over the area of the painting whereas in the boatshed painting the brushstrokes are less pronounced and more varied throughout.' She is right.

We then return inside to look at *Balmoral* painted in 1927. In this painting the surface is much smoother and the feel and tightness of the brush-work has much more in common with the boatshed painting. I had seen the reproduction of *Balmoral* in

An Artist Remembers but the similarities had not seemed so obvious. I note the problem of comparing a painting with others seen only in reproduction.

We return to the veranda where I offer to take my picture out of its frame. As soon as the fresh blue areas are revealed around the edges of the painting—edges which are free of yellow varnish and which had been protected for years from the sun—we see the similarity to the bright blue colours of *Balmoral*.

'When all of this old varnish is cleaned off,' says Keith, 'it will be a cool painting rather than a golden, warm painting.' We try to imagine it without the yellowed varnish. Then Alan brings out *Balmoral* and we rest both paintings in the light, placing the blue edges of the boatshed painting over the opalescent water of *Balmoral*. The pigments are pretty similar.

Keith comments again on the rigid composition, even despite the slightly curved horizon. We know Rees's compositions in his Sydney University drawings were rigid, due mainly to their architectural form, but could he ever have been so rigid in his oil paintings? We think about whom he might have painted with or whom he might have been influenced by in the 1920s. The obvious answer is Wakelin. Jan and Alan lead us to a small oil by Wakelin of houses on a hillside. While the brushwork is not similar at all, the composition is all squares—horizontals and verticals.

The red of the roofs and the boatshed is still a bit of a problem. When it is cleaned it will probably be softer, more coral-coloured. Jan tells us that she has come across references to paintings titled *Red Roofs*. 'Red' is also used in other Rees titles such as *The Red House*, *The Red Door* and *The Red Bank*.

'Any ideas on the location of the painting's subject?' I ask. 'If it is by Dad', says Jan, 'it is unlikely that you will find a topographically correct location.

He almost always changed things around.'

I promise faithfully that I will return and show them the painting after it has been cleaned. I assure them that I will keep an open mind and bid a warm farewell.

While my mind is struggling to stay 'open', it is also racing ahead, figuring out my next move.

Sunday, 25 April

Now to find the best restorer. I decide to discuss this with Frank McDonald, the Sydney art dealer. I phone him to tell him about the painting and he says that he would love to see it. We arrange to meet in a few days.

Frank has been something of a mentor and provided me with my early training in art research. He has been dealing in Australian art since the 1960s. He pioneered art research in the commercial gallery scene in Sydney and has trained many researchers, including myself, who have gone on to work in both private galleries and public institutions.

▭

It is 1967. My friend, and later business partner, Jim Berry, who is studying accountancy and working part-time as book-keeper for an art gallery, asks me if I'd like a part-time job as an art researcher. I know very little about art. I don't quite know what an art researcher is. But I'm working part-time pumping gas in a service station and anything would be better than trying to find dipsticks under car bonnets in the dead of night for two dollars an hour. I go for an interview with this art dealer.

Not knowing what to expect, I dress casually. The gallery, in Macquarie Street and opposite the

Mitchell Library, turns out to be genuine colonial Georgian (I am studying Australian History at university), filled with masterpieces and appears to have servants, although I wonder whether these might be 'art researchers'. I explain to the art dealer that I am qualified for the job because I draw cartoons. It is the only qualification I can think of. Later in the interview, I am mildly surprised when he hires me.

'How much do you want per hour?' he asks. I am stunned. I have never been asked this before. Up to this point in my employment history I have just been given two dollars per hour for pumping gas and finding dipsticks whether I liked it or not. I was a lad from the working classes living with my parents in a rented semi-detached house in a gully in North Sydney, a suburb which in 1967 was so unfashionable that they put a ten-lane expressway through it. I was a bit worried that I could be trapped there, a luckless victim of an unfair class system.

'I'll tell you what,' says the art dealer, with a slight American twang in his voice, 'you write down what you think you're worth per hour on this piece of paper and I'll write down what I'm prepared to pay you on this other piece of paper and we'll split the difference.'

My eyes spun quickly around the opulence. I looked at him as he wrote. Although in reality he didn't seem like a class enemy, I imagined him with a gold watch on a chain and a fat cigar in his mouth, like a Noel Counihan caricature. I decided to go high: I had nothing to lose and plenty to gain. A chance for an upwardly mobile boy to bound right into the upper class without even having to stop to mingle with those classes in the middle. It was worth a go. I wrote down the absurd sum of $15.

Now here is the interesting thing. Maybe he was affected by the smell of the carbon monoxide fumes in my mohair jumper and torn jeans. Maybe he thought that I'd write only $2 on my piece of paper because I thought that searching for dipsticks was on par with searching for art information. Anyway, he had written $10. When the difference was split I was on a salary of $12.50 an hour. I became the highest paid art researcher in the world. Without flinching very much the art dealer told me to start the next morning.

On the way out I noticed on the brass plaque that the gallery hours were eleven to six. The next day I turned up promptly at eleven o'clock. The art dealer sat me down and explained that art researchers' hours were nine to five like any other job. Then he asked me what I thought of Fox and Bunny. At first I thought the question related to my interest in cartooning. Fox and Bunny? Was it something to do with Disney? I replied obliquely: 'I have never got into animation but I'd like to.' He looked at me strangely. Later when he showed me a painting by Phillips Fox I tried to cover my tracks by saying, 'It's pretty animated isn't it?'

He put me to work in a room filled with art books and told me to write about a Drysdale which was on an easel. I had never really looked at a Drysdale before, let alone written about one. I looked at this one until it was five o'clock and time to knock off. The next day I still had writers' block. The art dealer replaced the Drysdale on the easel with a nineteenth century Australian painting signed J. H. Carse. I looked at it in terror. At least I had heard of Drysdale. Then, looking up the standard references on Australian art, I found that nobody else had ever heard of J. H. Carse either. Maybe I could make it up. How else could I write an account of someone who apparently nobody else had written anything about before? It was getting tough.

The next day he gave me a pastoral map of

Australia with a line drawn on it which apparently
showed the route taken by the colonial artist Eugene
von Guerard when he travelled from Adelaide to
Sydney painting portraits of homesteads along the
way. The art dealer explained that the job I had to do
was to write to the owners of all the existing homesteads along the way and ask them, politely, if they
had any Eugene von Guerards. He was organising
the first exhibition of work by this great colonial
artist. He also had to explain to me that the pronun-
ciation was 'Oigen' and not 'You-jean'.

That afternoon we had to go out to look
at some paintings that needed researching. The
art dealer ordered a hire car. It was the first hire
car I had ever been in. Later, after we had returned
to the gallery in the hire car, the art dealer told
the driver to continue on and take me home. I
got out just around the corner because a) I wasn't
sure whether I'd have to pay for the trip and b)
I didn't want my parents seeing me get out of
a stretch limo and have them start thinking I was
a class traitor. It might have been a bit too sudden
for them.

But after two years there could be no hiding it.
I was a changed person. I was able to put once
popular but now obscure artists, such as J. H. Carse,
back on the map. In fact for a while I could boast
that I was the only living person who knew what the
J. H. stood for.[1]

And I could say 'Oigen' with the best of them.

Tuesday, 27 April

I show the boatshed painting to friends who drop by.
I have to field some tricky, intelligent and sobering
questions.

Why couldn't it be by a 1920s artist whose work

is completely unknown today? An artist whose work bears a similarity to Rees's, coincidentally or because of an association? Perhaps a body of this artist's signed work may surface sometime in the future. Or, could it be by an artist who is, in fact, unknowable because all trace of his or her work has been destroyed?

The chances of it being by a currently unknown but potentially knowable artist are very slight, but I admit it is possible. The Society of Artists in Sydney included only work by professional artists, most of whom are still well known. However, the exhibition catalogues occasionally include artists who are now unknown apart from these references, and whose work is never seen. An example is Juanita Job who exhibited two oils in 1918: Number 131, *Harbour Sketch* and 132, *The Sea Beyond*, priced at two and four guineas respectively, which suggests they were small in size. Her name does not pop up again in any art literature until 1934 when she is listed as a member of an obscure group called Women Artists of Australia. A quick search reveals no other reference to her in any other publication, Australian or otherwise. No-one I know has ever heard of her. So until we have seen Juanita's work, and the work of others like her, we can't totally rule them out. Unless the evidence for Rees, say, becomes totally overwhelming.

It is possible that the artist of the boatshed painting was a 'bird of passage' and painted few works whilst in Australia. We do, however, know the work of many such artists. It is usually of a high quality because they came here as trained artists. They invariably made contact with other artists here, seeking them out and becoming part of the scene, albeit briefly, and they usually exhibited. They tend to be researchable. Aletta Lewis is a good example.[1] Another possibility is that the artist studied here and painted relatively few works before travelling and settling overseas where their career was pursued. Some never returned. Winifred Honey is such an artist.[2] There is also the chance that the boatshed painting is not by an Australian artist but happens to bear a similarity to Rees's work and Sydney Harbour topography and was brought to Australia sometime after it was painted. If this is the case then I've got Buckley's.

It is hard to imagine a competent artist in Australia being completely unrecorded during the 1920s. First of all, to paint the boatshed painting would have required tuition over a period of time, either self-tuition—which, for a professional artist, was unusual at the time—or training at an art school. There are extensive records of artists who trained with the two main schools in Sydney, Julian Ashton's and Dattilo-Rubbo's.[3] The National Gallery School in Melbourne is similarly documented.[4] And if the artist was unrecorded during this time, what happened to the works later? They would have to have been destroyed or else the artist's family perhaps is still sitting on them and they have yet to emerge. If Ms Juanita Job had not exhibited a couple of works in a well-known art society, she would be in this category.

An anecdote about Picasso may help to clarify some of these issues. It is told by Gertrude Stein in *Picasso* (1938) in her maddening prose style:

> [Picasso] was always interested in painting as a metier, an incident that happened once is characteristic. In Paris there was an American sculptress who wished to show her canvases and sculpture at the salon where she was *hors concours* but she did not wish to show sculpture and painting at the same salon. So she had asked Miss [Alice B.] Toklas to lend her name for the pictures. This was done. The pictures were

accepted in the name of Miss Toklas, they were in
the catalogue and we had this catalogue. The
evening of the vernissage Picasso was at my house.
I showed him the catalogue, I said to him, here is
Alice Toklas who has never painted and who has
had a picture accepted at the salon. Picasso went
red, he said, it's not possible, she has been
painting in secret for a long time, never I tell you,
I said to him. It isn't possible, he said, not
possible, the painting at the salon is bad painting,
but even so if anyone could paint at their first
painting a picture that was accepted, well then I
don't understand anything about anything. Take
it easy, I said to him, no she didn't paint the
picture, she only lent her name. He was still a
little troubled, no, he repeated, you have to know
something to paint a picture, you have to, you
have to.[5]

The boatshed painting is by someone who knew
something about a picture, had experience and is,
therefore, most likely to be recorded somewhere.
     But who? And where?

Friday, 30 April

Today is the day I have arranged to show the boatshed painting to Frank McDonald at his gallery and
to seek his advice on a good restorer. He knows that
I have progressed a fair way already with my
research. He is at a disadvantage in this respect and
is circumspect about offering an immediate opinion
without the advantage of reflection. Despite this, his
almost immediate response is that my boatshed
painting is *not* by Rees.
     He is, however, prepared to listen to my
arguments. When I give them, he agrees that the

next logical step is to have the painting cleaned. He recommends a restorer of whom I have heard but have not used. We discuss the subject of provenance, or the history of ownership of works of art. Frank is fairly fanatical about provenance. And rightly so: it is one of the best tests of authenticity. If we look at a painting and we know who bought it from the artist, and we have incontestable proof of each subsequent owner of this painting, then we can be certain that the painting is by that artist.

Frank turns the boatshed painting over looking for evidence of the previous owner or owners. The clues are, of course, minimal: a pencilled title, a couple of numbers and an indecipherable word. From the look on Frank's face I know he is thinking that I have absolutely no chance of establishing a provenance for this painting.

'I don't like the painting,' he says, and then jests unkindly: 'I think the only thing interesting about it is the fact that it is unsigned.' I am not amused. 'I think there's more to it than that,' I respond testily.

Our conversation drifts on to the problems of attributing paintings to artists, where the provenance is not known, on the basis of style and technique alone. This is a complex subject. If a painting is catalogued for an exhibition or auction, the cataloguer usually follows a convention. Sotheby's catalogues, for example, provide the following explanation of their cataloguing terms: 'A picture catalogued with the forename(s) and surname of the painter is in our opinion a work by that artist.' What are the legal ramifications of 'in our opinion'?

The next category is a work catalogued as 'attributed to ... (an artist)'. Sotheby's definition is that such a work is 'in our opinion *probably* a work by the artist'. (Their italics.) Further terms are employed as the level of their certainty decreases: 'Studio of ...', 'circle of ...', 'Follower of ...', 'manner of ...',

'school of ...', right down to 'after ...' which the
catalogue explains as meaning 'a copy of any date
after a work by that artist'.

Sometimes works in public galleries are 'down-
graded' as new information or expert opinion comes
forward. This was the case when the National
Gallery of Victoria accepted expert opinion on their
famous, and now ex-famous, *Rembrandt Self
Portrait*. Its label now sadly reads *18th Century
Portrait of Rembrandt in the manner of Rembrandt*.
Works can be upgraded as well. Frank makes the
point that in either case, the quality of the work is
sometimes so good that it really doesn't matter. True
works of art have a habit of standing apart from
whoever made them.

These questions of attribution are relevant to me
because I suspect that with the boatshed painting I
will have to at some point make a hard decision
about the use of those words 'attributed to' or even
one of the other terms above. Or will I be able to say
simply: 'by Lloyd Rees'?

I leave Frank to his work. He is presently in the
process of selling a large, multi-panelled mural to the
Art Gallery of NSW. He hopes that it will be incor-
porated into a room to be called 'The de Maistre
Mural Room'. The panels were purchased at
Christie's in London as being by Roy de Maistre.
They were put into the auction by a Somerset de
Chair. Christie's had stated in the auction catalogue
that Somerset's mother had commissioned them
from her friend de Maistre in the early 1930s.

Although the work is unsigned, Frank has
absolutely no doubt that the impeccable provenance
guarantees them as being by de Maistre.

Hmmm. A large unsigned painting.

Monday, 3 May

The restorer I have chosen, on Frank's advice, is David Stein. As I show him the boatshed painting I briefly outline the task at hand: I am recording the progress of my responses to the painting up until the time that I arrive at a firm attribution, whatever that might be. He guesses correctly that I already have someone in mind and then says, 'Don't tell me.' He takes a long look at the painting. After about a minute he says, 'Well, I would say Lloyd Rees,' and then looks expectantly at me.

'Good on you,' I say. Having chosen him on Frank's advice, David's response to the painting strikes me as pleasantly ironic.

I have already noted why the family of an artist can be relied upon to give an opinion which must be respected. The opinions of good restorers should also be respected. They work so closely with the brushmarks of so many different artists that it becomes like analysing handwriting. They develop a knowledge of the different pressures and angles of an artist's brush, the idiosyncratic methods of building up and 'working' the surface, as well as a highly attuned response to varying pigments. They are expert in analysing the minutiae of all the painterly details.

David fetches a weak solution of ammonia and water and offers to apply it with a cotton swab to a corner. I had thought that the painting had been coated in a yellowed varnish, but when the corner is gently cleaned, a lot of the yellow disappears. This suggests that the grime is not entirely yellowed varnish (which would have required a stronger solvent) but the accumulation of cigarette smoke and dust. Or perhaps it had once been hung over a fireplace.

It is probable that there will be a thin layer of yellowed varnish remaining on the painting after the grime has been cleaned off with a weak solution. We decide that David should remove the grime first, and then we will decide whether to remove any varnish. Some artists intended that their work should always be seen with a coat of varnish. On the backs of some of Max Meldrum's oils I have seen his written instruction that the dark varnish is intentional and should never be removed. Varnish is more problematic if the painting was done in the nineteenth century when public galleries were known to have 'varnishing days' (referred to by some wits as 'vanishing days'). In such cases layers of varnish were built up over many years until the paintings themselves were sometimes barely visible.

David tells me to expect some results within days.

Saturday, 8 May

David phones to say that he has cleaned off the surface dirt and the residue from the tobacco smoke and asks if I could look at it and instruct him on proceeding. When I arrive he fetches the painting from the safe. He is not treating it like any old unsigned painting.

The results are highly promising although it is still dirty-looking from the yellowed varnish that does, in fact, remain. This varnish has discoloured unevenly giving the painting a patchy look. In the hollows of the paintwork the varnish has congealed occasionally into black specks. But despite this, some colours that had not been apparent before have now miraculously appeared: a purple shadow under the eaves of the house; multicoloured brushstrokes in the trees at the right; strokes of blue which liven up the still-murky sky. But the most exciting part is that David has also used a test solvent on the varnish in the top left-hand corner and the result shows a crisp, white area of sky. Since the oil paint itself is quite hardened, there is little chance of damage to it from using the stronger solvent to remove the rest of the varnish, so we decide to go ahead.

Sunday, 9 May

I have decided to write to Joel's to see whether they will provide me with the name of the vendor—the previous owner—of the boatshed painting. If I can get this, I may be able to work backwards to the original owner and, from there, find a link to an artist. In other words ... establish a provenance. But asking for this information directly from auction houses is rarely successful. They tend to argue that they are respecting the privacy of the vendor. However, asking them to pass a letter on to the vendor can occasionally bring results. It might depend on the letter.

Dear Jon [Dwyer],
    I am currently researching, with the intention of writing about, a painting I purchased at Joel's auction on the 21st of April, 1993.
    This was lot 692, catalogued as Australian School, titled *Beachside Villas* and estimated at $100–$200. I purchased it for $340 and am most pleased with it.
    The piece I am writing explores the process of researching paintings where the artist is unknown.
    Would it be possible for you to pass my letter on to the vendor in an attempt to find out as much information as possible about the history of this work?
    If it is not possible I would appreciate knowing

the reasons, as this, in itself, would be useful information in documenting the process of the research.

I very much look forward to hearing from you,
Yours sincerely,
Stephen Scheding

Did I intend that hint of blackmail in this letter?

Monday, 10 May

I think about setting out around the waterfront in search of the location of the boatshed painting. If the painting is by Rees I may not find a location which corresponds exactly since Rees's oils were rarely topographically exact. In fact, if the boatshed painting turns out to be totally topographically exact it may be evidence against the Rees theory. Also if I were to find the location of the boatshed painting to be, say, the Georges River, it is unlikely that the painting is by Rees who is not known to have painted the Georges River.

In *Small Treasures of a Lifetime*, Lloyd Rees recounts his 'excitement on discovering, during a walk along the waterfront from Old Cremorne wharf to The Point, the location of Streeton's *Cremorne Pastoral* painted back in the 1890s'.[1] In 1953 on a visit to Suffolk, England, he located the subject for Constable's *The Haywain*. In both cases he notes the way each artist had organised the elements of nature to make it 'a creative work of painting and not just a transcription from nature'.[2] So, I may be looking merely for elements of the boatshed painting rather than the scene as a whole. I recall Jan Rees's comment about 'Dad' changing things around.

In preparation, I hunt out a map of the Harbour.

From Rees's writings I have narrowed my search
down to two locations worth checking as quickly as
possible: (1) from Balmoral around the shoreline as
far as Chinaman's Beach and The Spit in Middle
Harbour; and (2) the shoreline around Ball's Head
Bay and Berry's Bay west of the Harbour Bridge. I
will try these two locations first and then others such
as Mosman and Cremorne if necessary.

In his extensive autobiographical writings, Rees
refers to virtually no other 1920s painting spot in
Sydney close to a large body of water. A check of the
titles of his known 1920s oils confirms that he
painted his Harbour scenes exclusively at the above
locations. The exception, of course, is that he did
paint harbour subjects while overseas in 1923. But
this is irrelevant in terms of the boatshed painting,
since my feeling is that the subject is a Sydney one
because of the Federation-style architecture and the
clear, white light. The atmosphere of his overseas
work tends to be more subdued, more 'northern'.

A summary of Rees's residential activity might
help here. It has been gleaned from his autobiographical writings and Renee Free's publications,
and supplemented by information from my conversation with Alan and Jan Rees.

Following a brief trip to Melbourne Rees first
moved from Brisbane to Sydney in 1917 where he
lodged for a few weeks in Mosman above Balmoral.
It was such a short period that it is doubtful that he
would have had the time to paint from this address.
He would have been engaged in looking for more
suitable accommodation since his sister Amy was
about to join him from Brisbane. But one can never
doubt Lloyd's propensity to create, even at the most
unexpected moments. In *Peaks and Valleys* he
describes spending his first night in Sydney in the
Grand Hotel in Clarence Street alone and totally
traumatised. He eventually conquered his panic by

sketching self portraits through the night until dawn.
The next day, temporarily exorcised of the 'demons'
which were to plague him through his life, he took
the ferry to Cremorne to visit his ex-physics master
and his wife. They suggested a trip to Manly which
Rees describes as 'a delightful trip through Sydney
suburbia' (my italics—a promising use of the word
by the artist, remembering the inscribed title on the
reverse of the boatshed painting). Manly turned out
to be 'an exciting climax with its rows of pines'.[3]

When Amy arrived in Sydney to join him, Lloyd
and she moved from Mosman across the Harbour to
Edgecliff Road, Woollahra. By 1918 he returned to
the north side again, to Waverton. The location had
been suggested by Roland Wakelin whom Rees had
met while working at Smith and Julius. Wakelin was
now a neighbour. In 1919 Rees was living at Old
Cremorne above the wharf in Mosman Bay in a flat
with his Brisbane friends Peter Templeton and Wal
Taylor. Amy Rees had returned to Brisbane but by
1920 he was back in Waverton with her. Basil
Burdett lives with the Reeses at this address from
about 1921 and is to become not only a friend, but
a supporter, critic and an exhibitor of Lloyd's work.
In 1922 Rees moved to Parramatta with Amy and
Burdett. In 1923 he was overseas and from 1924 to
1925 he was back in Parramatta. In August 1926 he
married Dulcie Metcalfe and moved to Mosman.
Following Dulcie's tragic death in 1927 he moved
back to Parramatta and shortly afterwards he
stopped painting oils for a period of about five years.

It is possible that at any time while he was
at Parramatta he might have visited or stayed
with friends near Waverton or Mosman and painted
around the shoreline. Therefore I could say that
if the boatshed painting is by Rees it could have
been painted at any time between 1917 and
1927.

I return to the two possible locations.

   When writing about his painting *Balmoral* in *An Artist Remembers*, Rees recalls:

> ... there was a jetty on what I will term the western end of Balmoral Beach, not the area where the swimming took place but the area overlooking the submarine base at Middle Head ... The painting dates from 1927, which came within the first year of my marriage [in 1926. Dulcie died in 1927], and most of my painting was done down at the Spit and at Middle Harbour because of the proximity of my home to the tram service.[4]

Rees was living with Dulcie in Mosman at the time, near her parents' house.[5] Writing about *The Houseboat, 1926*, he records that

> I had no hope of living by painting, but I was on call from Farmer and Company to do commercial drawing for them. Some days would be free, and Dulcie often enough would suggest that I go out-of-doors painting. A natural source of subject matter was the foreshores of Sydney Harbour, which I could reach by tram.[6]

The second possible location is established from the same book when Rees is writing about *Old Boats, Wollstonecraft Bay* circa 1920:

> I formed a particular friendship with Roland Wakelin—that was my first lasting Sydney friendship ... There was a little agitation on his part to come across the harbour to Bay Road, now Waverton. I don't know who found it, but there

was a little more than half a cottage at Ross Street, Bay Road. It led down to the big gasworks ... The little cottage had a front room in which I used to sleep, with glass windows overlooking the harbour—and so I got a new sense of ecstasy concerning Sydney Harbour. When I looked out of a morning the sun would rise and shine on typical harbour headland with russety trees and golden rocks ..."[7]

This is a mouthwatering description when I look at the colours of the boatshed painting; I think again about my initial impression that the painting, if by Rees, could have been painted circa 1920. Whether the date is c1920 or c1927 it could still be a Balmoral subject as Rees could have travelled there by tram easily from either Waverton or Mosman ...

Wakelin was about half a mile away on the other side of the railway. You would have walked along a little narrow strip of land alongside the railway and then come into Carr street, Waverton, and diagonally across was Wakelin's tiny little double-fronted house ... But when you came to the corner there was a cubistic looking two-storey house that appeared in the paintings of the period done by both Wakelin and Roy de Maistre.[8]

It is probably far too optimistic to think that the house in the boatshed painting is the cubistic looking one which, in the paintings referred to, is much further away from the water's edge.

By checking a street directory I can easily work out the areas of shoreline that would have been within walking distance from Rees's address in Waverton

Or, I could explore the shoreline by boat.

Tuesday, 11 May

It is too cold and blustery for boating.

I decide to go to the Mitchell Library to find the exact addresses of Lloyd Rees from about 1920 to 1927. I also want to follow up the inscription on the frame of the painting, possibly 'Booth', 'Book' or 'Boon'. If it is a name, then this person might have been a one-time owner of the painting and, if so, it might be possible to establish a connection between them and Lloyd Rees. For example, if I can locate the exact address of Rees in 1927 and then find that living next door was a person by the name of Booth, then an assumption worth exploring might be that Rees gave Booth the painting as a gift.

It is difficult to know which year to begin searching first. The telephone books and the Sands' Sydney Directory for the 1920s are on microfiche and working with them is painstakingly slow. I only have time to do one year so I settle for 1927, partly on the basis of the similarity of pigments in *Balmoral* of 1927 and the boatshed painting which might date the latter to 1927 rather than the years around 1920. But it is really just a punt.

I first check the Sands' NSW Directory, looking for the Mosman address of Lloyd Rees for 1927, but to no avail. The Sands' Directory lists the residents of every street in Sydney in order of the house numbers, first on one side of the street, then down the other. Rees's in-laws, Rev. and Mrs Metcalfe, are listed at number 64 Muston Street, Mosman. I have remembered the name Metcalfe from Rees's *Peaks and Valleys*. I then get out the microfiche of the Sydney Telephone Directory for 1927. And there, surprisingly, I find Lloyd Rees. I had not thought that he could have afforded to have the phone on at this time since in his writings he describes himself as

hard up. Perhaps the in-laws helped out. The address
is 57 Cowles Road, Mosman.

Back to the Sands' Directory, where I find four
Booths who live near the Rees home but not in the
same street—let alone next door. The most likely is
perhaps Mrs J. W. Booth who lives at 48 Wolseley
Road, Mosman. On a street map it appears that she
may have lived just above the spot where Rees
painted *Balmoral* in 1927. If I find a boatshed
adjacent to her address then there could be a
connection, but it's a long shot. I note all the Booth
addresses in Mosman in case there are any in the
current Sydney telephone directory who are still
living at these addresses. I then go through the 1927
Telephone Directory again to see if there are any
Books. There aren't. In the current directory there
are four. In an old *Who's Who in Australia* I find
that there was a well-known Book in the 1920s, a
Crown Prosecutor and then Judge, but he lived
in Melbourne. Since I found the painting in
Melbourne, I may follow him up later.

Now, while looking up and down the lists and
lists of old telephone numbers in the 1927 directory,
I find myself becoming almost hypnotised. And then
I have a sort of deja vu experience! I suddenly
remember that the telephone number my family had
when I was a kid in the 1950s was XB 8619. I am
amazed that it has come to me. Then I realise that
the numbering system had not changed from the
1920s to the 1950s. All the numbers in the 1927
directory also have a prefix and four digits, except for
some city numbers which are listed as four digits
with 'City' in front of them.

What if the number 8930 written in pencil on
the reverse of the boatshed painting is in fact *a
telephone number*? Many of the four-digit city
numbers start with eight!

I look at more telephone numbers. Most of the

numbers around Parramatta also start with eight but
have a prefix 'UW'. I wonder if anyone in 1927 would
have written a telephone number without the prefix,
for example if they knew the prefix off by heart
because they also lived in the same suburb. I check
E. O. Rees at 'Bondo', Western Road, Parramatta
(E. O. is Lloyd's father) and the telephone number is
UW 8098. Well, three of the numbers are the same
but that's not close enough! I check all the Booths in
the directory but none have the four correct digits.

There is only one thing to do. Go through the
entire 1927 Telephone Directory looking for the
number 8930. Or, is it possible that Telecom has
scanned all the early directories and put the
information into a computer? Could they find the
1927 subscriber by simply keying in 8930? I decide
to call it quits in the Mitchell, to go home and to
phone Telecom in the morning.

Wednesday, 13 May

I first call a number listed in the front of the White
Pages as the Telecom Customer Help Centre, a
promising-sounding title. Joanne is very helpful and
suggests putting me through to Archives. Although
Archives is in Melbourne she connects me directly.

Rosemary in Archives tells me that they are in
the process of putting all Victorian telephone
numbers onto computer but that they haven't got
far. She doesn't know what the situation is in NSW
but suggests I try the Educational and Historical
Service. She also recommends someone by the name
of Bert Spratt at the Telecom Exhibition Centre at
Ashfield in Sydney. He only works one day a week,
on Wednesday, which is the only day the Centre is
open. As luck will have it, today is Wednesday. But
first I try the Educational and Historical Service.

There, Amanda takes an interest in my quest, despite the fact that it must sound somewhat bizarre. Finally she says: 'Look, I think Bert Spratt is your man.'

I think Bert had been waiting for my call for fifty-eight years. Bert was a trainee Post Master General's technician back in 1936 (he retired in 1982 and now works at the Exhibition Centre on a voluntary basis). As it turns out, he lives and breathes telephones—he knows more about the Australian telephone system than anyone else in the universe. We talk telephone systems for over an hour. Bert tells me that Telecom has put all Sydney numbers onto computer from 1882 when the system was begun but so far only up until the year 1895. 'Oh, no', I cry out. 'Sorry,' says Bert, 'but what is the number you're researching? I'll see if I can help.'

When I give him my number, his response is astounding. He tells me that it is almost certainly a city number south of Market or King Streets. From 1922, when the city went partly onto automatic, most city numbers would have had a prefix, as in the suburbs. In that year there were about 16,000 subscribers with city numbers: 10,000 to the north of the Market–King line went onto automatic with the prefix 'B', leaving about 4,000 to 6,000 with the prefixless numbers south of that line. To call these numbers, callers had to dial 'B9' for the operator and then be connected.

Impressive old Bert is coming up with this information off the top of his head. It means that I will only have to look really hard at 4,000 to 6,000 prefixless numbers out of the 10,000 city numbers in the 1927 Telephone Directory. Unfortunately, those 4–6,000 numbers will be dispersed through the total of 200,000 numbers in the book. Bert makes it sound almost like a treat—he is a man after my own heart.[1] Tomorrow I will search the 1927 Telephone Directory with a new respect for it.

In all the excitement, I forgot to ask Bert in what year the remaining city numbers became automated and were given prefixes. If I have this date, then I would know the latest date that the prefixless telephone number 8930 could have been written on the reverse of the frame.

Friday, 14 May

Could 8930 really be a telephone number? Before I go rushing to the 1920s telephone directories again, searching for 8930, I do some hard thinking about the inscription on the back of the boatshed painting. *Suburban Scene*/8930/Boo(?), and the sticker numbered 22.

I have decided that the inscription is almost certainly not a framer's inscription nor instructions relating to the framing. That is, 8930 is probably not an order number nor reference to a particular moulding, mainly because the painting does not appear to be put in the frame in a manner indicative of a *professional* framer. Also, such instructions are usually written on the back of the painting when the owner brings it in, and not on the frame which has not yet been made or prepared at this stage.

A fact that may support this conclusion is that the frame appears to be a standard size, that is, 6 inches by 12 inches (in pre-metric terms). It may be a stock frame. It seems possible that someone purchased it off the shelf, so to speak, and later placed the painting in the frame themselves. This person was possibly the artist since the painting was still wet when it was placed in the frame. If not the artist, then it was someone who would have been in possession of the painting within a few weeks of it being painted, while it was still wet. It is possible that this person may have had something to do with the book trade since the painting is held in with the assistance of what appears to be bookbinding tape.

The point is that 8930 does not appear to be related to the actual framing. It could, however, have been written there by the artist or a non-professional framer after the painting had been framed. It could, therefore, be the telephone number of someone close to the painting, or even of the next person to take possession of it.

But what about 8930 being an art gallery stock number? It seems too big. If stock was registered in consecutive progression by galleries in the 1920s, then it is hard to imagine that a gallery that existed then would have sold 8930 paintings. But perhaps they used a different system of registering stock. At any rate, it seems to me to be too quickly and casually written, too informal to be a stock number. And the only time I have seen stock numbers on the backs of paintings is when the gallery is so organised as to also use labels on which the numbers are written.

Was the painting even exhibited in a gallery? Most galleries sell paintings which have been professionally framed. It is not good practice to sell paintings to clients with the backs of the paintings in a tatty condition. In the 1920s, the back of the boatshed painting would have been in a fresher condition but it would still have been smeared with the mess of paint. My feeling is that a commercial gallery would have had this covered up before offering it for sale. The painting would have been presented professionally, the back of it probably sealed with brown paper.

A few commercial galleries that existed used a gallery sticker pasted on the back of the painting.

Macquarie Galleries' neat Bligh Street sticker is a
well-known example. The boatshed painting has no
label of this kind. But perhaps it was exhibited at a
gallery and there were circumstances which led to
the back not bearing a label and it being in such a
haphazard condition. Perhaps the gallery was a new
one and the owner inexperienced. Perhaps the
gallery owner believed so strongly in the art on the
gallery walls that not much attention was paid to the
backs of paintings.

After all, the boatshed painting also has what
appears to be a gallery exhibition sticker (number
22) on the reverse. If it is a gallery sticker, it was
probably on the front of the frame initially, during an
exhibition, and later removed to the back, possibly as
a record for the purchaser. It is not uncommon
practice at the conclusions of exhibitions to remove
such a sticker from the front to the reverse of the
frame as a record of the painting's provenance.
Someone purchasing the painting from an exhibition
would, no doubt, always remember the exhibition
from which it came. In the case of the boatshed
painting, as it is unsigned, the purchaser would be
able to prove authorship by referring to the number.
This would be proof, along with the exhibition
catalogue, that the painting was by the artist who
exhibited number 22.

Could the sticker be an auction sticker? When a
painting is bought at auction, the new owner might
possibly cut the catalogue entry out and paste it on
the reverse of the painting. I have often seen this
done. But re-pasting the lot number alone on the
reverse wouldn't help greatly. Furthermore, I cannot
recall a serrated-edged sticker being used by the early
auction houses. On the other hand, I think I can
recall seeing old paintings bearing such a sticker
together with a circular red 'sold' sticker of the type
used by private galleries decades ago.

But what about the pencilled number 8930
being an auctioneer's reference number? The inscribed title, *Suburban Scene*, the number 8930 and
the word Book, Boon, or Booth appear to be written
in the same hand. Now, while an auctioneer usually
writes a number on the reverse of a painting when it
is brought in by a vendor, they do not write the title
and other details as well. This would be recorded in
a book and be referred to later when cataloguing a
sale—writing the description on the painting as well
would be time-wasting duplication. As an example of
all this, on the reverse of the boatshed painting is a
number written in white chalk which is the number
Joel's used to record it when it was first given to
them for sale earlier this year. But this chalked
number is the only thing written on the reverse by
the staff at Joel's. All other details—the vendor's
name and address, a description of the work, an
estimated sale price, the reserve if any—are all listed
in a carbon book and a copy is provided for the
vendor. These days, the information is then typed
into a computer which can create receipts, invoices,
and so on. I am pretty sure then that the number
8930, being part of a larger inscription in the same
hand, is not an auctioneer's number.

Apart from telephone numbers, what other sort of
four-digit numbers existed in the 1920s? A Lottery
number? A bank balance? A car registration? The
number of an incredibly long street? As a child I
went train spotting for a week in the Blue Mountains
and became attached to a dark green steam loco-
motive with the number 3313 which used to pass
daily. I am having trouble thinking of any more possibilities for 8930.
    The person who wrote 8930 must have had a

purpose or motive in doing so. And it almost certainly must have had something to do with the painting. Is it a record of some past transaction to do with the painting? It seems more likely that it is a reminder of something relating to the future, an aid to something that is to be done with the painting. But no matter what the purpose of the number is, *I think it has to be a telephone number*.

It may have been put there by someone in a gallery—the number to be called, perhaps, when the painting was ready for collection ... The number of the next person to take possession of the painting. If I can find out who had the number in the 1920s, I may be able to work out the writer's purpose in putting it on the back of the boatshed painting. And hopefully begin to establish a provenance.

Saturday, 15 May

Straight to the 1927 Telephone Directory in the Mitchell. I have decided to focus the search on the year 1927 again because to do the same research for each of the years in the early 1920s is simply too daunting.

I find that there are actually two directories for 1927, one published in April and one in October. When I begin to go through the October directory from the beginning, I find that the numbering is different from the April edition which I was looking at the day before. Incredibly, it seems that the city numbers actually became automated between April and October 1927. By October they *all* have prefixes! So if 8930 is a telephone number, then the boatshed painting must have been painted prior to October 1927! I return to the April 1927 edition, the last edition to have prefixless, four-digit telephone numbers.

It takes me an hour-and-a-quarter to get through the As. By the Bs I am getting better at it and it takes only fifty-five minutes. But what if the subscriber's name is Zyznik or something? I could be here for days. I find myself racing against the old, sedate Mitchell Library clock high up on the end wall which seems to admonish me each time I try to speed up to save time. It is imperative to be thorough. When I come to 'Commonwealth Dental Supply Company' City 8932, I take heart. Only two off. I keep going with renewed hope.

And then, there it is! City 8930! It belongs to a W. C. Crawford at 139 King Street. I can't believe it. I want to shout out in the vast muffledness of the library. I want to tell all the other researchers. I know that they would just love to share my triumph. But shouting out in here just isn't done.

I double-check the entry. Who was W. C. Crawford? There is also a W. C. Crawford at 42 Carlotta Road, Double Bay, surely the same person. I have twenty minutes, before the library closes, to find out. I rudely jump the queue at the front desk to get the Sands' NSW Directory off the reference shelf. I haven't got time to explain my frenzied manner, but I'm sure the other researchers in the queue would understand if I spent an hour or so with them.

I bring King Street up on the microfiche. Number 139 is a building called Boomerang House. I have heard of it before. The Directory lists seven floors. I start at the bottom. First floor—vacant. Second floor—McGovern J. F., Dentist and Crawford W. Charles (office). Now I have a Christian name. Is W. Charles Crawford a dentist too? It doesn't seem so. What was the office for then?

Floors three and four are occupied by a skin specialist. On the fifth is the caretaker. On the sixth are Lodge E. H., an architect; The Hoover Depot (for vacuum cleaners, it says) and Leake J., oriental handwork. On the seventh floor is Moore, Miss May, photo studios. I have heard of her too. With her sister Minna, she was a society portrait photographer in the 1920s. The sisters also moved in artistic circles and their portraits of writers and artists survive.

And then the big surprise: also on the seventh floor is the Australian Fine Art Gallery, W. R. Bennett. I know all about this. It is the gallery run by the artist Rubery Bennett. So this is one of the reasons why Boomerang House rang a bell. Another reason is that I now remember that the building was once owned by the Alberts, the music family which published the Boomerang song books of my childhood. There is no time to consider all the possibilities now. I run through the microfiche until I come to the Trades Directory to try to find the occupation of Crawford. I try under Accountant, Architect, Dentist, Doctor, Solicitor ... and then the librarians are asking me to leave. I am not happy about this.

Back home, I look for Crawford in the *Australian Dictionary of Biography* and *Who's Who in Australia*, but he was not famous. I do a quick scan of a number of other reference books but without success. His identity must remain a mystery until I can get back into the library. But I speculate. Perhaps Crawford was a well-off professional gentleman with a house in Double Bay and an office in the city. On the top floor of his building is an art gallery. He gets to know the owner of the gallery, Rubery Bennett, from seeing him in the lift. Being a person of some money and perhaps taste, Crawford visits the gallery. One thing leads to another, and he purchases a painting—the boatshed painting. For some reason he does not take immediate possession of the painting. Maybe it is part of an exhibition and is to remain on the wall until the show is over. Rubery Bennett

writes Crawford's telephone number to call him
when the painting is ready for delivery in case he
doesn't see him in the lift …

It will be interesting to see whether any of it
stands up when I find out more about W. Charles
Crawford. I am fairly confident that I will. The problem is, I have never before come across any reference
to a connection between Lloyd Rees and Rubery
Bennett.

Sunday, 16 May

I get a call. The painting is ready. Collecting it
from the restorer takes precedence. I go and pick
it up. It looks terrific. I make some initial
observations:

(1) All the brushwork and modelling of the
surface is now fully revealed and the pigments are
fresh and alive. This will make comparison with
other works from the period much easier. Some of
the thick impasto has been smoothed while the
paint was wet (a technique that Rees is recorded
as having used and which is known sometimes as
'ragging').
(2) There is clearly no signature. Any speculations based upon promising squiggles can be
abandoned.
(3) The area of blue water in the centre and
surrounding greenery is even more complicated
and ambiguous than I had first realised.
(4) The chimney has a shadow and if I discover
the actual house on the waterfront, I may be able
to establish the time of day that the painting was
done. Perhaps even the time of year.
(5) The foliage is still dark and I suspect has
darkened since the work was painted. I think Rees

himself has noted somewhere the tendency for dark pigments to become even darker over time.

I put the boatshed painting next to the colour reproduction in *An Artist Remembers* of *Balmoral, 1927* for a comparison and note the following:

(1) The pylons in Rees's painting of Balmoral wharf, compared to the cream lines (railings and posts or outlines of stone windbreaks?) in the boatshed painting, reveal a similar slow dabbing and dragging of paint with additions of highlighting.

(2) The same pigment seems to have been used to create the effect of light on surfaces in both paintings: the creamy yellows on the top of the wharf, on the steps and on the front of the rowing boat in *Balmoral* are similar to the pigments used for the wall of the house, the railings and the foreground rocks in the boatshed painting.

(3) The red pigment used for the boatshed and roof of the house is similar to that used for the figures in *Balmoral*. On the eaves below the roof of the house in the boatshed painting is a smear of unusual red violet, the same colour that is dragged lightly in a horizontal line across the water at the centre right of *Balmoral*.

(4) Similarities also exist in the use of black, perhaps the khaki green and certainly in the blues used for the water.

But it is difficult to compare an original with a reproduction and now that the boatshed painting is cleaned I will take it, as promised, to show Alan and Jan Rees and put it next to their original *Balmoral*.

Monday, 17 May

I drive over to Mosman to look at the house that
Lloyd Rees was occupying in 1927 (the date that
Balmoral was painted). It is a compact, free-stand-
ing, double-fronted Federation bungalow which has
been newly renovated. Coincidentally, it has been
painted approximately the same colour as the house
in the boatshed painting. Perhaps less of a coincidence
is something to do with the windows. The original
windows at the front of the house have been replaced,
but judging from the adjacent houses which are in a
more original condition, in the 1920s there would
have been a pair of windows in the same relationship
and of the same proportions as the pair of windows
in the painting. If the boatshed painting is by Rees
and painted in 1927, could there have been
something unconscious going on when he painted it?

Tuesday, 18 May

I am now looking for a connection between Lloyd
Rees and Rubery Bennett's gallery at the Art Gallery
of NSW. Its library has an excellent collection of
artists' catalogues kept in boxes and filed in alphabetical order. There are three boxes of Lloyd Rees
catalogues. Later I'll walk across to the Mitchell
Library and track down W. C. Crawford, the subscriber to telephone number 8930 whose office was
in the same building as Bennett's gallery.

I know that Rees held several solo exhibitions
around the 1920s. Most of these are listed in Renee
Free's monograph but the only catalogue from that
decade held by the AGNSW library is the 1922 New
Art Salon exhibition organised by Basil Burdett. I
will probably be able to get other 1920s catalogues
from Alan and Jan Rees. I peruse the titles in the

1922 catalogue to get a flavour of Rees's titles at the
time. Two of the twenty-five oil paintings have 'red'
in the title: *The Red House* and *The Red Bank*. While
the subject of the boatshed painting does not fit either
of these, at least we know Rees was emphasising the
colour red in some of his paintings at this time.
(Could the boatshed painting have originally been
titled *The Red Boatshed*?) Other titles suggest atmospheric or mood paintings: *Early Morning*, *Noon*,
and *Storm Shadows*. Others are direct descriptions:
The Gum Tree, *A Parramatta Lane* and *The Farm*.

I think of the sticker numbered 22 on the
boatshed painting. What is number 22 in this 1922
catalogue? It is titled *The Bay*. Could the boatshed
painting have originally been titled *The Bay*? This
would mean that *Suburban Scene* would have been
added later, some time after the exhibition. I look at
the photograph of the boatshed painting that I now
carry about with me. At first *The Bay* seems an
unlikely title because the bay is not the obvious,
central subject of the painting and Rees's titles often
refer to the obvious. But, then again, *The Bay* has to
at least be possible because the painting certainly
seems to include a bay. And, in fact, I realise that the
title holds my interest because I am forced to try 'to
put the bay together'. Interesting.

But there is evidence against the boatshed
painting being *The Bay*. The price is fifteen guineas
and perhaps this is too high to be identifiable with
the small boatshed painting. *The Red House* was
priced at seven guineas and *The Red Bank* at eight. If
the boatshed painting was exhibited by Rees in the
1920s, my feeling is, from its size, that it may have
been a seven or eight guinea picture.

There are no titles with the word 'suburban'
in them, nor for that matter 'scene'. In one title he
has used the noun 'view'—a much more Reesish sort
of word. I now go through the library's collection of

press clippings and correspondences relating to Rees.
I come across an article by Renee Free from *Art and
Australia*, Winter, 1989, which has an illustration of
a 1964 oil titled *Summer in the Suburbs*, proving
Rees used the word 'suburb' within a title at least
once in his lifetime. In the article, Renee writes:

> It has been something of a mystery to me to hear
> Lloyd Rees divide his paintings into light and
> dark. The paintings he referred to as dark, such as
> *Drama in the Valley*, seem simply to be dramatic.
> It must be that behind the dark paintings he was
> struggling against depression, which he from time
> to time battled and which deserves document-
> ation. While it affected his early period in an
> intrinsic way, from 1953 at least, it had no
> significant meaning in his art.[1]

The title of Lloyd Rees's second autobiography is
fittingly titled *Peaks and Valleys*. Forgetting for the
moment the quest at hand I continue reading about
Lloyd Rees. He is quoted in *Lloyd Rees—the Last
Twenty Years* by Renee Free as saying:

> I had a phobia about flake white because there
> is so much lead poisoning in Queensland, and
> kidney trouble due to lead. Being a very dirty
> painter, I found myself worrying about the
> amount of white lead under the fingernails, and so
> on. I was subconsciously underusing white in the
> early Werri pictures [1940s]. When I saw Tuscany
> and the key of the landscape, I turned to titanium
> white and could use it from then on.[2]

It might be possible that the lead content of the
white oil paint was related to Rees's early bouts of
depression. Something else worth noting in the
above quote is the reference to being a dirty painter.

The reverse of the boatshed painting is smeared and daubed with a mess of oil paint.

When discussing the issue of light and dark in Rees's paintings of the 1920s, Renee Free continues in her *Art and Australia* article:

> The first opalescent vision of Sydney required a lifetime of painting to capture, but the course of his life was set by that glimpse through the porthole. The first major period of depression began in 1923 on the first visit to Europe, when Daphne Mayo [the sculptor] broke off their engagement because of her own destiny as an artist.[3] The twenties can be called the darkest decade. For years after his return, Rees drew at night obsessive variations of European buildings, ink black and Australian fantasies of castle landscapes with dancing figures, full of Druid mystery from his Welsh heritage—without contact with nature. These were clearly seen by him as expressions of a brooding depressive state of mind ... The dark gave way to a brief period of light with sparkling paintings, for example *Balmoral* [1927] in the period of his marriage to Dulcie Metcalfe. This was swiftly brought to an end with her death and that of their child in childbirth. The few paintings done at home in the following breakdown were sombre still lifes.[4]

The breakdown continued through 1928 and is documented by Rees in *Peaks and Valleys*:

> Life went on, as it had to, and I was surrounded by friendship and help, but in view of my general record [of ill health] it was probably inevitable that I would suffer a collapse. I had been back at 'Bondo' for six or nine months [after the tragedy in late 1927] and I had begun to paint again

when, on a week that I had devoted almost
entirely to painting, I broke down. It had been
a week of furious activity and at the end of it I had
a consciousness of some advance, some development I had been hoping for, and I was elated. 'At
last I know how to paint!' I almost shouted, 'At
last I know how to paint!' But almost immediately, at dusk, on this final day, an overwhelming
dying sensation descended upon me which was to
be with me for many days and nights to come ...
It was a sensation that had been there all my life
and now with Dulcie's death, it took control. My
brain collapsed under the strain ... The death
conviction was so absolute that I visited doctors,
not with the hope of a cure, but to find out what
was killing me.[5]

A visit to one doctor led to 'one of the most disturb-
ing experiences' he had ever known. This unnamed
'specialist' turned out to be a chiropractor who
attempted to mesmerise Rees, had him X-rayed and
violently manipulated his spine, causing him great
pain and shock.

Does the painting have a mood of foreboding
which might relate to the impending crisis in his life,
of which he was aware quite early in his wife's
pregnancy in 1926–27? Or am I reading too much
into it? There are numerous references in Rees's
writings to his depression and to his many visits to
medical people regarding various ailments. The
novelist William Styron (*Sophie's Choice*, etc) has
recently published a brilliant, illuminating little
book, *Darkness Visible*,[6] which details his own episode of depression. He regards 'depression' as a
wimp of a word and feels a better one to describe
'the blacker forms of the disorder' would be 'melancholia', a word which appears in English from the
fourteenth century. He notes the historic connection

between melancholia and hypochondria. He also documents the high incidence of artists who have suffered from the disease, including many who have ended their lives because of it.

Styron refers to a book on suicide titled *Self-Destruction in the Promised Land* by Howard I. Kushner, using it to explore the idea that the creative drive of some artists suffering depression might be intertwined with a self-destructive impulse, the idea being that the artist is attempting 'to vanquish death through work honoured by posterity'.

The causes of depression are not fully understood, but a genetic cause is strongly indicated as well as environmental factors, such as a traumatic loss not fully mourned. Chemical factors may also be involved. For Styron this was a tranquilliser he had been prescribed some years prior to his breakdown. For Rees the chemical trigger may have been exposure to lead in the white paint he used.

While I am researching and reflecting away, I meet Barry Pearce, Senior Curator of Australian Art, and tell him a bit, but not all, about what I am doing here. He offers to show me the Gallery's photographic file on Rees's work. I do not expect any real clues here as most of the paintings I have seen already in reproduction. Included in the file, however, are installation photographs of the Rees Retrospective Exhibition in 1942. There are photographs of a group of 1920s oils hanging together on one wall. At least one of these seems to have an almost identical frame to the boatshed painting!

I begin to search the Art Gallery library for information relating to Rubery Bennett, at least during the time that he ran his art gallery in Boomerang House from about 1925 to about 1928. *Did* Bennett ever sell paintings by Lloyd Rees? *Could* W. Charles Crawford, working in the same building, have bought the boatshed painting from Bennett?

I start with *The Life and Work of Rubery Bennett*
by Katherine Campbell Harper.[7] (Bennett, later in
life, was to become better known for his work as a
painter than as a gallery director.) The book is not in
my own library because it is expensive and I have
been unwilling to fork out the money since I'm
afraid I have never really thought much of Bennett as
an artist. The first thing that strikes me in the book
is the number of times the artist John Banks appears
in Rubery's story. I wonder whether I have to recon-
sider Banks as a possibility for the boatshed painting.
He seems to be the artist most associated with
Bennett in the 1920s. It would make sense that
Crawford, if he had bought a painting from Bennett,
would select one by Bennett's most popular artist.

I know Banks's work. I dismissed him early on.
But not before I noted his fondness for waving trees
and the fact that he usually painted scenes near water.
His surfaces can also have the sort of grittiness that
is evidenced in the foreground of the boatshed
painting. But Banks mainly specialised in depicting
elegant, ethereal women draped in exotic clothes
drifting through landscapes which are usually
blatantly romantic. I have always regarded Banks as a
superficial painter—highly successful in his time, but
ultimately shallow. I have suddenly become highly
anxious at the prospect of Banks proving to be the
artist of the boatshed painting. Firstly it would mean
that my judgement is way out. And secondly, I realise
that I really want the boatshed painting to be by
Lloyd Rees. With trepidation I read on ...

It was Banks's habit to spend time in Brisbane
each Australian winter and involve himself in the
local art scene. It is worth quoting at length here
from *The Life and Work of Rubery Bennett*:

It was at the 1920 Annual Exhibition of the
Queensland Art Society that John Banks first saw

Rubery's work. Banks was the son of a wealthy
Sydney family, a painter of figure compositions
and sea and landscapes, and a member of the
Royal Art Society of New South Wales. He was
also interested in helping young artists: *it was he
who suggested Lloyd Rees should move to Sydney
from Brisbane* [my italics—this occurred circa
1917].[8]

That's more promising. Banks was impressed by
what he saw of Rubery's painting and called to tell
him so. He invited Rubery out to dinner and told
him he was 'wasting his time' in Brisbane, that he
should move to Sydney. Rubery was interested but
not convinced and it was not until several years later
that he first visited Sydney.

    Now, since Rubery knew Banks and Banks knew
Rees, it is most likely that Rees knew Rubery. It is
even possible that Rees might have sold some works
through him when Rubery set up as a dealer in
Sydney, even though no solo exhibition by Rees at
Bennett's gallery is recorded. (In fact, I have to
admit that there is no documented connection at all
between Rees and Rubery.) And what about Rubery
Bennett himself as a possibility for the boatshed
painting? In 1922 Rubery made a week-long business trip to Sydney. The impact of the Harbour was
immediate and overwhelming:

It was staggering. I had seen it through
reproductions in *Art in Australia*, Streeton and
Jimmy Jackson, but the beauty of it! I took a tram
to The Spit. I can still see the sparkling blue of the
harbour … Within a year I had moved to Sydney.[9]

The comparison to Lloyd Rees's first response to
seeing Sydney Harbour is striking. Although Rubery
continued to paint following his arrival, he did so

clandestinely. He did not exhibit until the 1940s, at which point he became a highly successful artist. His re-emergence as a painter surprised even his closest friends who thought he had long given up his art.

Rubery Bennett painted landscapes almost exclusively, and he almost invariably appears to have used a palette knife technique. The surfaces are shiny, if not slick. Possibly because of his long, self-imposed period of 'training' they appear to have been painted easily—perhaps too easily. There is no conflict in them, no ambiguities. Lots of clever depictions of attractive but predictable atmospheric effects and romantic landscape subjects. Which is probably why his work consistently sells today for between $10–20,000 at art auctions. It is not, however, given prominence in public galleries.

On stylistic grounds there is no way the boat-shed painting could be by him, unless it is a very early work. And even though I have seen no early examples, it seems unlikely that he would ever have painted so radically differently. But Bennett's important contribution to the support of traditional art in Sydney cannot be denied.

He first lived at a boarding house in Musgrave Street, Mosman, recommended by John Banks, where he stayed until at least 1925. If he was still there in 1927 then Bennett and Lloyd Rees would not have been too far apart.

[He first made his living] with a number of whole-sale agencies including footwear and a profitable line in Dutch cigars and cigarettes ... In late 1923, the Federal Government imposed a duty on imported cigars and Rubery's living dwindled ... Gayfield Shaw was looking for a buyer for his Fine Arts Gallery and Rubery thought this could be a possible opening. While Gayfield Shaw was on holiday, Rubery managed his gallery for a

Lloyd Rees's Near Old Cremorne Wharf *(1920-21), oil on board, 28 x 34.5 cm, signed lower right.*

Lloyd Rees's The White Horse *(1921-22), oil on board, 19 x 16.5 cm, signed lower left.*

Lloyd Rees's Villa Medici, Rome *(1923-24), oil on canvas on board, 29.2 x 39.4 cm, signed lower right.*

Will Dyson's lithograph Compensation (Back at the waggon lines), *(1918) 52.2 x 78 cm.*

The house next door to where Lloyd Rees was living in 1927. Rees's house would have had identical windows.

Be Modern —

Let us demonstrate to you the use of Electricity in your home

For Lighting, it is more economical than gas, and our various styles of fixtures for indirect and direct lighting offer many ideas in home decoration. The use of electricity is not limited to lighting only, but may be used to operate many other home conveniences, such as electric fans, radiators, toasters, flat-irons, &c.

Australian General Electric Co.

"Mazda House,"
Cor. Wentworth Avenue and Goulburn St.
SYDNEY.   Agents in BRISBANE, PERTH, ADELAIDE, TASMANIA,
NEW ZEALAND.

"Mazda House,"
Cor. Queen Street and Little Collins St.
MELBOURNE.

Advertisement from Art in Australia, *first series, no. 1, 1916.*

A Smith and Julius advertisement (illustration by Lloyd Rees) published in Art in Australia, *first series, no. 6, 1919.*

ART AND COMMERCIAL PROGRESS

AS our cities grow in size and importance, our ideas expand with them. As a community we are now more exacting in our taste. In becoming conscious of our past deficiencies we awaken to the possibilities of the future. The thing that in pre-war days would pass muster is not good enough to-day. What we produce must be equal to the best, or as a nation we will not progress. Therefore, when you require art work for the advertising of your goods, let it be the best. It is always worth paying for. The Smith & Julius Studios are a complete organisation with a large staff of experienced artists. We undertake all classes of art work for advertising purposes.

Smith and Julius Studios

24 Bond Street, Sydney.

DIRECTED BY SYDNEY URE SMITH, HARRY JULIUS AND ALBERT COLLINS

A Lloyd Rees drawing of Basil Burdett.

John Banks by Lawson Balfour.

Wal Taylor. Photograph reproduced from The Home, *1 June, 1921, p88.*

Rubery Bennett. Photograph reproduced from Fifty Years of Australian Art, 1879-1929, *published by the Royal Art Society, Sydney, 1929.*

Lloyd Rees. Photographed by, and courtesy of, Greg Weight.

King Street in the 1920s. Photograph by W. J. Hall.

Advertisement for the New Art Salon (illustration by Lloyd Rees), published in Art in Australia, *third series, no.2, 1922.*

The title page of Sydney University – Drawings by Lloyd Rees, *published by Smith and Julius, Sydney, 1922.*

SYDNEY UNIVERSITY

DRAWINGS BY
LLOYD REES

PUBLISHED BY
SMITH & JULIUS
24 BOND STREET
SYDNEY
1922

IN THAT POSITION, WITH GUN COCKED, HE MUST REMAIN MOTIONLESS.

The Fox from His Lair in the Morning

"The ricochetting echo crackled thro' the hills . . . Reynard was dead."

By E. W. CRAWFORD

FOX-HUNTERS have been very busy this winter. Experienced men took note of the fox "crop" for the season in the autumn months; they noticed the hills where the rabbits were thickest; where the fox spoor was most frequently seen; and on cold, clear nights, they listened for that eerie, undulating howl to which is the

Frost crunched underfoot. The granite slabs were as "fast" as ice, fingers ached cruelly, and nostrils dripped and almost froze.

Arriving at the base of the steep, rocky hill, a strenuous climb took me to the summit. Here I determined which way the decoy

Lloyd Rees's An Old Barn, Parramatta.

Stolen Rees and Dobell works found

By SUSAN WYNDHAM

Four paintings stolen from the Manly Art Gallery in 1956 have been recovered from a home in the Eastern Suburbs.

The missing works came to light after a Darling Point businessman asked a Melbourne art dealer, Mr Joseph Brown, last January to sell two early Lloyd Rees paintings and a pencil drawing by the late William Dobell.

Mr Brown, a collector of early works by Rees and a friend of the artist, was eager to check the date and title of one of the paintings, which he described as "a very, very early painting, very unlike a Lloyd Rees painting but nonetheless very beautiful and obviously the work of a skilled painter". So he contacted Mr Rees.

As soon as Mr Rees saw a photograph of the painting, he recognised it as one which had been stolen from the Manly Art Gallery nine years ago.

One night in May 1976, thieves had forced the front door of the gallery and taken six of its best works; so important to buy Tom Roberts stolen *A Flower Seller*, a watercolour by Norman Lindsay called *Swans and Peacocks*; Lloyd Rees's oils, *An Old Barn, Parramatta*, and *Grecian Monastic*; Dobell's pencil drawing, *Portrait of Billy Perer*; and an Arthur Streeton oil, *Nude*.

Police recovered two of the paintings, the Roberts and Lindsay, from a Darling Point home in December 1982, after someone reported seeing them there. They returned the paintings to the gallery and no charges were laid.

When Mr Brown was told several weeks ago that he had the stolen Rees painting, *An Old Barn, Parramatta*, he was also able to identify the other Rees and the Dobell. He had already sold the second Rees painting, but recalled it, refunded the buyer's money and returned all three to the council-owned Manly gallery.

Mr Brown had rejected the Streeton nude as unworthy of his attention. Police have since taken it from the Darling Point home of the vendor and have it in their possession while they renew their inquiries into the theft.

The vendor, who was referred to Mr Brown by a friend, claims that the paintings were left to him by his father-in-law.

The director of the Manly Art Gallery, Mr Peter Pinson, said: "It was remarkable that Joseph Brown happened to ring Lloyd Rees and that Lloyd Rees recognised the painting. The really amazing thing was that the Streeton painting still had a label saying 'Presented to Manly Art Gallery'."

At the time of the theft, the six paintings were valued at $50,000. Mr Pinson said that the Tom Roberts would now bring about $100,000 at auction. Mr Rees said that early paintings by him, similar to those stolen, had fetched as much as $40,000.

Top: Article by Embrey Crawford illustrated by Will Mahony, published in the Australian Sporting and Dramatic News, *31 August, 1929.*

Left: Sydney Morning Herald article by Susan Wyndham, 28 March, 1985.

Above: The boatshed painting in its frame.

The inscription on the reverse of the frame.

"Reanah"
East Crescent St
Mc Mahons Point
Saturday.
1933?

Dear Mr Gill,

I have received your two letters dealing dealing with this mr Clark and his strange attitude and actions.

as I have only a little time in which to catch the week end mail and as I can see the matter has caused you great worry, I must see that this short letter gets away in time.

To begin with I can assure you that I will have ~~two~~ no dealings at all with Mr Clark through any agency but yourself and if he cannot accept the very generous offer we made him he cannot have the pictures.

Anyway when one hears of such men it makes one think works of art are dishonoured by going into such hands.

If I read your thoughts aright I feel you would rather lose the money than put up with further indignities from such a man

Part of a letter by Lloyd Rees to W. H. Gill, Fine Art Society, Melbourne, 1933. Reproduction courtesy Mitchell Library.

Left: A detail of the Roy de Maistre Mural Room.

Below: Roy de Maistre's Flowerpiece *(1926), oil on canvas on board, 78.5 x 64.5 cm, signed lower right.*

couple of weeks, but he did not in fact buy it.

Instead he went into partnership with S. A. Parker, the picture framer, to whom he was introduced by John Banks, and formed the Australian Fine Arts Gallery in March, 1924. Parker had three-storey premises at 219 George Street of which his framing business occupied only the ground floor. The top floor was let to Thea Proctor who had her studio there. The first floor, which had been Basil Burdett's New Art Salon, fell vacant when Burdett moved to Bond Street in 1924.

Rubery took over most of the first floor, with Wal Taylor, who later established the Grosvenor Galleries, occupying one end for his bookbinding workshop.[10]

Whoa! *Bookbinding workshop*? Did Bennett fetch some bookbinding tape to help stick the boatshed painting in the frame? And to return to the frame for a moment. Katherine Campbell Harper notes that S. A. Parker was 'a sleeping partner and the management of the gallery was left to Rubery. Parker's intention was to expand his framing business with custom from artists who left their work on consignment at the gallery.'[11]

Bennett, therefore, as well as providing trade to Parker in terms of the demand for custom-built frames, had access to Parker's stock frames. This access may have continued after the arrangement between Bennett and Parker broke up around 1925 and Bennett moved to the seventh floor of Boomerang House, 139 King Street, between Pitt and Castlereagh Streets. Even after this date it is possible that Bennett may have kept an existing stock of Parker's frames from which to select. Stock frames, perhaps, like the one on the boatshed painting?

We know the occupants of 139 King Street from the Sands' Directory. Harper gives us the additional information that Bennett was introduced to the photographer May Moore on the seventh floor by John Banks. (How did Banks find time for painting?) Harper writes: 'May Moore agreed to let Rubery have two rooms, one for the gallery and a smaller store room, but space was still limited.'[12] She adds that 'May Moore had important people passing through her studio all the time one of whom was Dame Nellie Melba.'

It is hard to imagine that my man Crawford could have resisted the temptation to wander upstairs to Rubery Bennett's gallery. It is quite possible that as a fellow tenant, he attended the openings. Did he purchase the boatshed painting there?

In 1927 or soon after, 'Rubery moved down King street to number 88, Beaumont Chambers.'[13] He also changed the gallery's name to the W. Rubery Bennett Galleries.

Now, if the boatshed painting had been purchased by Crawford from Bennett when his gallery was down the street at number 88, then this would be more reason for the gallery to write Crawford's telephone number, 8930, on the reverse. There would be less chance of Bennett bumping into Crawford to tell him that his painting was ready. He would have to phone.

Bennett's gallery had two more changes of address, to 324 George Street sometime around the end of 1932 and to 1A Hunter Street in 1934 where it remained until 1956. It is possible that the stockbooks of Rubery Bennett's gallery still exist. I intend to write to his widow, Violet, whom I have met once before.

What of the other painters in Bennett's circle or who exhibited with him? *The Life and Works of Rubery Bennett* records a few others apart from

Banks whom, I suppose, might be worth reconsidering, such as Albert Sherman or Henry Hanke. But surely not. Sherman routinely painted technically accomplished flowerpieces and Hanke's formula was in square brushstrokes.

Having got a fix on Bennett, I need to know more about W. Charles Crawford. I leave the Art Gallery of NSW library and head across the Domain to the Mitchell Library.

On the way across I am thinking about bookbinding. If it is a type of bookbinding tape holding the boatshed painting into its frame then there is possibly a promising connection to Lloyd Rees's close friend Wal Taylor. But I can think of two problems with this. Firstly, such tape may have had a variety of household uses, and its leather look may have been simply decorative. It could have been used to repair books or periodicals but not exclusively. Secondly, the tape is torn crudely into the required lengths rather than cut neatly. I feel that a professional bookbinder would not have been so messy. When I reach the Mitchell I decide to try to resolve these problems.

In 1921 when Lloyd Rees held an exhibition of pen drawings at the Gayfield Shaw Gallery, Wal Taylor jointly exhibited examples of his bookbinding. In *Small Treasures of a Lifetime* I note with interest that whilst the two were in Brisbane before moving to Sydney, Wal would mount and frame Lloyd's work![14] However, this probably refers to the framing of works on paper which requires the skill to cut mounts. Also, Lloyd was not painting many oils while in Brisbane. So perhaps I can't make too much of this.

In 1922 Rees had a solo exhibition at Basil

Burdett's New Art Salon, which occupied one end of the first floor of 219 George Street. Wal Taylor, the bookbinder, had his workshop at the other end. By 1924, Burdett had vacated and Rubery Bennett took over the space, trading as the Australian Fine Art Gallery. The picture framer S. A. Parker occupied the ground floor. In 1925, after Bennett had moved to Boomerang House, Wal Taylor established the Grosvenor Galleries on the whole of the first floor.

In 1924 Lloyd Rees actually gives his address in the catalogue of the Royal Art Society Annual Exhibition as 219 George Street. This address may refer to a studio that he had in the building but it is more likely that it means c/ Wal Taylor, his close friend. But I can still find no documented connection between Rees and Rubery Bennett at this time. But Basil Burdett, or even Rees himself, may have used Wal's bookbinding tape to seal the painting. That is, if it is bookbinding tape.

I check the Mitchell card index for trade catalogues of the period, in particular for a catalogue from the stationers W. C. Penfold.[15] Wading through these catalogues I can find no illustrations of or reference to the tape on the reverse of the boatshed painting, although other types of tapes are listed including a transparent one for repairing books and sheet music. Failure to find a reference is not necessarily a bad thing, since it may mean that this tape was not distributed or used widely. In other words, the tape probably had an exclusive use. Given its leather-like texture, it may be bookbinding tape.

Where does this leave me? The tape may have been used by bookbinders, but it does not seem likely that Wal Taylor, a quality bookbinder, would have applied it in such a slap-dash way to seal in a painting. I recall Lloyd Rees's comment about being a 'very dirty painter' and wonder whether it is possible that he could have framed the boatshed painting in such a messy way. Could he have used Wal's tape? And then inscribed it *Suburban Scene*?

The Penfold's catalogue, which is dated 1939, is certainly an absorbing read, though. For example, it has information about stock frames and stock canvas sizes. Unfortunately, there is no stock size of 6"x12", the size of the boatshed frame. Penfold's stock frames were 8"x6", 10"x8", 12"x10", 14"x12" and 16"x12". There are sixteen stock sizes for stretched canvases smaller than 16"x12"—but no 6"x12". But perhaps S. A. Parker made a stock size frame of 6"x12" in the 1920s. The family still operate an art supply and framing business in Sydney. Perhaps someone there will know.

Now on to W. Chas Crawford who had telephone number 8930. He first appears in the Sands' NSW Directory in 1904 when he is listed at Linden Court, Market and Castlereagh Streets. He is described as General Manager of The Dr McLaughlin Company! What on earth could that be? In 1905 he is at number 107 Castlereagh Street with his private address listed as Busaco, Ithaca Road, Elizabeth Bay. In 1908 he is in the Commerce Buildings, Ash Street (and still living at Busaco) and in 1914 he is living at Toowong, Bakewell Terrace, Darling Point (still with his office in the Commerce Buildings). In 1917 he is not listed at all but returns by 1920 and is listed at 139 King Street (obviously his business address now) and 42 Carlotta Road, Double Bay. His business telephone number from 1917 is 8930 and remains this number until October 1927 when it changes following automation of the exchange.

The Sands' Directory listing, which, frustratingly, never gives any information about his occupation (which is unusual, since it was common practice for Sands'), is still the same until 1933 when the Directory ceases publication. I transfer to the Sydney

Telephone Directories from 1933 and again track him forward. His addresses do not change. In the 1950s he is still at King Street and Carlotta Road. But by 1963, according to the directory, he has given up the King Street office and retired (?) to Carlotta Road. By 1966 he is not listed at all, presumed dead.

This sounds straightforward enough but it has taken about two hours to establish this most flimsy information. The library staff, observing me feverishly switching between Sands' and the Telephone Directory, become curious and ask me what I am looking for. I tell them a little of the story and that I am looking for Crawford. They suggest the electoral rolls, which might list his occupation, but they are not sure.

But I am just about searched out for the day and, besides, I have already found what I really came looking for. The most important piece of information at the moment is the approximate year of Crawford's death since it will help me search for his will. On the way home on the bus I fantasise about finding W. C. Crawford's will and, in it, the words: '... and to my friend ... of Melbourne, I leave the small oil painting titled *Suburban Scene* by Lloyd Rees ...'

Wednesday, 19 May

The Office of Wills and Probate is in the Law Court Building on the corner of King, Phillip and Macquarie Streets. I am so eager to find the will that I spend on a cab. I ask the driver to approach the Law Court Building by driving up King Street and letting me out at number 139. I am curious to see what's there.

A disappointment, of course. Boomerang House no longer exists. Someone has demolished the evidence. A giant office block stands on the site that probably held at least three lovely old buildings. I am denied the chance of finding any trace of Crawford's office or having a look at what used to be the gallery on the seventh floor. I may never know whether or not there was a lift, as I have assumed above. I walk on up the hill to the Law Court Building.

Wills are, believe it or not, public property. Evidence of this can be seen in the recent wrangle over the will, or rather, wills plural, of the artist Brett Whiteley which became front page news. Anyone can go along to the Wills and Probate Office and pay ten dollars for a copy of a will if they have the right information. They are listed alphabetically under each year from 1800 to 1982 on microfiche.

According to Nick Vine Hall in *Tracing Your Family History in Australia*,[1] it has been estimated that some 20% of people in NSW who died in the year 1900 left a will. By 1980 this figure had risen to 50%. He notes that the earliest will on the NSW index is that of Curtis Brand, dated 4 July, 1800, in which he leaves his property to a blind boy in Sydney and a shilling to his wife Elizabeth.

I begin to search for Crawford's will between 1963 and 1966, the period when he drops from the Sydney Telephone Directory, but without luck. I search through to the 1980s by which time I calculate he could have been close to 100 years old. Still no luck. I can't believe that a gentleman who owned a property in Double Bay did not leave a will and start searching backwards from 1963. The diligence is rewarded: his will is recorded in the index for 1954. The Sydney Telephone Directory must have forgotten to delete him after 1954. I pay my ten dollars and go up to the next floor to collect the photocopy.

This is a big moment. I settle down in a comfortable chair in the foyer to read the will.

It begins: 'This is the last will and testament of me William Charles Crawford [at last, his full name] of 139 King Street Sydney in the State of New South Wales Company Director and Radiographer.' At last we know what he did for a living. The will appoints as his Trustees his son-in-law Fergus Foster Munro and Ethel Gwendoline Bushell of 139 King Street, Secretary. I wonder whether either is still alive. Ethel is bequeathed 'my carved chair used by me in my office and also a legacy in the sum of one hundred pounds'. His son Hugh Maynard Crawford is bequeathed 'my diamond cufflinks'.

There is a reference to his shares in McGovern Radiology Pty and also to 'the Optical Department of the business [which] together with all furniture and fittings ... shall be sold to Charles Gordon Willings of no. 14 Albert Avenue Chatswood who is at present employed by the said company in connection with the said optical business'. I recall that on the same floor as Crawford in King Street was a J. F. McGovern, listed as a dentist. There is provision for his wife Dorothea Crawford. If she were to predecease him then the residue of the estate would go to 'my son Hugh Maynard Crawford and my daughter Ithaca May Munro'. There is also a reference to 'the Dental Section of the Company's business'. The equipment is to be offered to a C. L. Harvey.

There is no reference to any paintings, let alone one by Lloyd Rees.

I am still sitting in the comfy foyer chair working out my next step. On the other side is a telephone and next to it a nice new set of directories. I get up and go over to them, will in hand. Of those beneficiaries mentioned above, at least one is still in the current telephone directory: C. G. Willings, now at Balgowlah. There is an H. M. Crawford in Sylvania but because the name Crawford is more common—this may not be the son. There is an E.

Bushell in Chatswood but not an E. G. Bushell.
There may be a connection since Charles Willings
once lived at Chatswood. There is no C. L. Harvey.
There is no F. F. Munro but there is an I. M. Munro
at Canley Vale. Could this be Crawford's daughter? I
have an interesting day of telephoning ahead of me.

But first, I go downstairs again and search for
the will of William Charles Crawford's wife,
Dorothea. I am getting used to the system and I find
it easily. It was made in 1970. The clerk to whom I
give my will application form is getting interested. I
outline what I am looking for, which is getting
difficult to do with so many possible strands, and he
offers some valuable information that had not
occurred to me: when wills are processed there can
be an Affidavit of Assets and Liabilities in which the
entire estate is itemised and valued. Unlike the will
itself, this is not available unless the person requesting it can prove they are a member of the family or if
they can show a good cause as to why they wish to
see it. A letter must be written to the Principal
Registrar of the Probate Office. Could I show a good
cause?

I thank the clerk for this information and go
upstairs again to collect Dorothea's will. Then I head
up to the cafeteria on the fourteenth floor to have a
coffee and read it. I take a seat near the window
which, I find, has a panoramic view of Sydney
Harbour. I automatically run my eye around the
shoreline from Kirribilli to Manly looking for red
boatsheds ...

Which reminds me. In 1990 the National Maritime
Museum in Darling Harbour, Sydney, was given a
twenty metre long panorama of Sydney Harbour
painted in 1907 by the amateur painter and inventor

Muriel Mary Sutherland Binney.[2] It had been painted for the First Australian Exhibition of Women's Work held in Melbourne in October 1907 and was selected for the Franco-British Exhibition in London in 1908. It then disappeared from public view, and Muriel Binney was forgotten, until the artist's family offered to donate the panorama to the museum in 1990. Reportedly it is currently in pieces and being restored. I must arrange to see it. Perhaps I will find the boatshed on the shoreline, somewhere in the jigsaw puzzle.

Referred to in Dorothea's will are her daughter Ithaca May Munro, who, apart from a sum of money, is bequeathed 'my dutch chair, my lamp with coloured metal and glass top [I wonder if it could be by Tiffany, the most famous producer of such lamps], my jewellery and articles of personal use ... and the residue of my household effects excepting my furniture.' Following references to friend Leila James, and Dorothea's grandson Fergus Ferguson Crawford Munro and granddaughter Catherine Ann Ives, her son, Hugh Maynard Crawford is bequeathed 'my late husband's diamond ring, American twenty dollar gold piece and watch fob'. The residue was to go to her son and daughter. In a codicil to the will dated 1971 (and I think she may be in a nursing home because it is witnessed by a J. Paton, Matron) she changes her trustees from the Public Trustee to Fergus Foster Munro (her son-in-law) and Julia Beatrice Crawford (probably her daughter-in-law).

Back to the telephone book. There is no Julia Beatrice Crawford. The grandson and granddaughter are not listed either. But it has been a productive day. I return home to write some letters and make some key phone calls.

Thursday, 20 May

A summary of the telephone calls:

(1) To H. M. Crawford, possibly Hugh Maynard Crawford, the son of William Charles Crawford. There is no answer throughout the day. When the phone finally answers in the evening, a woman tells me, laughingly, that Hugh Maynard is not of their clan.

(2) To I. M. Munro, possibly Ithaca May Munro, William Charles Crawford's daughter. But it isn't. It is Ivy Marjory Munro, no relation.

(3) To E. Bushell, possibly William Charles Crawford's secretary in 1954, Ethel Gwendoline Bushell. A young woman with an American accent answers. No, she says, Mrs Bushell does not live there any more. Was she Ethel Gwendoline Bushell? The young woman doesn't know. Letters still arrive at her house, addressed to E. Bushell. It does not sound like Ethel Gwendoline. I think this is a dead end.

(4) To C. G. Willings, possibly a business partner of Crawford's. I am more sure of this one because of the fairly unusual name. A woman answers the phone. I tell her that I am attempting to contact a Charles Gordon Willings. She asks me why and I briefly explain my mission.

Mrs Willings tells me that although I do have the correct number, her husband Charles died last year. I offer my condolences before asking if she knew a Mr Crawford. Indeed she did. She is happy to talk about the business operated by Crawford and for which her husband worked from 1934.

The business, she affirms, was in Boomerang House which was owned by the Albert family whose business was music. They also owned the 'Holly-wood-style' harbourfront mansion called Boomer-ang. Occasionally, Mrs Willings herself would work in the office 'when one of the girls did not show up'. She is not sure whether Crawford collected paintings but he did have various things in his rooms in King Street including a number of amusing little drawings. She thought they were American because Crawford was an American. This would explain the reference, in Dorothea's will, to the American $20 gold piece and possibly to the lamp with the coloured metal and glass top which I had questioned whether it was by Tiffany, an American firm.

Mrs Willings says she had never visited the Crawfords' home and describes him as 'rather gruff' in manner. He did not talk much about himself. Her husband's relationship with him had been very much a business one. Both Mrs Willings and her husband Charles had been interested in art and had painted themselves, studying for a time under an artist by the name of Sid Sullivan. They had 'picked up things' by other artists and collected art books but she could not recall them ever having discussed art with Crawford. She does not remember the boatshed painting when I describe it to her, but she is happy for me to send her a photograph, just to make sure.

Crawford, she continues, had go-ahead ideas for his time, introduced, she thinks, from the United States. The business was like a modern-day medical centre with a number of associated professions in the one place by the 1950s. Mrs Willings had seen Mrs Crawford shortly before her death but she had had no contact with the Crawfords' son and daughter for many years and did not know where they might be.

As a final question I ask whether Boomerang House at 139 King Street had a lift. 'Oh yes,' she chuckles, 'and lovely white marble stairs. All gone now of course.'

I now have a clearer picture of Mr Crawford. If it was in his nature to be gruff, perhaps keeping his emotions to himself, could this have meant that he would be the type of person who would have responded to the boatshed painting? It has such a strong sense of reservedness about it, a sense of holding things inside—of having a secret. Or is this too far fetched?

Sunday, 23 May

I compose a letter to Mrs Violet Bennett, the widow of Rubery.

Dear Mrs Bennett,
   Some years ago I spoke to you about a painting I was researching which was said to be by Rubery Bennett, and you kindly offered to have a look at it. Your opinion about it—that it was not by Rubery on stylistic grounds—was later confirmed to be absolutely correct on technical grounds.
   I am currently researching another unsigned painting which I believe may have been purchased from Rubery's Australian Fine Art Gallery on the sixth floor, 139 King Street known as Boomerang House (or later at 88 King Street) by someone who had an office downstairs on the second floor. The purchase may have taken place prior to October 1927.
   The painting is exactly 6" x 12" and the original frame may be a stock frame by S. A. Parker although there are no framing labels on it. The painting is held into the frame by bookbinding tape. Inscribed in pencil on the frame is a title *Suburban Scene*, the number 8930 and the name 'Booth', 'Book' or 'Boon'.
   The telephone number for the office on the

second floor of Boomerang House prior to October 1927 was CITY 8930. A Mr William Charles Crawford was listed as the subscriber to this number. The painting also has a sticker on the reverse with the number 22 which is probably an exhibition number.

I am wondering if catalogues or even stock books exist of works exhibited at the gallery around this time. Is it possible that you may recall any of the above-mentioned people and whether they might have purchased work from Rubery? Mr Crawford was married to Dorothea and while working as a radiographer also had interests in dental and optometrist practices. The Crawfords lived in Carlotta Road, Double Bay.

Enclosed is a photograph of the painting. I have some ideas about who the painting might be by, and would be happy to discuss them with you. I realise that this is a 'tall order' and hope this request is not putting you to too much trouble.

I look forward to hearing from you.

Yours sincerely,

Stephen Scheding

Monday, 31 May

I have not received a reply to my letter to Joel's. I phone Jon Dwyer. He says he has passed my letter on to the executor of the estate of an F. J. Sainsbury, the vendor of the boatshed painting. And, just like that, I have a name! Sainsbury. I now have to see whether a link can be established between this Sainsbury and one of the other names that has emerged from my research so far.

Jon Dwyer also recalls that the boatshed painting was one of three paintings in Sainsbury's estate. The executor 'walked in off the street' and

asked Joel's to sell them. He remembers the boatshed painting well. 'I thought it was by Harry
McClelland,' he says. Harry who? I've never heard of
him. Jon tells me that he has sold a similar work
which was clearly signed 'Harry McClelland'. He
tells me that Harry McClelland is best known for
starting the McClelland Art Gallery at Frankston in
Victoria. But his work is not at all well known.

This is a bit of a shock. But Jon is only going on
a comparison with one other painting so perhaps I
shouldn't get too depressed just yet. But I will have
to check this Harry McClelland out. Jon promises to
phone the executor of Sainsbury's will and ask him
to contact me regarding my research.

Thursday, 3 June

The letter from Mrs Bennett has arrived:

> Dear Mr Scheding,
>   Herewith I return your photograph—I am very
> sorry I cannot help you, as I have no recall of this
> painting, and no records. If we had any record or
> information about the painting it would have
> been passed on at the time of sale.
>   Yours sincerely,
>   Violet Bennett

Since the Sydney end of the research is not proving
fruitful at the moment, the next logical step is to
write to the Victorian Probate Office requesting the
will of F. J. Sainsbury. If I can locate the will of F. J.
Sainsbury, I will at least have the names of some
people who may know something of the boatshed
painting. Like how he or she came to possess it.

Saturday, 5 June

In today's edition of the *Australian* is an article by
Hazel Rowley, the author of the just-published
biography of Christina Stead.[1] In this article Rowley
touches upon some of the problems faced by the
researcher who is desperate to get information from
certain individuals or families who may not wish to
give information, or who may simply not be interested. Rowley cites the case of her attempt to talk to
Walter George Keith Duncan whom Christina Stead
had followed to England. Duncan wrote a reply to
Rowley that he was too ill to see her and she knew
from other sources that he was dying of cancer. She
writes:

> The need for certain information, that could only
> have come from him, overrode all notions of
> moral decency. I would have to turn up in a busy
> nursing home, loom up by the bed of a dying
> man, explain who I was and why I had taken no
> notice of his letter. Duncan was known to have a
> formidable temper …
>
> I locate Duncan's room, knock, go in. [He] is
> sitting by the window … a slight figure dressed in
> baggy flannel trousers and a waistcoat … It takes
> him a while to realise who I am—he is rather deaf.
> Then his brown eyes flash at me from behind his
> heavy glasses. 'I have no intention of talking
> about that woman Christina Stead.'
>
> I sit down. We talk, about him, about me and
> eventually about that cursed woman. At one stage
> he pauses, looks out at the garden and mutters: 'If
> that's what women are like, God preserve me
> from them.'

Another episode in Rowley's investigations was more
productive. By tracking down the name of a relation

of a friend of Stead in the London phone book she eventually located the friend herself and wrote to her and received a reply. Initially this friend did not want to see Rowley, saying that her friendship with Stead had ended sadly. But Rowley then sent her 'the most persuasive letter I was capable of'. She continues:

> One can spend hours on such letters, and the reply is stony silence. A week passed and I came home one evening to find another envelope ... Inside a long letter. It began: 'Dear Hazel Rowley, what a temptress you are ...'

This response led to the eventual uncovering of 360 letters by Stead which had been written over the years to this friend.

I am heartened by reading about these exploits in uncomfortable circumstances. After all, I intend to probe the life of a recently deceased person whose relatives may be in no mood to talk about a potentially valuable painting that they have just sold for a song.

Sunday, 6 June

It is a glorious winter Sunday and I take my four-year-old son, Sam, for a drive to Middle Harbour. We head off with a photograph of the boatshed painting and a camera.

I have shown the boatshed painting to numerous people over the past few weeks and have been eliminating many of the possible sites that have been suggested. I am becoming convinced that the general inspiration for the boatshed painting is somewhere along the strip of shoreline from The Spit to Balmoral. The other sites suggested, mostly located in the inner Harbour, have the problem of

having high hills in the backgrounds. But where I am
headed there is the possibility of a glimpse of an
uninterrupted view across water to the horizon. I
also remember there being houses with boatsheds at
Chinaman's Beach which is about midway between
Balmoral and The Spit.

I have decided against using a boat for this
reconnoitre. Lloyd Rees and other artists had
travelled to these spots by trams which terminated in
the 1920s at both Balmoral and The Spit. The tram
would have gone down Parriwi Road which runs
high above Chinaman's Beach, but it is more likely
that an artist would have stayed on the tram until
The Spit and walked around the rocks if he or she
wanted to get to Chinaman's. It would have been
easier than descending the hill loaded up with
painting equipment.

So, we start at The Spit. Being low tide, we find
we can walk fairly easily from The Spit around the
rocks. The rocks beyond Chinaman's which lead
from the southern side around towards Balmoral
look a bit more forbidding. We will have to drive
around to Balmoral later. Along the rocks we pass a
couple of boatsheds as well as some rusty slips where
boatsheds had once been. But none of the sites are
promising. There are no significant promontories
similar to the one in the boatshed painting and the
background cliff to the south is wrong in any case.
When we reach Chinaman's Beach we retrace our
steps and return to the car.

At Balmoral we walk along the rock shelf for a
short distance back towards Chinaman's Beach but it
is obvious that there will be no signs of boatsheds
along this stretch as it has a bare cliff face. So we turn
around and stroll on the sand to the other end of
Balmoral Beach, past the place up on the hill where
theosophists had built an amphitheatre in 1924 from
which to witness the second coming of the Messiah.

We approach the spot where Rees painted *Balmoral* in 1927. At first glance, this south-western end of Balmoral does not look promising either. We pass what used to be the wharf depicted in *Balmoral* (now a swimming pool and marina) and walk along the small, crescent-shaped beach which curves around the piece of water called, appropriately, Hunter's Bay.

At the end of this strip of beach is a building, a scout hall with a boatshed. They are too new to be the buildings in the boatshed painting. They are juxtaposed in roughly the same manner but are not in the same position in relation to the promontory. The view behind the promontory is quite similar to that in the boatshed painting. What is missing are the trees to the left, at the end of the promontory.

I walk back to a point at which the artist of the boatshed painting might have stood if this was in fact his subject. Where I am now standing is only a few paces from where Rees must have painted *Balmoral*. I look at the scout hall and boatshed again. I imagine an older building, perhaps a previous scout hall, and a red boatshed in the place of these new buildings. I mentally stick in a tall tree at the left, as Rees might have done.

This could almost be the spot! It is certainly not topographically correct, but I think it has a certain *feel* to it. Perhaps there is something about the distance I am from the possible subject. It seems to be about the distance Rees often positioned himself from his subjects in the 1920s.

Away in the distance across the water is Manly. One can even see the tall Manly pine trees. In the boatshed painting, in the absolute centre of it, is a splodge which had been puzzling me. But now I see that it could be an impressionistic representation of a Manly pine. It is a little large, almost a caricature of one. Has the artist left me a big clue smack bang in the middle of the painting? I also note that the headland in the left of the boatshed painting could be Grotto Point.

If this is the spot, then it could explain the similarities of the pigments used in the boatshed painting to those in *Balmoral*, painted only metres away in 1927. Could both paintings have been painted within a very short space of time and distance? I will now have to discover whether any older buildings ever stood near the end of the promontory and, if so, whether they relate in some way to the ones in the boatshed painting. I need to look at old photographs.

It has been a pleasant day at the beach. Not perfect, but better than a poke in the eye with a wet paintbrush. Sam has tripped fully clothed into the water, accidentally on purpose, and is gurgling with pleasure.

Monday, 7 June

On phoning the Mosman Library, I find that they employ an 'historical librarian', one Sharon Muir. Sharon tells me that the library holds a collection of old photographs of Mosman and Balmoral Beach and invites me to view them. We make an appointment to do this at the library for the following Saturday.

Tuesday, 8 June

I collect the photographs which I took of Balmoral Beach from the chemist and scrutinise them carefully. I am reminded of Antonioni's film *Blow Up*, the difference being that I am not trying to solve a murder, but an act of creation.

The first thing I realise is that when painting *Balmoral* in 1927 Rees may have foreshortened the distance to the headlands in the background, confirming that he did change his subjects. 'I never claimed to be a topographical painter' he once wrote.[1] Sydney Ure Smith wrote in 1917: 'He is not a realist ... his drawings of buildings and streets would sometimes annoy the historian, as he has a way of donating trees and ornamental devices where they are often unfortunately not to be seen.'[2]

But there is little else I can tell from the photographs. I will have to wait until I find out whether there was an old building and boatshed on this promontory, hopefully from the library's photographs.

Thursday, 10 June

When I arrive home from work there is a message on my answering machine from the Probate Office in Melbourne. It is good news—Mary O'Brien says that she has located the will of F. J. Sainsbury (died 1993), who has turned out to be Florence Jane, and if I would like to send $31.80 she will send me everything I have asked for. What service!

Saturday, 12 June

At the Mosman Library, a cursory search through early photographs of Balmoral does not prove helpful. I find only one photograph, dated 1929, which shows a view of the south end of Balmoral Beach. It is a distant view taken from the northern end of Edwards Beach back towards Balmoral, perhaps a kilometre away. I blow it up on the library's photocopier, focusing on the approximate spot of the Balmoral scout hall. But these photocopies do not have enough clarity to be able to tell for sure whether there is a house and boatshed where I think they should be. I can't see them.

I also find out the names of some local historians and the address of the Mosman Historical Society. Perhaps some local octogenarian will remember the spot in the 1920s: 'Oh, yes. The old boatshed. I remember young Lloyd Rees used to come down to Balmoral to paint it.'

Sunday, 27 June

I phone the Parker Gallery in Sydney which has a direct connection to S. A. Parker and speak to Derrick Parker whose great-great-grandfather was S. A. Parker. Apparently S. A. (Sidney Albert) had a son by the name of Clarendon who continued the framing business and is still alive, aged 89. This Clarrie works for the Parker Gallery once a week and Derrick feels he would be happy to talk to me about Parker frames from the 1920s. A key question to him will be whether S. A. Parker had stock frames measuring 6 x 12 inches. I tell Derrick I will be in touch again after I have worked out all the questions I need to ask Clarrie.

Monday, 28 June

I phone Lloyd Rees's son, Alan Rees, to let him know that the painting has been cleaned. He says he and Jan would love to see the painting again. To prepare them for my visit, I write them a letter giving the basic information I have to date, in the hope that they may dig something up before my arrival. Some names might ring bells.

It is a very long letter, during the course of which I pose some questions:

(1) Do you know of any Lloyd Rees paintings from the 1920s which definitely have Parker frames on them?

(2) I have been surprised at Rubery Bennett's connection to Lloyd's friends Wal Taylor and Basil Burdett. It seems possible that there might be a connection between Lloyd Rees and Bennett who was for a while in partnership with Wal Taylor and had an arrangement with Parker to direct framing jobs to him. In 1924, Parker was on the ground floor of 219 George Street, below the gallery space run variously by Burdett, Bennett and Taylor. Do you have any information that might connect Lloyd Rees more closely with Rubery Bennett?

(3) I would like to locate all the catalogues of solo and group exhibitions by Lloyd Rees in the 1920s as well as *all* the dealers who sold Lloyd's work. Is that possible?

(4) I have to admit it is rare for an artist not to sign a work that is intended to be exhibited publicly. I wonder if Lloyd Rees was ever known to have done this?

(5) I don't suppose the name Crawford has ever turned up in your records as an owner of a Lloyd Rees painting?

(6) I have managed to extract from Joel's the name of the person who put the painting into auction. It was a trustee of the estate of the late Florence Jane Sainsbury. I am currently in the process of tracking down any relatives Florence Jane Sainsbury may have had in the hope that they may remember something of the painting. Is the name Sainsbury anywhere in your records?

(7) Did Lloyd Rees ever develop his oils from his

pen and pencil sketches? If so, would it be possible to look through any sketchbooks you may have in the hope of seeing a connection between the boatshed painting and a sketch?

(8) I am struck by the similarities in the pigments of the boatshed painting, now that it has been cleaned, and *Balmoral* painted in 1927. I am currently investigating a possible site for the boatshed painting which is within a hundred metres from where *Balmoral* was painted. Do you know of any other paintings done in this area around 1927?

(9) Would you have any examples of Lloyd's handwriting in the 1920s? I need to convince myself that the inscription on the back of the frame is not by Lloyd himself.

Thursday, 1 July

Back to the Mitchell.

I locate some useful articles on Wal Taylor and his bookbinding.[1] After all I have come to know about Wal, it is nice to finally see some illustrations of his bookbinding and other tooled leather work. Unfortunately, while his methods are described in some detail, there is nothing to indicate he could have provided the tape used for sealing the boatshed painting into its frame. However, the examples of his meticulous work convince me that he, personally, would never have sealed the painting in so sloppily, even if it is his tape.

I discover a treasure chest of manuscript material: the personal papers, etc of William Henry Gill. Gill was the art dealer who ran the Australian Fine Art Gallery at 100 Exhibition Street in Melbourne from the early years of this century until the 1930s. His papers contain hundreds of letters from Australia's major artists who exhibited with him at the time. In one box there is what could be a complete set of his gallery's exhibition catalogues.

I find one letter from S. A. Parker to Gill (unfortunately not dated) advising Gill that 'all the pictures for your show—with the exception of John Banks—have been sent ... to Thomas Whitelaw and Company, with instructions to deliver them to you'. This indicates that Parker framed the work of John Banks. There is also a reference in this Parker letter to Rubery Bennett: 'Re the matter of the Etchings— I handed your letter to Mr Bennett, and I thought he had replied to same; I have spoken again to him and hope he will reply by this mail.'

Since I know that the business arrangement between Parker and Bennett did not work out and was dissolved in 1925, the date of this letter could be 1925 or shortly after, judging by its tone. The letter links Parker to the dealer Gill at this time. And as it turns out, the arrangement whereby paintings by Sydney artists framed by Parker and then sent to Gill continued for some years.

More to the point, a letter by Lloyd Rees to William Henry Gill dated 4 March, 1933, mentions that Rees's drawings being sent for exhibition to Gill's gallery 'will go to Thallon's [a Melbourne framer] in two boxes. One box of 20 from Fleming, framer, Hunter St and another of 22 from S. A. Parker, George St.' Presumably they were sent to Thallon to repair any frames which might have been damaged en route from Sydney. So, as I suspected, Lloyd Rees did use Parker for his framing. But I would like to. be certain that he used him earlier than 1933, and for oils.

It is vaguely possible that the boatshed painting may have been framed by Parker in the 1920s and, later, sent to Gill for sale. If this is so, then it would explain how the painting got from Sydney to Melbourne and eventually into the hands of Florence Sainsbury from whose estate it entered Joel's auction. If this is the case, then I would have to rethink the number 8930. Maybe it's a Melbourne telephone number! I may have to get back to Bert Spratt. However, this possibility is unlikely if the boatshed painting is, in fact, by Rees because there is no mention by Rees, in his dozen letters to Gill in the early 1930s, of having had prior dealings with Gill. Also, the Australian Fine Art Gallery catalogues which form part of the Gill collection of papers do not include any reference to oil paintings by Lloyd Rees.

In all, there are about a dozen handwritten letters by Rees to Gill, each referring to his impending exhibition of drawings which was to be held at the Australian Fine Art Gallery in March, 1933. On 2 March, 1933, Rees writes to Gill that

> although many of the drawings depict certain parts of Sydney, I have never stressed the topographical aspect for its own sake. Certain combinations of landscape and architecture have appealed to me and I have tried to make the most of those aspects that lend themselves to pencil treatment; and my aim whether in success or failure has been the attainment of pencil quality in relation to design and form.

One imagines that the same basic aim was present when working in oils. But does it have relevance to the topographical accuracy, or otherwise, of the buildings in the boatshed painting?

The humility of Rees in these letters is incredible when we consider the greatness we associate now with these early 1930s drawings.

I photocopy all the letters by Rees.

At home, I set the boatshed painting up on my desk
with the reverse side facing me, the inscription showing. I find the 's' for 'such' in one of the Rees letters
I have photocopied, and compare it to the 'S' in
Suburban Scene.

It is uncannily similar—it is incredibly similar!
There is precisely the same movement of the line at
the bottom of the letter which reverses horizontally
before moving on to join the next letter. The next
letter turns out in both cases to be a 'u'. Again, a
striking similarity.

This is too good to be true. I begin to read
through all the photocopied pages, marking the
similarities as I come to them. Rees's writing of the
letter 's' is fascinating. Almost invariably he uses the
form 's' to begin words starting with 's' and the
cursive form '*ſ*' if it is not the beginning letter of a
word. But there are exceptions. In one letter the
word 'such' appears three times on one page. In two
cases the form 's' is used and in the third, the cursive
'*ſ*' begins the word. This correspondence needed to
be written in a hurry 'to catch the week-end mail'
and this may partly explain Rees's inconsistency. But
what is the real reason why a writer might switch
from one form of a letter to another? What subconscious brain messages are being sent? That's
heady stuff.

There are plenty of examples of the letter
combination 'an' and 'ne' and many of these appear
similar to these combinations in *Suburban Scene*. A
'look' and a 'took' both show promise in relation to
the inscription 'Booth' or 'Book' or 'Boon'. There is
less similarity with the capital 'B's. However, the
movement at the bottom of the 'B' in the inscription
strongly resembles the movement of the line at the

bottom of the 'S's in *Suburban Scene* suggesting it is
in the same hand. If it is by Rees then the word is
most likely to be 'Book'. Rees's way of writing 'th' is
quite distinctive and is unlike the end of the 'Boo'
word in the inscription. For example I can find no
examples of uncrossed 't's, even when he is writing
in a hurry. His 'n's are also quite consistent and also
unlike the end of the 'Boo' word. And now to the
numbers. Do any in his correspondences resemble the
inscribed numbers '8930'? The answer, I think, is yes.
I find enough examples of the four numbers in Rees's
letters and these numbers bear a distinct similarity.

But surely the inscription on the back of the
painting can't be by Lloyd Rees. Surely Alan and Jan
Rees would have picked it up when I showed it to
them. Both must have been familiar with his
handwriting—Jan had typed the manuscript for
Small Treasures of a Lifetime from Lloyd Rees's draft
manuscript which was later donated to the Mitchell.
But, perhaps, like me, they assumed that since the
inscribed title *Suburban Scene* was so atypical of a
Lloyd Rees title of the 1920s, they did not look
closely at it. But this is very far fetched.

The similarities are probably just a coincidence.
But I will certainly have to get examples of Rees's
handwriting done in the 1920s and make a proper
comparison. Perhaps get a handwriting expert in.

Wednesday, 7 July

I show Frank McDonald my very long letter to Alan
and Jan Rees so that he can catch up on my progress
with the boatshed painting. I can see that he is still
highly sceptical about it being by Lloyd Rees. And
even more sceptical about the possibility of proving
it, even if it is. Not only that, he says 'even if it is by
Rees, why put all this effort into researching a

painting that at best is going to be fairly minor in
Rees's oeuvre? Why not write a book about discovering something major like a lost American impressionist painting, or even a whole collection?' But
making a grand discovery is not entirely the purpose
of my exercise.

As Frank reads through the letter to Alan and
Jan he mutters things like 'you're such a miniaturist'
and 'this is quite orientalist'. He has a pencil poised
to make notes. I leave him to mumble to himself and
wander around his library in the adjacent rooms.
When I return he has finished reading and I detect
that the mood has changed slightly. He has not
pencilled any notes on the letter. He asks me whether
I have checked this fact or that lead.

He then asks whether I have rung all the
Sainsburys in the Melbourne phone book. I tell him
I'd thought about it, but have been waiting for
Florence Jane Sainsbury's last will and testament to
arrive so as to know which relations to phone, and
also to get a sense of the family. Frank seems to nod
his understanding but gets down the Melbourne
Telephone Directory, an old one—1988, and goes to
the Sainsburys. We see F. J. Sainsbury listed at 11
Elgin Avenue, Armadale, not too far, in fact, from
Joel's office. 'Elgin' has an interesting resonance.
The Elgin Marbles were shipped by Lord Elgin to
England in the first years of the nineteenth century.
The Marbles were, in fact, 250 feet of the Parthenon
frieze. Elgin was imprisoned by the French but
returned to England in 1806 to be met by misgivings
about his vandalism and doubts about the authenticity of the Marbles. They looked too good to be
true. But in 1816 they were purchased by the British
Parliament, an act which fuelled the British passion
for collecting. The debate over their ownership
continues today.

Frank reaches for the phone and starts to dial.

'No, stop, Frank! Put down that telephone!' I yell. I know that I need to have all the available information on the Sainsbury family before going off half-cocked. If a relation answers Frank's call, I have not thought through a complete list of questions to ask. I don't want to have to make a second call which may sound as if I am hounding them. Frank reluctantly accepts my point and replaces the phone. Even though he does not think the boatshed painting is by Rees, he would like to know what Florence Jane's family has to say about it.

Over lunch I tell Frank about my amateur handwriting analysis. 'Well,' he says, 'if the inscription is in Lloyd's handwriting, that could be interesting.'

Friday, 9 July

The will for Florence Jane Sainsbury has finally arrived together with the list of her assets at the time of death. At first I find it disappointing, since none of her beneficiaries are the same as William Charles Crawford's beneficiaries. Nor is there mentioned a 'Booth', 'Book' or 'Boon'. Therefore there is no immediate link to my research into the painting's possible Sydney existence.

However, there is plenty of information to work on. Florence Jane's address on the Inventory of Assets dated 4 May, 1993, is the Lynn Private Nursing Home at 11 Elgin Avenue, Armadale—her 1988 address. This means that from at least 1988 until her death she was in this nursing home.

The assets are exclusively monies in various bank accounts. The total amount adds up to almost $200,000. Under the heading 'Furniture and Household Effects' the only items listed are '2 Paintings'. These are 'valued by Executor at $700'.

So it seems that when Florence died, her only material possessions of significance were these two paintings. There is not even any listing of jewellery. I wonder whether the paintings may have had sentimental value and meant a great deal to her. It is a nice feeling to know that the previous owner of the boatshed painting might have cherished it to the end and in preference, perhaps, to other possessions. It also means that it may be possible that an acquaintance or family member may know the reason why she so cherished it and chose to spend her last days with it.

The main beneficiary of the will is a Mrs Dunkley. Token sums of money are given to various people including Robert E. Blain, noted elsewhere in the will as the 'alternative executor'. The will has been witnessed by Peter Merrylees, the appointed solicitor, and Audrey Pavlich, Nursing Sister, presumably employed at Lynn Private Nursing Home when the will was drawn up on 19 December, 1988.

I wait 'til late at night before phoning Telecom to get the telephone numbers for the people mentioned in the will. I figure that the operator will not be so busy and will give me seven or eight numbers in one go. I am successful with all but the main beneficiary, Mrs Dunkley. I do not have enough details on her. All the others are still living at the addresses listed in the will and now I have their telephone numbers.

Sunday, 11 July

The first call is to the Lynn Private Nursing Home. Sister Pavlich is still working there and is friendly and helpful. She locates Florence's card and provides me with some details: Florence Jane Sainsbury had entered the nursing home on 26 August, 1988. She had, at this time, been a long time widowed, with no children. She had a sister from whom she was long estranged, who lived in the country.

Following her death, someone had come to collect her things, including the paintings, and had taken them home. This person's name was Robert Blain and she gives me his telephone number. This latter piece of information tallies with mine, Robert Blain being listed in the will as the alternative Executor. The phone number is the same as the one I got from Telecom.

To prepare for the next phone call I write down the information I need to find out—the list that I did not have prepared when I last saw Frank McDonald.

(1) Florence Jane Sainsbury's maiden name. (Crawford or Booth, perhaps, would be nice.)
(2) Her age when she married and when she died. (Perhaps the painting was a wedding gift.)
(3) Her husband's full name and occupation. (Radiographer? Dentist?)
(4) Whether she had a Sydney connection. Had she been born there or had she ever worked there (perhaps in Mr Crawford's rooms?)?
(5) How, when and where had she come by the boatshed painting? ('Could you possibly be more specific? What year was that exactly?')
(6) Did she have it hanging in her apartment at the nursing home? ('Could you perhaps tell me why this was? Did she have any particular attachment to the painting? Did she have other things with her?')
(7) Who else might be able to give me information? Who is Mrs Dunkley? ('I have a list of people referred to in the will. Would it be worthwhile phoning them? What about her sister, could you tell me her name?')
(8) And what was Florence Jane Sainsbury like?

(9) I don't suppose she left any letters, that sort of thing?

Robert E. Blain answers the phone. I explain who I am and why I am ringing him. He doesn't seem at all put out by the call nor the rather bizarre reason for it. In fact, it turns out that he has a great sense of humour. My letter to Joel's had been passed on to him. He had been intending all the while to reply but somehow hadn't got around to it.

He remembers the boatshed painting well, but the artist is 'a complete mystery'. There were actually three paintings in Florence's room at the nursing home. The boatshed painting was not listed in the statement of her assets as it was not considered to have much value. Robert Blain had taken the three paintings to Joel's himself. The other two were an Archibald Colquhoun oil titled *Lorne*, 29 x 38 centimetres (signed) and a Harley Cameron Griffiths titled *Autumn Shadows*, 26 x 34 centimetres (signed and dated '45). Both are fairly well-known Melbourne painters. Robert Blain in fact knew Harley Griffiths' father, also an artist. Harley Griffiths Senior had got him a job with Mobil.

It is interesting that both the signed paintings owned by Florence were small and by Melbourne artists. If I had only this information available to me I would probably conclude that the small unsigned boatshed painting was also by a Melbourne artist. So this information is not at all helpful to the whole Rees theory. It is sounding like Florence collected small Victorian landscapes—although two paintings is not enough to be in any way certain of this. Besides, both Colquhoun and Griffiths could be considered Meldrumites and so the boatshed painting, stylistically, seems to be the odd one out. It may even have been a gift and not an indicator of her taste in collecting.

So what of Florence Jane Sainsbury herself?
'Tough old bitch,' replies Robert Blain with a laugh.
'A suspicious personality, very difficult to deal with.'
He then tells me she was 96 when she died.

Robert fills me in with some details about her
life. She was born and grew up in the Dandenongs
where her father was the local undertaker. His name
was Garner, or at least that's what was on F. J.'s birth
certificate. Robert thinks that it might be a mistake
and that the family name was Garnar. Mr and Mrs
Garnar had six children—five girls and a boy.
Florence would have been born in 1897. In about
1913, after she had left school, she worked for a time
as a governess in a town in the Western District of
Victoria, employed by a Mrs Elsie Ross who had two
young daughters. Then she taught in school for a
short period before marrying Bert (probably
Herbert) Sainsbury in 1918. Bert was a policeman
whose father had been Commissioner of Police. It
was Bert's second marriage and he already had three
teenage children. At the time of his marriage to
Florence he was 38, while she was 22. Bert died in
1931. There was a niece still living in Melbourne but
Florence did not have contact with her. Florence
herself had no children.

Florence lived for some time in St Kilda. Robert
described her as one of those women who would
wander around junk and antique shops. Depres-
singly, it may be at one of these shops that she picked
up the boatshed painting, in which case it will be
almost impossible to trace the painting's history
backwards prior to the point of sale. She was survived by one sister but apparently they had fallen
out, hence no mention of the sister in the will. In
fact, she had apparently given away some things
before her death in order that the sister would not
get her hands on them. These things included an
antique writing desk given to the daughter of her

solicitor. Robert does not know how Florence's sister might be traced.

Robert does not know whether she ever spent time in Sydney. He does know that she used to spend her winters in Brisbane before falling out with the people that she stayed with. This is a bit more promising—perhaps she stopped off in Sydney sometimes. And then there is Lloyd Rees's Brisbane connection. And John Banks used to spend his winters in Brisbane ... Robert tells me the others mentioned in the will were friends. They might be worth writing to, but he doesn't think that they were really close to Florence.

And Mrs Dunkley who was left the bulk of the estate? 'Over $175,000,' says Robert. 'She is certainly going to get a surprise when she gets the solicitor's letter next week. She doesn't know anything about it yet ... Do you remember I mentioned that Mrs Sainsbury worked as a governess to Mrs Elsie Ross back in 1914, looking after her two young children? Well, Mrs Dunkley is one of those children. The really amazing thing is that the only contact Mrs Sainsbury appears to have had since that time appears to be through the exchange of Christmas cards.'

Well! Mrs Dunkley is probably not going to be of much help to me but I will write anyway. Florence seems to have kept thoughts to herself if the surprise will is anything to go by. But who knows, maybe Mrs Dunkley was a confidante. But I will wait awhile until she gets over the shock (or is it?) of her inheritance. I thank Robert Blain and ask if it is OK to phone him again if I need to. He happily agrees.

Monday, 12 July

A clue?

I am re-reading the events surrounding 1927 as

recorded in *Peaks and Valleys* to check whether Lloyd
Rees returned to Brisbane for a visit around this
time. I am looking to see if it is remotely possible for
there to be a connection between Lloyd and Mrs
Sainsbury. Were they ever in Brisbane at the same
time? Of course I would have to find out what years
Mrs Sainsbury visited Brisbane in the winter and this
might be impossible. But there is no harm starting
on Lloyd's movements.

As it turns out, there is no firm evidence that
Lloyd returned to Brisbane until 1932 when he may
have been there for an exhibition of his work at Miss
Sheldon's Gainsborough Gallery and when he
presented a still life painting to the Queensland
National Gallery in memory of his father. But the
exciting bit, the possible clue, comes from re-reading
the section about his visits to doctors, owing to his
acutely depressed state from 1927 following the
death of Dulcie, and in particular to the chiropractor
who had caused him such pain. The thing that leaps
out now are the words: 'The "specialist" was undoubtedly American, for his first words had proclaimed him ...'[1]

American! William Charles Crawford, a subscriber to the telephone number 8930, was an American
as well! Not only that, but the 'specialist' had 'got
some X-rays done which [demonstrated] his diag-
nosis'. And Crawford was a radiographer! Rees writes:

> My chiropractor had been, of all things, a butcher
> in China. I don't think he was a bad man but he
> had the same type of closed mind often associated
> with religious sects from America and his main
> fixation was that all human ills stemmed from the
> spinal column.

Following a visit to this chiropractor, Rees describes
running dishevelled and in panic and pain from the

'surgery' in Martin Place down to the sanctuary of the Macquarie Galleries in Bligh Street where Basil Burdett, by this time directing the Macquarie Galleries, managed to talk some sense into him. It is quite possible that Lloyd at this time was suffering what is now termed Post Traumatic Stress Disorder following the recent personal tragedy in his life.

Later, Lloyd consults 'Dr Royal and Dr Bickerton Blackburn'. But not before he returns to the chiropractor to retrieve his X-rays to show to Dr Royal who gave him 'one of the most authoritative X-ray readings in Australia'. So, Dr Royal did not order his own set of X-rays. Therefore it is unlikely Dr Blackburn would have ordered another set.

So where would the chiropractor have got these X-rays? The radiographer William Charles Crawford! And his office in Boomerang House was only one street away from Martin Place. It must be possible that these two Americans did business together. Rees also comments on the exorbitant fee of the chiropractor: seven guineas, 'which was quite a lot at that time'. (*Balmoral* was priced at 12 guineas when it was exhibited at the Royal Art Society in 1927.) Is it possible Rees may have exchanged a small painting (the boatshed painting) for the X-rays from Crawford?

I will now try to trace Crawford's children, Ithaca May Munro and Hugh Maynard Crawford with renewed vigour.

Ithaca? The name rings a bell. I remember the Sands' Directory listing Crawford in Ithaca Road as a young man from about 1908 to 1911. He probably enjoyed living there since he named his daughter, who may have been born around this time, Ithaca.

Lloyd Rees attended the Ithaca Creek School in Brisbane from 1907 to 1909, which he describes as a wonderful place which 'opened up new vistas' for him.[2] (In later life Rees visited Ithaca in Greece and sketched and painted there.) Is it possible that these

two men chatted and touched on this coincidence?
Any mention of family names, schooling or addresses
may have brought it out. Were there any other
connections that could have led to the sort of
relationship between the two men which might have
enabled Lloyd Rees to offer a painting rather than
pay money for his X-rays?

What about this scenario? Let's say Rees does in
fact summon his courage and suggest that the
radiographer Crawford might like one of his
paintings in lieu of a bill. He then has to decide
whether to present one to Crawford sight unseen, or
to organise for Crawford to see a group of his
paintings and make a selection. If he chooses the
latter option, then perhaps the paintings should all
be much the same size. He is unable to resolve the
dilemma on the spot and, telling Crawford he will be
in touch, he seeks out Basil Burdett at the Macquarie
Galleries again for advice. Burdett has some small
Rees oils in the stock room. Sizing up the situation,
Burdett selects a small unsigned oil, the boatshed
painting, and, seeing how uncomfortable his friend
is, offers to settle the matter for him. Burdett needs
a phone number to seal the deal. Rees looks it up—
it is 8930. Rees (or Burdett) writes the number on
the reverse of the painting and presto! Or perhaps
Rees approached Rubery Bennett for help because
Bennett's gallery was in the same building as
Crawford's practice.

Wednesday, 21 July

By phoning the Australian Medical Association I
find that there is an Australian Institute of Radiography based in Melbourne. I phone the number
I am given and eventually get on to Ernie Hughes,
the General Secretary. Ernie is most helpful. The

institute keeps extensive archives and has an honor-
ary archivist who does research on request. If I
send the details which I have on William Charles
Crawford they will be able to tell me if they hold
any further information on him. If they have nothing
on him then my information will be of interest to
them.[1]

Another question occurs to me. Does Ernie
know anyone who X-rays oil paintings? Yes, he says,
there are several radiographers who would do this for
me. He gives me the name of Joe Petroni at Westmead Hospital near Parramatta, west of Sydney.
Ernie implies that it is a fairly simple process. I
wonder what chance there is of X-rays revealing
another painting underneath the boatshed painting.
Perhaps one signed 'L. Rees'.

I send the letter to the Institute, including all
the information I have about the radiographer
Crawford.

Thursday, 22 July

A letter arrives from Alan and Jan Rees. Judging
from the weight of the envelope it is a rather lengthy
letter. Is this a good sign? I'm hoping it means that
I haven't put them off-side by my numerous
questions. I settle down into an easy chair for what I
pray will be a good read.

The first thing that slips out of the envelope is a
colour photograph of Lloyd Rees's *The Cafe at the
Spit* of 1927. There is an immediate gonging in my
brain. The composition and colour are uncannily
similar to the boatshed painting. I had previously
known *The Cafe at the Spit* only from a black and
white reproduction. But my hopes that this photograph was being sent by Alan and Jan as further
evidence for the boatshed painting being of the same

date, 1927, are shortlived as I begin to read the accompanying letter.

> Dear Stephen,
> Your letter was waiting for us when we came back from Melbourne on Friday (we went down for the opening of a Lloyd Rees/Brett Whiteley exhibition at the Museum of Modern Art at Heide) —gosh, you really have been doing some detective work.
> We don't have your confidence that, if it is a Rees work, it was done in 1927. The more we look at the photo, we feel that *if* it is one of Dad's, it was probably done before he went to Europe— in fact, probably c1918–20—there's not much evidence that he did many oils before then. This feeling is based on the style—the later 1920s oils that we have photos of were lighter and more detailed—the earlier ones were heavier. We enclose a photograph of an oil that we know is 1927 (it's *The Cafe at the Spit* that was exhibited in the 1928 Gainsborough Gallery exhibition in Brisbane), and I think the difference in style is obvious—though the pigments are similar.

Before continuing I compare the two works more closely. What they have seen is probably right. Not only that, but another difference is also becoming clear. The boatshed painting does not have that hazy, misty quality of *The Cafe at the Spit* and the other known 1927 paintings (including *Balmoral*).

Alan and Jan have put a great deal of effort into their letter to me. They have included a chronology of Lloyd's movements and associates from 1917 to 1931. More incredibly they have included a list of exhibitions from 1913 and have listed all oils known to have been exhibited up until 1932. Although they say that the list is not exhaustive it is certainly likely to be the most exhaustive listing of early oils known at this stage.

There is a comment in their letter about the title *Suburban Scene*:

> The title seems an unusual one, but we have seen a number of his works get new titles over the years, and if the painting went through a number of owners this is even more likely to happen. But we must say that *Suburban Scene* is not the title that springs to mind when you look at the picture—even if you had no idea of what the artist called it. The title may have been written on the back of the painting by the framer—or even more likely, a later dealer ... After all—if it was done by Dad, and if it was done when we think it might have been done, that gives it at least seventy years of life, and it's pretty unlikely that it stayed with one owner for that time.
>
> Parkers were in business at that time—so it would be interesting to hear what Clarrie Parker says—and so was John Young's framing workshop —the framer was H. Fleming—we have some frames with his labels.

And about Lloyd not signing works?

> There were times when Dad didn't sign (or forgot to sign) his work—the only one at that time that we really know about is a drawing of St Mary's that was bought by the Queensland Gallery in 1920—the newspaper report refers to '[the artist] to be requested to sign the picture, it being the opinion of the trustees that his work is sure to command greater attention and increase considerably in value.'

And about developing oils from sketches?

He did develop his oils from sketches—the early drawings that we have are with the AGNSW (Hendrik Kolenberg, Curator of Australian Prints, Watercolours and Drawings, has them). We don't recall any of that subject, but there were about 880 separate sheets of paper covering 1912–1988, so that is not surprising.

This is great news. What excitement it will be going through them! A handwritten note on the typed letter at this point tells me that the Art Gallery of NSW also has examples of Lloyd Rees's handwriting. This is also good news since it means that they have not dismissed the possibility of the inscriptions being in Lloyd's hand.

Any reference in Lloyd Rees's records to those characters I have come across in my research?

Dad kept no records—we are trying to build up a list, and none of the possible names you mention appear in any of the 400 plus records we have— we think there are probably another 400 or so that we haven't got on the database yet, and of course there are lots we don't have the provenance for, so that really isn't much help.

The letter concludes with the following handwritten note:

We will be in Queensland for a week or so at the beginning of August—but apart from that we should be here. We'd love to see you and talk about the picture and your research.

With our very best wishes,

Jan & Alan Rees

I spend some time melding the exhibitions and titles
of oil paintings given by Alan and Jan with the Royal
Art Society exhibition titles, and begin to organise
the result into a complete list. As I read over the list,
now in chronological order, I notice again the oil
with the title *The Bay*, exhibited at The New Art
Salon, 219 George Street, Sydney (Manager, Basil
Burdett), December 1922 to January 1923. I note
the catalogue number again, number 22, the same
number as on the sticker on the reverse of the
boatshed painting. That exhibition is discussed by
Jean Campbell in *Early Sydney Moderns*:

> ... retaining 'The New Art Salon' title, Basil
> [Burdett] moved [from Vickery's Chambers, 76
> Pitt Street] into the gallery above S. A. Parker,
> sharing the area with Wal Taylor and his book-
> binding activities. Later, of course, Wal Taylor
> established the Grosvenor Gallery on these
> premises. Here [at 219 George Street] in
> [December 1922 to] January 1923, prior to
> Lloyd Rees's departure for Europe, Basil held an
> exhibition of Lloyd's drawings [and twenty-five
> oil paintings] and also a rollicking party to fare-
> well the artist.[1]

The Bay, therefore, may not date precisely to 1922
but may have been done up to a few years earlier
since Rees obviously collected together as many
unsold oils and drawings as he could for this exhibition. If the boatshed painting is not of circa 1927
but of 1918 to 1922, then this could add a little
more weight to its being identifiable with *The Bay* of
the New Art Salon exhibition. It may even have
remained unsold and stayed in Burdett's stock room
through the 1920s to be sold to ...

As I scan the list, interestingly, the title *The Bay*
comes up again. At the exhibition of 'The Pen

Drawings of Lloyd Rees and Bookbindings by Wal Taylor' at Gayfield Shaw's Gallery in June 1921, number 24 is titled *The Bay* and priced at ten guineas. It is possible that this drawing may be related to an oil titled *The Bay*.

Then I come across the title *The Bay* again! There has to be *more than one Rees oil with this title* because in the 1922 exhibition of the Art Society of Tasmania, a Rees painting of the same name is catalogued at thirty guineas. This is twice as much as the New Art Salon painting which was exhibited only months later, and therefore is almost certainly not the same painting. Pricing practice was conservative in those days and it is unlikely that the price of a painting would have halved in a couple of months.

In 1928 at the Gainsborough Gallery, Brisbane, number 10 is *The Bay*. It may be the same picture as the New Art Salon painting although it is still priced at the 1922 price of fifteen guineas. Or it may be yet another picture. In 1921 at the Royal Art Society, Rees exhibited an oil titled *The Little Bay*, number 98, also priced at fifteen guineas. But since it is not exactly the same title, it too may be a different painting, perhaps, but not necessarily, of the same subject.

Perhaps contemporary reviews of these exhibitions will mention these bay works. If so, and if there is a description of one which exactly matches the boatshed painting … It could be proof. But it may only be absolute proof if I can discover who bought a painting titled *The Bay* in the 1920s and then trace its subsequent history, or provenance, down to me.

Monday, 26 July

An hour in the Mitchell Library is all it takes to get the name of the rogue chiropractor in Martin Place

who 'treated' Lloyd Rees and organised for him to
be X-rayed. This is a good start.

I have some spare time to browse through the
Sydney Telephone Directory for 1918 to 1922, the
years now considered more likely as the date of the
boatshed painting, if it was done by Lloyd Rees. I am
still looking for likely Booths, Books or Boons who
might have had something to do with the painting
then. But there are no likely candidates with these
names. In fact there are no Books or Boons at all.
There is one Boot and this person lives at 17 Muston
Street, Mosman, the same street as Lloyd's first in-
laws in 1927. But even if this Boot was still living in
Muston Street in 1927 I don't really think the
inscription reads 'Boot'.

The 'Boo' word has just about got me beat. But
as I run my eye down the subscribers whose names
start with 'Boo' a startling possibility comes to me. I
need to go home and look closely at the inscription
again.

Back home, I look at the word inscribed on the
back of the painting and I can see that my thought is
indeed possible. If Lloyd Rees or Basil Burdett or
anyone else wrote Crawford's telephone number on
the back of the boatshed painting then that person
may have started to write Crawford's address as well.
He may have got to 'Boom' for Boomerang House
before stopping because he knew he would
remember it anyway. If Rees, or Burdett, was writing
it in 1927 he would have been quite familiar with
Boomerang House because it housed Rubery
Bennett's art gallery which was booming at the time.

The last letter does not really look like one of
Lloyd's 'm's. But could be half an 'm'. If Lloyd Rees
wrote the inscription around 1927 he was possibly,
given his circumstances, in an agitated state when he
wrote it. This might explain a wayward, half-
completed 'm', which could make the beginning of

'Boomerang House'! It seems so obvious. Why hadn't I seen it before? Because I was looking for a whole word, not half a word. Can I blame myself for that? Or have I become unfocused and can't see the trees from the wood? I must find a sample of Basil Burdett's handwriting as well. And Rubery Bennett's.

I write the following reply to Alan and Jan Rees and send it off:

Dear Alan and Jan,
   Just a quick note. First of all thank you for your most helpful letter. In particular, thanks for the list of exhibited oils.
   I agree with your thoughts about the date of the painting if it is by Lloyd. I think what you have seen (that it is less detailed and the paint is heavier than in *The Cafe at the Spit* and *Balmoral* of 1927) is right. Not only that, but another difference is also now clear to me. The boatshed painting does not have the hazy, misty quality of *The Cafe at the Spit* nor *Balmoral*. In looking at the 1920s oils of which I have colour reproductions, this atmospheric effect is an accomplishment which seems to have developed over time. Unfortunately there are not enough 1918–22 oils known to be absolutely sure of this.
   When I first showed you the painting some months ago I had guessed at the most likely date, if the painting was by Lloyd Rees, as being 1919–1922. This was largely due to the heaviness of the paint and the fairly rigid composition which was without the curves and roundedness of Rees's later works. It was only when comparing the pigments to those in *Balmoral* that I began to focus

on 1927 as a probable date. Then, as I got completely carried away with the issue of the ownership, I continued to focus on 1927 (Crawford, Rubery Bennett, et alia) which probably fed my belief that the painting was done in 1927.

But the fact that it may be unlikely to have been painted in 1927 does not exclude the possibility that the painting could have been done by Rees in, say, 1920 but not sold or swapped (to W. C. Crawford, the radiographer, for example) until 1927.

I have just discovered some information which may support this theory. In *Peaks and Valleys* Lloyd Rees describes his experiences with a chiropractor in 1928 which caused him great distress. This chiropractor (who is not named) had his 'surgery' in Martin Place and is described as an American. He organised for X-rays to be made of Lloyd's spine. Lloyd later retrieved these X-rays and took them to Dr Royal and later, possibly, to Dr Blackburn.

Now, the radiographer Crawford, who had the telephone number 8930—which is the number inscribed on the frame of the boatshed painting— was also an American. He had his office in King Street, one street away from Martin Place. It seems possible that these two Americans may have known each other and done business together. If this is the case it may explain how the number 8930 came to be on the reverse of the boatshed painting. While Lloyd commented on having to pay an exorbitant fee for the chiropractor's services, could it be that he was able to settle his bill for the X-rays from Crawford with the boatshed painting?

I have been able to discover that the chiropractor's name was J. (possibly James) F. Courtney. (There were only about four chiropractors in

Sydney in 1928.) His 'surgery' was on the fourth
floor of Ocean House at 34 Martin Place. Ocean
House was so named because it housed the Ocean
Salt Company Limited. Interestingly, on the top
(7th) floor was the studio and/or retail premises
of the jeweller Rhoda Wager. Her work along with
the bookbinding of Wal Taylor was the only craft
work exhibited at the Society of Artists around
1927–1928.

J. F. Courtney is first listed in the Sydney
telephone book in April 1927 with an entry in
bold. Business may have dropped off after this
beginning because by April 1928 Courtney's
entry drops to normal type. By November 1931
he is no longer in the Directory and does not
appear to return. Almost certainly out of
business—probably left the country. Sounds like a
bit of a fly-by-night.

At any rate, I now have something to go on when
trying to link Courtney, the chiropractor, closer
to Crawford, the radiographer, whose office was
in Boomerang House at 139 King Street. Incidentally, 34 Martin Place is in line with 139 King,
one parallel street away. A very short walk ...

I will probably have a fair bit more to tell you
later. Until then, best wishes and thanks again,

Yours faithfully,
Stephen Scheding

Tuesday, 3 August

Is anyone in William Charles Crawford's family
still alive and living in Australia? A telephone call to
the nursing home in which Crawford's wife,
Dorothea, died in 1971 reveals that they have no
records of her relations. Sister Margaret Edmonds is
quite apologetic.

I go back to the wills of both William Charles and Dorothea Crawford and construct a family tree. None of the family are in the Sydney Telephone Directory. But in the Melbourne directory there is an F. F. Munro. In the will there are two F. F. Munros: Fergus Foster who marries William Charles's daughter, Ithaca, and Fergus Ferguson, the son of Ithaca and Fergus Foster.

If this F. F. in the directory is related to William Charles Crawford then this could explain how the boatshed painting travelled from Sydney, if it is by Rees, down to Melbourne, if William Charles Crawford gave it to F. F. Munro and he took it with him when he moved interstate. Now to think about my questions to the unsuspecting F. F. Munro of Melbourne.

Friday, 6 August

A man answers the phone, and I introduce myself. 'This is Fergus Foster speaking,' he says, 'but I can't for the life of me think how I could help you.'

I take a deep breath. 'Have you got a few minutes?' I ask. Yes, he is happy to talk. I ask him if he is related to William Charles Crawford. Yes, Crawford was the father of his wife, May. Would that be Ithaca May Munro, nee Crawford? Yes it is. This is wonderful. I had thought I would be dealing with Crawford's grandchildren who would be less likely to have any knowledge of the boatshed painting.

I briefly and carefully summarise my story. At the end, I describe the boatshed painting and ask if Fergus remembers it. 'Oh, yes,' he says, 'but May would probably remember more about it. Just a moment.' When Fergus gets back to me it is bad news. May does not seem to remember the painting. I ask if they would be interested in seeing the painting next time

I am in Melbourne. Fergus tells me that would be fine.

I ask a leading question, whether William Charles Crawford had a lot of paintings or just one or two. 'Just one or two,' replies Fergus. Was he interested in art? Yes, says Fergus, in fact, Crawford had been a bit of an amateur painter himself as a youth! Painting could be another thing he had in common with Lloyd Rees which may have come out in any possible conversation between them and which may have meant that Crawford valued paintings enough to accept one in payment for the X-rays. What about the possibility that the boatshed painting may be by Crawford? Not likely. It is hardly an amateurish painting.

I tell Fergus how grateful I am for his help.

Monday, 9 August

I follow up my telephone conversation with a letter to May and Fergus Munro, telling them that I will be in Melbourne on the weekend of 21–22 August, and asking if they mind me showing them the painting. The trip will coincide nicely with the next Joel's auction.

Wednesday, 11 August

I have made an appointment with Hendrik Kolenberg to view the 880 sketches by Lloyd Rees on loan to the Art Gallery of NSW. I take the boatshed painting with me in case there are also examples of Rees's handwriting from the 1920s on these sketches to use as comparisons to the inscriptions on the reverse of the painting.

Hendrik meets me in the Gallery's Study Room

where the prints, drawings and photographs are stored. I have only spoken to him a couple of times on the telephone in the past and this is the first time I have met him in person. He is the Curator of Australian Prints, Drawings and Watercolours and is also the author of *Lloyd Rees—Etchings and Lithographs*.[1] He is currently organising a major exhibition of Rees's drawings to be held in a couple of years' time.

Since I have the boatshed painting with me and since I am asking to see the Rees material, I feel obliged to tell him something of my project. When I get to the point where I say that I am considering the possibility that the boatshed painting is by Lloyd Rees, he looks at the painting and says, 'Well, I can't say that I agree with you'. He gives, as his main reasons, the clumsiness in the handling of the paint and the stolidness of the composition. Those and the fact that he regards it as an 'awful little painting'.

'That's OK,' I reply bravely. 'I'm interested in the process of reaching a conclusion. If it was obviously by Rees then I wouldn't be researching it.' Hendrik nods thoughtfully and then, after bringing out the volumes of Rees drawings done prior to 1930, he leaves me alone to wade through them.

Despite my cocky reply to his opinion, I am a bit unsettled. It is the most negative response to the painting so far.

Of the hundreds of images in the volumes, none bears any close resemblance to the composition of the boatshed painting, although there are scores of sketches of waterfront scenes executed between 1916 and 1922. There are some similar details, such as the shadows made by chimneys or the placement of trees against buildings, but certainly nothing conclusive.

It is now almost closing time. I go and fetch Hendrik from his office. I tell him I have not found anything, joking that if I had he probably would have heard me yell. We return together to the study room and he takes another look at the painting. I turn it over and show him the handwriting on the reverse, telling him that I think that it is possible that it is Lloyd Rees's handwriting. He has seen a lot of Rees's handwriting and agrees that the inscription is in a similar style. I have brought some photocopies of Rees's letters and I show him these, pointing out some similarities.

He now appears a bit more interested. I tell him that if it is Rees's handwriting on the frame of the painting, including the number 8930, then the only explanation I can come up with for the number is that it is a telephone number. Hendrik can't think of any other explanation for the number, off the top of his head. Then I tell him about Crawford, the radiographer, and Rees having had X-rays done.

Before I leave, Hendrik fetches a form which I need to be able to take the painting out of the gallery—one of the guards may think I am trying to steal one of the gallery's paintings. It seems I have been a bit naughty bringing my painting in without approval. As I walk through the gallery, I look at the form that he has given me.

At the bottom of the form, in the section headed 'Artist and description', he has written: 'A small painting, possibly by Rees.'

Friday, 13 August

A Mrs Catherine Ives phones from Melbourne to say that she is the daughter of May and Fergus Munro. She has read my letter to them and would like to organise a time for my meeting with them. She would like to be there as well. We agree on Saturday morning, 21 August.

Catherine tells me that, from my written description of the boatshed painting, Fergus thinks that he remembers it. May, on the other hand, still does not. She warns me that her mother is rather deaf. I tell her I understand—so is mine. I ask her whether she, too, lives in Camberwell. She says that she used to. Before that, the family lived in the Dandenongs, where she still lives.

The Dandenongs covers a lot of hills. But could it be that the family knew Florence Sainsbury when she lived in the Dandenongs? I save that question for later.

Friday, 20 August

I fly down to Melbourne.

Saturday, 21 August

The Munros' house is gleaming white with a large bay window overlooking a leafy park. Catherine Ives, with a welcoming smile, shows me into the front room. Fergus is there and we shake hands. May will be 'out in a minute'.

The room is furnished with objets d'art and pictures and prints. Immediately I notice a large still life by Albert Sherman out in the hallway! Sherman exhibited with Rubery Bennett whose gallery was in the same building as May's dad. I pretend to admire it while rapidly doing another assessment as to whether Sherman could have painted the boatshed painting. No. I'm still certain it's not a Sherman. I dismissed him early on because he almost exclusively painted very finished, traditional still lifes.

On a sideboard near the bay window is a stunning, huge metal and glass lamp. This must surely be

the lamp bequeathed in the will of William Charles
Crawford to his daughter Ithaca May Munro. I have
to stop myself from going straight over and heaving
it up to see if it is stamped 'Tiffany' as I suspected.
Crawford, after all, was American. If it is Tiffany,
then it is worth squillions. And if they don't know,
then they could be in for a nice surprise.

After some brief chit-chat, I offer to show
Fergus the boatshed painting. He takes it in his
hands and says 'never seen that before'. Catherine
seems disappointed. 'Are you sure, Dad?' she presses.
Fergus is quite sure. Although in his nineties, he is as
sharp as a tack.

We talk about William Charles Crawford, and
Fergus begins to tell me about a Miss Bushell. 'You
mean Gwendoline,' I say. He is somewhat taken
aback but then compliments me on having done my
homework. She had been mentioned in the will and
I gently explain how I came to see the will. Fergus
tells me that Miss Bushell was Crawford's secretary
and knew as much about his business as anybody. He
thinks she had lived in Kogarah in Sydney, but
doubts that she is still alive.

May enters the room. She is very frail and I can
see that it is an effort for her. She is helped into a
chair opposite me. May and Fergus have been
married for over sixty years. They moved from
Sydney to Melbourne in 1984 after Fergus had
suffered a stroke. Their daughter and son-in-law in
the Dandenongs are not far away.

Catherine shows May the painting, who shakes
her head. She has never seen it before. 'It's not a
terribly good painting, is it,' she says impishly. 'Oh,
I think it's a lovely painting,' announces Catherine,
as if coming to my defence. She is a warm and
generous person. I can see that she is fascinated with
my story. She asks to hear more of it.

I tell them what I have learnt about 139 King

Street. Fergus and May both remember Rubery
Bennett's gallery upstairs but did not know whether
William Charles had any dealings there. May tells me
that there was a lift in the building which was oper-
ated by ropes. Could the Albert Sherman have come
from Bennett? Yes, it's quite possible, they say. He
certainly knew the other occupants of the building.
They tell me that Crawford was friendly with Old
Man Albert, the music magnate who owned
Boomerang House. Both had been members of the
Motor Yacht Club at Rose Bay—Crawford had been
Rear Commodore. He had been interested in boats
and had owned a speedboat.

Information is tumbling out now. I try to sort it
into chronological order. Crawford was the son of an
American Supreme Court Judge. He arrived in
Sydney from Los Angeles in about 1900 on his
honeymoon with Dorothea. He was also representing the company in America for which he worked
which sold aspirins and patent medicines. I am able
to tell Fergus and May that the name of the company
was almost certainly The Dr McLaughlin Company
because this is the company name listed next to
Crawford's name in the 1904 Sydney Telephone
Directory.

It is likely that Crawford stayed in Australia as an
agent for the company, either because he fell in love
with the place or because his stay was part of a pre-
arranged business plan. In 1902 Crawford returned
to California possibly to tidy up affairs and to
arrange for his things to be sent to Australia—
including, presumably, the metal and glass lamp over
on the sideboard. Around 1905 he is living at Ithaca
Road, Elizabeth Bay. Ithaca May was born at this
time and she confirms that this is why she was
christened Ithaca. It's a nice feeling to know that my
conjecture on this point was correct.

The office in 139 King Street was leased around

1917. Crawford had no training as a radiographer
and it is not known how he came to be teamed up
with the dentist McGovern at this time, but
McGovern apparently left the practice soon after.
Both Fergus and May remember that the telephone
number of the office was MA 2930. This, of course,
was the post-1927 number. With a bit of prompting
they say that they can vaguely remember the previous
number, 8930. I show them the inscribed number
on the reverse of the frame. And also the 'Boo' word
which could be the start of 'Boomerang House'.
They nod. Ah, yes.

It was in these rooms at 139 King Street, that
Fergus had anxiously asked William Charles Crawford
for the hand in marriage of his daughter, Ithaca May.
Fergus tells me this, still bashful at ninety. Crawford
had, apparently, agreed but with 'extreme doubt'.

So what was William Charles Crawford like?
Apart from his interest in speedboats he was also
fascinated by cars and over the years owned many of
them. He was one of the first, if not the first, to drive
a car from Sydney to Melbourne (so he did go to
Melbourne and could have taken the painting then—
if he owned it). He may also have gone flying in the
early 1920s because a friend was W. S. Hart the
aviator. Fergus recalls the story of Hart being pulled
over for speeding on the Harbour Bridge by a
policeman who asked him: 'Hey buddy, have you got
a licence to fly?' To which Hart replied: 'Yes, I have.'
I am surprised to hear that Hart was a dentist. A
flying dentist. His advertising slogan was 'Take it to
Hart'.

Crawford had been a member of the Admen
Club. He had been mad about publicity and
advertising. It seems that Crawford was a 'modern'
man. He had an interest in machines and speed
which were themes picked up by some of the
modernist artists in Sydney: in 1929 Margaret

Preston titled an essay *From Eggs to Electrolux*; John D. Moore wrote of aeroplanes, cars and wheat silos as being 'unconscious expressions of Modern Art'; and many images of the Harbour Bridge under construction exist because artists saw it as a technological triumph and were inspired by it.

But Crawford was not really interested in paintings—at least not in the 1920s. As a boy of about sixteen he had tried painting—Catherine has one of his works copied from a famous American painting. But he had not painted during his life in Australia. Fergus claims Crawford was more interested in the 'entertainment field' rather than the artistic field. While he was a naturalised Australian and proud of it, he remained, unlike his wife Dorothea, 'American to the core'. He never missed an issue of the *Saturday Evening Post*. He was a very methodical man: his motto was 'A place for everything and everything in its place'.

This last piece of information comes from May. With the vivid picture I am now getting of her father it is hard to imagine that he has been dead for over forty years. She even tells me 'Dad would go to work and put six pipes out on his desk and then, very methodically, he would fill each of them in turn. He would then smoke them one by one at set times during the day.' Is it still possible that the boatshed painting hung in Crawford's rooms, unnoticed by May, slowly developing a yellow glaze from the pipe smoke?

By this stage we are all quite immersed in the saga. Both Fergus and Catherine have spent some time researching. Fergus has researched a book on characters in early Australian history while Catherine has been researching her family history.[1] I have tapped right into a real interest of theirs. I am allowed deeper into this family's history. May had a brother who died. Embrey Crawford was a talented journalist who left Sydney for Melbourne in about 1927. Catherine tells me she has some wonderful letters from him, written before he died in 1931. I do not ask how he died—whatever the answer, it will be tragic because he would have died quite young. Which explains why he isn't in the wills of William and Dorothea.

Could Embrey have been the original owner of the boatshed painting? As a journalist in Sydney, he may be more likely to have been an acquaintance of Lloyd Rees who mixed socially with journalists as well as newspaper artists. Could Rees have given or sold Embrey the boatshed painting and had it delivered to his father's office in Boomerang House? Or could Embrey have been given it by his father, William Charles Crawford, unbeknowns to the rest of the family? The more I am thinking about it, the more I find myself swinging away from William Charles Crawford as the original owner of the boatshed painting. The main reason is that no-one remembers Crawford ever having the painting, and I know they would if it was possible.

Then Catherine pours a flood of cold water on previous speculations. As part of her family research Catherine has gathered together memorabilia that belonged to William Charles Crawford. She tells me that amongst the memorabilia there are even the little boxes that Crawford used to keep his X-rays in.

'Did you say *little* boxes?' I ask. 'How would spinal X-rays fit into *little* boxes?'

'Oh, no,' says Catherine, 'he only did X-rays of teeth.'

There is no way Crawford could be connected to Lloyd Rees via the chiropractor Courtney's ordering of spinal X-rays. Oh! Damn it! Double damn it!

I gather the strength to ask them whether they are aware of any connection between William

Charles Crawford and Lloyd Rees. They all shake
their heads blankly. They have not heard of Florence
Sainsbury either. By this time I have been offered tea
and cake and we are winding up our investigations
for the moment. We promise to keep in touch and
exchange any information we might find.

As I am leaving, I say carefully: 'I mentioned
before that I had seen William Charles Crawford's
will. In the will there was a mention of a metal and
glass lamp. I am wondering whether that could be it
on the sideboard?'

'Oh, you mean the Tiffany,' says Catherine with
a smile.

Monday, 23 August

Will I have to resort to dental records to crack this
case?

Checking back through the Sands' Directory at
the Mitchell Library I am able to determine the
dentists who were associated with radiographer
William Charles Crawford. Prior to 1928, the dentist
J. F. McGovern was Crawford's partner and in the
early 1920s was at the same address, Boomerang House. He seems to have left by the mid
1920s with Crawford retaining the business name—
McGovern Radiography. Dentist George Campling
was associated with Crawford from 1927. (Dentist
C. L. Harvey—mentioned in Crawford's will—was
associated from about 1928. That is, *after* Crawford's
number changed from 8930, so I can forget him.)

So. Could McGovern or Campling have attended to Lloyd Rees's teeth? Could Crawford have done
the X-rays? Could Lloyd have paid Crawford with
the boatshed painting after all? Could McGovern or
Campling have owned the boatshed painting (a
payment for dental work?) and taken it to Melbourne

and then given it to Florence Sainsbury? Could I prove a connection between Florence and McGovern or Campling?

I had hoped that I would not have to harass Alan Rees again for a while, but now, back home, I am on the phone asking him who his Dad's dentist was! Alan says he does not mind my calling. When I pop my question he says 'ooh ... ah ... I'll have to think about that.' And then: 'Of course, Dad had all his teeth out early on.' I think it too rude to ask 'how early?'—a person's false teeth are not something so abruptly discussed. Not at the beginning of a conversation anyway. But I am desperate to know if Alan knows whether his father had a major teeth job done prior to 1928, in the period when Crawford's telephone number was 8930.

Alan says that when he was growing up in the 1940s and 1950s, his dad had taken him to a dentist by the name of Ian Muir in Longueville Road, Longueville, which is the next suburb over from the Rees house in Northwood. Alan supposes that his father may have also used the same dentist. Ian Muir, he remembered, was quite old at the time. The names McGovern and Campling ring no bells for Alan. He offers, though, to give it some more thought.

While tracking down McGovern and Campling, I had made a note of their various other addresses. Although they were linked to Crawford in Boomerang House, they also operated out of other practices. In fact, in 1920, McGovern had operated in Longueville Road, the same street as Alan Rees's and possibly Lloyd's dentist, Ian Muir! Could Ian Muir and McGovern have been partners in Longueville Road? Could McGovern be the dentist who extracted Lloyd's teeth following the X-raying done by Crawford, McGovern's radiographer partner?

I reach for the current A–K volume of the Sydney Yellow Pages and flip through to dentists. How many dental surgeries are there in Longueville Road now? The road is about a kilometre long and, from memory, only bits of it are commercial. The answer is at least four. These are listed in the locality guide under Lane Cove. There may be more, if I had the inclination to check through the hundreds of dentists listed in the main alphabetical section.

As I look at the names of the dentists in Longueville Road, one of the names starts to wobble and float off the page. It is the most extraordinary thing. The name is Brian G. Sainsbury!

Sainsbury—surely not! *Could* he be related to the late Florence Jane Sainsbury who owned the boatshed painting before me? Is his address the same as Ian Muir's and/or J. F. McGovern's? My brain boggles.

I find myself phoning the number. A secretary answers. She tells me that Brian Sainsbury has sold the practice and moved to Adelaide. She provides me with his number. Robotically I dial the digits. My hopes drop when he answers. His voice is young. It is unlikely he would have been in practice at the time I am thinking the boatshed painting changed hands. But maybe his father, Sainsbury Senior, was/is a dentist too and had his practice (with McGovern?) in Longueville Road before Brian.

But Brian has never heard of Florence Jane Sainsbury. His family hails from Perth. He had been educated in Adelaide before practising dentistry for a time in Longueville Road in Sydney. This practice had not been a family concern. Nor had it been connected to J. F. McGovern nor to Ian Muir, the Rees's dentist.

He is not the missing link. His name and ex-Sydney address are just a cruel coincidence.

By phoning the NSW Dental Association I am able to track down J. F. McGovern's son, also a dentist, who lives in Wollongong. But after a lengthy conversation with him I come to the conclusion that there is no way McGovern Senior would have owned the boatshed painting.

Campling is a fairly unusual name and by phoning the handful in the book I am eventually able to get a fix on George Campling, dentist. It turns out that he wouldn't have owned the boatshed painting either. Why? Well, the families of both McGovern and Campling are certain that these dentists *never* owned an original work of art!

I think I am done with dentists.

Tuesday, 24 August

I write a follow-up letter to Catherine Ives.

> Dear Catherine,
> I am writing to tell you how much I appreciated the help from your parents and yourself last Saturday. Our conversation has provided me with much information to go on with. I hope it was not too taxing for your parents. Please pass on my thanks to them.
> From the information, I think I can just about rule out William Charles Crawford as having had the boatshed painting in his possession, at least for any length of time. May or Fergus would surely have remembered it. Nevertheless, I still believe that his telephone number 8930 on the reverse of the frame is an important clue to its history.
> I was interested to hear about May's brother, Embrey, and that he was a journalist. I am wondering if there is an outside chance that *he* may have had something to do with the painting. The artist

whom I am thinking is most likely to have done the painting is Lloyd Rees. (The reasons for this attribution are rather involved and I will tell you about them later, if I may.) Rees was part of a wide circle of artists, writers and journalists which was centred at the studios of the firm of Smith and Julius in Sydney, run by Sydney Ure Smith.

I am wondering whether Embrey may have been part of this circle. I remember you saying how talented he was as a writer and journalist. He may have even been about the same age as Lloyd Rees who was born in 1895. It may be possible that Embrey used his father's telephone number, 8930, as a city contact number. And if the boatshed painting was owned by Embrey it may explain how it ended up in Melbourne.

William Charles Crawford's interest in publicity and advertising may be worth my exploring. The largest advertising agency (there weren't many) in Sydney during the 1920s was Catts Patterson. One of the partners, George Patterson, had developed close links with Smith and Julius from 1919. He is described, by Nancy Underhill in *Making Australian Art 1916–49—Sydney Ure Smith Patron and Publisher*, as an 'aggressive advertising agent'. Ure Smith in fact published Patterson's autobiography *Life has been Wonderful—Fifty Years of Adventures in Advertising at Home and Abroad* in 1956. Much of Patterson's time abroad had been spent in America. Patterson had close contact with many of those associated with S. & J. I wonder whether William Charles Crawford may have used the services of Patterson's agency, to sell his pills and patent medicines for example. It is likely that Patterson, like Crawford, was a member of the Admen Club. If so, they would almost certainly have known each other.

Perhaps Crawford's journalist son, Embrey, was associated with advertising or even with Catts Patterson and through this company became connected to the Ure Smith circle and to Lloyd Rees.

The circle held get-togethers at the workshop of John Young, the picture framer. There were also some wine bars such as Pelligrini's, located in a basement in Hunter Street in the early 1920s, which later moved to George Street near the *Bulletin* office. Jack Lindsay describes it in *The Roaring Twenties*[1] as being a centre for artists, writers and musicians for many years and it is referred to in Louis Stone's *Betty Wayside*.[2] It was the haunt of journalists including Leon Gellert, for example, who was co-editor with Ure Smith on *Art in Australia* from 1922. Mockbell's Cafe is also referred to by Jack Lindsay. There were Mockbell's Cafes in Hunter Street and Angel Place. Jean Campbell writes that her father, John Young, met at Mockbell's with artists and that they also enjoyed counter lunches at the Royal Exchange Hotel. Bernard Hesling in *Stir this Stew* writes that he knew the artists Arthur Murch and Jimmy Cook 'around Pakie's Club in the late 1920s'.[3] This was probably at the time that the modernist painter Roy de Maistre had decorated Pakie's in 'a daring and uncommon arrangement of colours'.[4]

Dance halls were the rage in the 1920s but I can find no evidence that artists attended in any organised way. But they probably did. And vaudeville shows. An annual event (from 1922) that many certainly attended was the Society of Artists' Ball.

Would it be possible for you to discover whether there is anything in Embrey's letters which supports the possibility that he moved in Lloyd's circle? Do you know which newspapers he worked for and whether he published anything outside of newspapers? I would be interested to see the things that he wrote. Would you be able to tell me his year of birth and whether he worked in Sydney prior to leaving for Melbourne? Did he ever marry? He must have been very young when he died in 1931. Do you know what happened?

I hope this is not putting you to too much trouble.

Yours sincerely,
Stephen Scheding

Wednesday, 25 August

I phone the Mitchell Library to find out who the library uses for handwriting analysis. I am put through to Paul Brunton, head of the Manuscripts Department, for his advice. Paul invites me in, this afternoon, with the painting and the samples of handwriting. I do not tell him I think the painting might be by Lloyd Rees. I feel that this may influence his judgement if he, himself, attempts an analysis of the writing. I do not wish to contaminate the evidence.

Paul meets me and we go up in a lift and then burrow through rooms stacked with books, manuscripts and files. His office is done out in the same style. He seems to enjoy my story about the painting, even though I leave out one of the crucial characters—Lloyd Rees. I tell him that there could be about ten years' difference in the two exhibits. He looks from the inscription on the frame of the painting to the copies of the (Rees) letters which are dated 1933. Finally, after a long time, he says: 'Well, the only thing that I can say is that it *could* be the same writing.'

Paul explains that the writing is of a particular style that many people used in the 1920s. It was the way that they had been taught to write. It was a fairly bland style and therefore difficult to pick out any useful idiosyncrasies to make comparisons. At this point I reveal that I think the painting might be by Lloyd Rees. He looks at it and says: 'Well, it could be. It's a lovely painting.'

'What do you think I should do now?' I ask.

'I think you should go to the Police,' he replies seriously. 'They have experts who deal with this sort of thing.' I agree that this is my best move. On the way out he chats warmly about my project. I go down in the lift feeling cheered.

Friday, 27 August

I am not absolutely certain of my facts in the following letter, but I decide to send it off anyway. No harm in trying.

Att: The Registrar of Probates, Victoria

RE: Request for the will and statement of Assets and Liabilities for Embrey Crawford.

As part of the research I am currently undertaking on an unsigned Australian landscape painting, I am requesting the will and statement of assets and liabilities for Embrey Crawford who died in Melbourne about 1927.

Could you please advise me as to whether these exist and, if so, the cost of photocopies.

Yours sincerely,

Stephen Scheding

I telephone Police Headquarters and ask to be put through to the section that deals with handwriting analysis. 'Document Examination,' answers Senior Constable Debbie Battersby. I explain the job.

Debbie tells me that, at the moment, her unit has a lot of murder, big fraud and kidnapping on. She does not think that my job could be given priority. In any case, they don't really take on private jobs. She recommends a private expert, adding that most private experts have been trained through the Police Department. She sounds very professional and proud of her work, which makes me determined to have Document Examination look at the inscription on the boatshed painting and the handwriting samples of Lloyd Rees.

I ask her if she has done much work in the art field. Oh, yes, she says. They have recently identified a number of Albert Namatjira fakes by analysing the signatures. I ask her whether it is more difficult analysing handwriting from the 1920s. Echoing what Paul Brunton had said she tells me that it helps if one knows which State the handwriting is from because each taught its own style. I tell her that I know that my main suspect was taught in Brisbane. She offers to call me back—if the crime rate slackens over the next few weeks—to see if she can help me out.

Thursday, 2 September

If Lloyd Rees did not write the inscription on the reverse of the boatshed painting, then it is possible that someone with similar handwriting wrote it. Basil Burdett, Wal Taylor and Rubery Bennett were all educated in Queensland at around the same time. If the boatshed painting is by Lloyd Rees, then each may have had the opportunity to write the inscription: Basil may have sold it from his New Art Salon

or, later, from the Macquarie Galleries; Wal may have
framed it, using his bookbinding tape, when he was
working with Basil, or later when he established the
Grosvenor Galleries; Rubery may have sold it from
the Boomerang House gallery, but this is less likely
since his connection to Rees seems tenuous at this
stage.

    I will have to check the handwriting of all of
these Queenslanders.

Friday, 3 September

I am still puzzled by the title *Suburban Scene*. Is it
possible that someone like Lloyd Rees or Basil
Burdett (or whoever) would have used it in the
1920s? Or is it simply the sort of title that someone
resorted to, because they didn't have time to think of
a better one? Joel's, for example, had catalogued the
boatshed painting as *Beachside Villas* which is equally
inappropriate. For a start, there is only one 'villa'.

    The fact that it was written alongside a 1920s
telephone number on a 1920s frame indicates that it
is a 1920s title. *Suburban Scene* does not seem like a
title that anyone would use for this painting today. If
the title *Suburban Scene* is in the handwriting of
Rees, Burdett, Taylor or Bennett, it is unlikely that
it would have been applied hurriedly or lazily—it
would have been somehow appropriate. It must have
felt right. So what was the connotation of the word
'suburban' in the context of the early 1920s? In what
various ways was it used? Was it a term of mild
derision as it can be today? Or was it, rather, something to be admired? A dream that many yearned for?
Did it have a conservative connotation? Or a
modernist one?

    A check through the Society of Artists' cata-
logues from 1917 to 1932 reveals a few uses of the

word in the titles of paintings. In 1917 Albert Collins exhibited a small painting titled *The Suburb*. Now I am sure the boatshed painting is not by Collins, whose work is crisper and more pristine, often with distinctive, neat, square brushstrokes. But the interesting thing is that Rees knew Collins—they worked together at Smith and Julius around 1920. The next use in a title is by B. E. Minns in 1923. He exhibits a watercolour titled *Suburban Road*. Minns painted some fine impressionist watercolours in the 1890–1910 period and by the 1920s his work still had much the same spirit—but in the context of the 1920s it now looks more traditional and conservative. Then there is the use of the word by, not surprisingly, Herbert Badham: in 1929 he exhibits *Suburban Landscape*. Badham was a master of getting the most out of the most ordinary. His street scenes, interiors of pubs or trams and domestic situations, painted in the realist style, may initially appear bland but they have a psychological element that has the power to create uneasy reconsiderations. It is certain that Badham's *Suburban Landscape* was referring to more than just a place.

Was 'suburban' ideologically sound in the early 1920s after the first industrialised war? Was it seen as a haven perhaps? A new life? Or was the general meaning more prosaic? Were the suburbs simply a fact of the modern, expanding world? Or all of the above? Whatever the connotations of the word, I have a strong feeling that it could easily have applied in the 1920s to somewhere like the Balmoral area— if this is, in fact, the site of the boatshed painting. My feeling is that this area could easily have been seen as the quintessential suburban landscape at the time.

I check the *Dictionary of Australian Quotations* edited by Stephen Murray-Smith[1] but most of the references to the suburbs are fairly recent. Hugh Stretton is quoted from *Ideas for Australian Cities*.[2]

'You don't have to be a conformist to choose suburban life. Most of the best poets and painters and inventors and protesters chose it too'. Where else could I get information about the word in a 1920s context?

I have an idea. I reach for the phone and call the office of the Macquarie Dictionary Pty Ltd, located at Macquarie University. Maureen Lesley answers and quickly becomes interested in my word. She does not think that 'suburban' is all that modern, though. She goes off to look in the twenty volume *Oxford Dictionary*.

There are about a dozen citations of 'suburban' in the *Oxford*. The first is in 1625! It was later in use at the time of the First Fleet, meaning the word 'suburban' probably came over with the convicts! It continues to be recorded in the *Oxford* up to the present. So, its origin, at least, is certainly not modern. Maureen then tells me that they have a computer which has scanned all major Australian literature, from circa 1788 to 1993. The program is called OZCORP, short for Corpus of Australian Literature. It has a database of over sixteen million words. By feeding a word into the computer, the computer will provide all the references to the word in the literature scanned.

'Here goes,' she says. Click, click, click ... Eight clicks. Then after a while she tells me that the computer has come up with 380 uses of the word 'suburban'. She reads one at random: it is a quote from Louis Stone's *Jonah*, published in 1911, and 'suburban', here, has a social realist ring to it.

'Does the computer give printouts?' I ask naively. It does. 'Could it put the 380 quotations into chronological order?' It could. Maureen says she will have to charge a nominal fee and arrives at a sum of $25. This will include the 380 references in full, plus photocopies from the *Oxford Dictionary* of the meanings of the words 'suburban' and 'scene'. I do not request a computer printout on 'scene'. That might be asking for trouble. The $25 includes postage. I reckon I have got a bargain.

Wednesday, 8 September

The 380 references to 'suburban' arrive in a large package, jammed rudely into our letterbox by our 1990s suburban postperson. There is half a ream of A4 paper inside with closely typed quotes, all including 'suburban'. Each quote is about fifteen lines long and headed with the date, the title of the work it was taken from (novels through to newspaper articles), the author and the page reference.

   The first quote is dated 1867. Surprisingly late, given the *Oxford Dictionary* tracing of its usage back to 1625. The quote is from a novel titled *Mr Hogarth's Will* by Catherine Helen Spence. 'Suburban' is associated with a pioneering spirit, hard work, unexpected capital gain, and eventually being overrun by the 'monster, Melbourne'. In the next recorded use, in Marcus Clarke's *For the Term of His Natural Life* published in 1874, one character is horrified that land is being cut up into building allotments to be accessed by 'a suburban line'. In 1893, Philip E. Muskett in *The Art of Living in Australia* lauds the quality of the fish for sale at certain suburban markets. There is a sense of equality if not superiority over city fish sources. The suburbs, in his view, are where it's happening. At least in terms of fish.

   Ada Cambridge's use of 'suburban' in her 1904 novel *Sisters* suggests an association with a cosy 'escape from [the] treadmill'. The most desirable thing described about a suburban house is the view. The sisters could 'look out upon as pleasant a rural

landscape—the Malvern Hills—as any suburban
villa could command'. A sense of routineness is
present in C. E. W. Bean's 'suburban' in *On the
Wool Track* (1910). He uses the phrase 'every
suburban front lawn'. There is also a gentle hint of
new-found respectability, of something separate
from the tramp, swaggie, sundowner or unemployed
'that pokes its head over suburban back fences'. The
sense of respectability has lent itself to parody by
1913 when Norman Lindsay in *A Curate in Bohemia*
refers to a character, Bunson, as being addicted to
'playing the dissolute Bohemian in suburban
drawing rooms'.

A poem by William H. Ogilvie (1916) titled *The
Flying Scotsman* sounds modern, with its emphasis
on trains and speed:

> The grey suburban stations hold out their lifted
>   names,
> A painted roof beam flashes, a golden flower-
>   bed flames;
> We have no time to heed them, to pity or
>   admire;
> Between the sleepy platforms our wheels go by
>   like fire.

The use of 'grey' hints again at routineness and
uniformity. As well, 'suburban' seems an entity away
from the action. The psychologically charged con-
cept of dissociation (of the viewer) seems to be a
modernist one. And even the contention that suburb-
anites have the potential to be either pitied or
admired seems to sum up the contradictions in the
perceptions of 'suburban'.

By 1924 the notion of respectability reappears in
The Invaluable Mystery by Lesbia Harford. There is a
reference to 'a great suburban public school' and to
'cyclone fences which had recently become

fashionable for suburban gardens'. The inference is that the suburbs themselves have become fashionable. The final reference from the period is by Henry Handel Richardson in *The Fortunes of Richard Mahony* (1929): 'a jogtrot little suburban affair', referring to a medical practice (?) gone broke. A sense here of being out of the action. There are no more recorded uses until *For Love Alone* by Christina Stead in 1944 (unless I count *Blinky Bill* in 1939).

The word, as used around 1920, seems to me to contain the sorts of contradictions that are still present today. It can be a sanctuary, a place of refuge and peace. Or it can be used derogatorily to denote uniformity or recent respectability. For an artist, the derogatory use would be largely irrelevant. I doubt it would have entered the heads of Rees, Wakelin and the dozens of other professional artists living in the suburbs in the early 1920s. And for a landscape artist the benefits would be obvious.

For Lloyd Rees, the pioneering sense of the word may have had some meaning since, when he moved to the Sydney suburb of Northwood in the early 1930s, it was, Rees has written, an 'unknown suburb' to most people in Sydney.[1] He writes lovingly about his years in the Northwood house, from circa 1932, and about his 'mental marriage' to Marjory, his second wife, who was nurturing in every way. Northwood was a place of refuge and peace.[2] And the Mediterranean design of his house counteracted any charge of uniformity.

It would appear then, that someone in Rees's circle could easily have been the creator of the title *Suburban Scene* for the boatshed painting. It could have embodied for Rees in the 1920s a yearning or desire for a haven, as well as foreshadowing the pioneering move he was to make to Northwood in the early 1930s. It could also acknowledge the picturesque or scenic attributes claimed for the suburbs. It could also validate the waterfront suburbs as the domain of artists.

I still have the word 'suburban' ringing around my head. I remember seeing it recently in something written about Lloyd Rees. I rifle through my files and eventually find the reference. It is in the introduction which Basil Burdett wrote to *Sydney University—The Drawings of Lloyd Rees* published by Smith and Julius in 1922.[3]

The significant passage, referring to Rees's development as a painter, reads: 'Mosman [the suburb above Balmoral] was the *scene* of the first tentative efforts in oils, but the essentially *suburban* atmosphere seemed so limited that a move to the at least more varied interest of Bay Road [Waverton] was made.' The italics are mine, for obvious reasons: Burdett, the art dealer and close friend of Rees, uses both words of the inscribed title of the boatshed painting.

Burdett had established his New Art Salon in 1922. It was at this gallery that Rees's December 1922–January 1923 exhibition was held, which included catalogue number 22, *The Bay*. Rees's other close friend, Wal Taylor, was using part of the gallery space for his bookbinding activities. If *Suburban Scene* is not Rees's title, could it have been added to the boatshed painting, sometime after it was painted, by Burdett?

Saturday, 11 September

Tragic news regarding Embrey.

He shot himself. It is not known yet whether it was accidental or intentional.

I hear this from Catherine Ives. I had not heard

from her since I wrote on the 24th of August and had been getting worried that she might not have received my letter.

On the phone Catherine tells me that she had been meaning to write to me with a bit more information about her grandfather, William Charles Crawford, and in particular about this news of the death of his son, Embrey. She has recently had a long discussion with her mother about Embrey. I ask her whether it is a problem, my delving into what must be a delicate family matter. She says that her mother, Ithaca May (Embrey's sister), does not like to talk about it much. Within the family, Embrey's death is regarded as 'mysterious'. However, Catherine, herself, says she feels distanced enough for it not to be a problem. Maybe, like me, she believes that secrets in families should be unveiled, acknowledged and dealt with, so as to defuse the destructive power they can have. Whether this is the case or not, Catherine is curious.

She has discovered that the date of Embrey's death was probably February or March 1931. She is pretty sure that it occurred in the Dandenongs. He had been born in 1901, so that he was only about thirty when he died. In the last years of his life, from about 1927, he had worked as a journalist on the Melbourne *Argus* and was, for at least part of this time, the shipping correspondent. He had written letters to relatives in America, discussing which ships were listed to voyage there. This information was later used to discount any suicide theory: it was assumed he was making plans to travel and therefore could not have been contemplating suicide.

Catherine tells me that she has dug out Embrey's letters and articles and that the contents reveal a contradiction. While some of the writing is warmly descriptive of places such as Melbourne, there are some rather violent articles about hunting, fishing and shooting. Embrey had loved the bush: he had been a jackaroo in North Queensland. A couple of his articles describe gruesome kangaroo hunts. Embrey also wrote under a nom de plume, using Embrey as his surname. She offers to try to discover the sources of the articles. I wonder whether any of the publications he wrote for are from the stable of Syd Ure Smith.

I ask Catherine whether she minds my seeking out Embrey's will and the coroner's report on his death. Not a problem.

Catherine regards her late uncle Embrey as a much more likely owner of the boatshed painting than his father William Charles Crawford—she seems to sense something of Embrey's character. From what she knows about him, she believes it is likely that he moved in creative circles and may easily have come into the possession of a painting.

What might a close study of Embrey's letters and articles reveal? A definite link with Lloyd Rees? Or with another artist? A connection to Florence Jane Sainsbury, the last owner of the boatshed painting? Florence died this year at the age of 96 and would have been 34 in 1931. Not much older than Embrey.

Florence Jane Sainsbury was born and grew up in the Dandenongs, where Embrey had died, and may have been living there in 1931, the year of his death. I will have to double-check with the executor of her will, Robert Blain, about this. But is it possible Embrey and Florence have known each other? Could the boatshed painting have passed in, say, 1922, from Lloyd Rees to twenty-one-year-old Embrey Crawford (and, in the process, have acquired Embrey's father's phone number on the back) and been taken in about 1927 by Embrey to Melbourne where it eventually passes to Florence Jane Sainsbury? How did it pass? Were they neighbours? Friends? Or is it as simple as the painting somehow ending up in a junk shop, following Embrey's tragic death, and Florence finding it there? Is this the only connection between the two owners? Did Florence browse in junk shops in her mid-thirties, as she was known to have done when she was much older?

And then there's Florence's father who was an undertaker in the Dandenongs. Could he have organised Embrey's funeral and have also been involved in the disposal of his possessions, giving the boatshed painting to Florence? Also, Florence's husband, Bert, was a policeman. Could he have investigated Embrey's death and have been involved in the disposal of any possessions, including the boatshed painting, to his wife?

Was Florence's husband still around in 1931? I go back to my notes of the conversation with Robert Blain. I remember he had mentioned the year Bert died. I find it easily. Chillingly, it is 1931. Did he die in the Dandenongs too? From my notes I work out that he must have been only 51 when he died, and unlikely to have retired from the Police Force. Did he die in the line of duty? Did his death have something to do with Embrey?

Were Embrey and Florence lovers? Was the boatshed painting a gift from Embrey to Florence? Was there a lover's triangle? She 34, he 30, Bert 51. How did Bert die? It is probably just a coincidence. A lot of unrelated people died in the year 1931. Although Bert and Embrey could have been related through the boatshed painting. Could their deaths have been related too? I have to find out exactly how, when and where Embrey and Bert died. Death certificates would be a start. And the Coroner's report on Embrey's death. What will that reveal? Could there be a Coroner's report on Bert Sainsbury's death?

Meanwhile, my main hope for information is that their deaths were news, or that one or both received obituaries in a newspaper. In either case, the place to start is the *Argus* for 1931.

First thing tomorrow, into the Mitchell.

Sunday, 12 September

The Mitchell is closed for some reason. Then I realise it's Sunday. I'm losing track of time. But the general reference section of the State Library is open and it holds the *Argus* for 1931 and the index.

First the index. I first check under 'suicides'. And there it is: 'Crawford, Embrey W.: Skeleton in Bush: Discovery at Ferntree Gully, Apl. 27 [page] 4; Identified, Apl. 28 [page] 5; Inquest, May 13 [page] 17.' I also check under 'Accidents', 'Hunting' and 'Crime'. But there are no references. Under 'Obituaries' I find: 'Sainsbury, Sen.-Detective H. W., May 8 [page] 6.' He must have died a few days after Embrey's body was discovered and identified, and just before the inquest!

I thread the microfilm into one of the machines that doubles as a camera. This way I can photograph any pages of interest and take them home to be fully absorbed later. I work in chronological order. From the *Argus*, 27 April, 1931, page 4:

SKELETON IN BUSH

Discovery at Ferntree Gully

About 70 yards from the track leading to the lookout on One Tree Hill, Upper Ferntree Gully, on Saturday afternoon, two members of a walking party found the skeleton of a man lying beneath a tree with a pea rifle between the legs. The Ferntree Gully police took the skeleton to the city morgue yesterday. It is about 6ft in height. The tattered remnants of a pair of gabardine trousers, a grey sports coat, and a grey hat, were also found. The boots on the man's feet were size 10.

From the Argus, 28 April, 1931, page 5:

SKELETON IDENTIFIED

Missing Journalist

From clothing and other articles, the skeleton found in the bush at Ferntree Gully on Saturday is believed to be that of Embrey W. Crawford, aged 31 years, a journalist who had been missing since January 20. In a pocket of a grey sports coat and on the skeleton were found a handkerchief bearing the monogram 'C', and several keys. Attached to one key was a disc bearing the number 236 and it proved to be the key to a room at the Young Men's Christian Association building, Sturt Street, South Melbourne, which was formerly occupied by Crawford. Another key fitted the lock of a private letter-box at the YMCA which was formerly used by Crawford.

The skeleton was found on Saturday by Mr Charles Biggs, of Moreland Road, East Brunswick, who was walking down a hillside near the bush track leading to One Tree Hill. There was a pea rifle, with a pistol butt, between the legs of the skeleton, and yesterday the Government pathologist (Dr C. H. Wollison) found a bullet in the skull.

From the *Argus*, 8 May, 1931, page 6:

Senior-detective H. W. Sainsbury, of the Commonwealth Investigation branch, died at the police hospital yesterday after a short illness.

Senior-detective Sainsbury who was aged 51 years, was a son of a former chief commissioner of police (Mr A. G. Sainsbury). He was appointed to the criminal investigation branch in 1903, without any previous police experience. After 13 years in the Victorian detective service, Senior-detective Sainsbury was transferred to the Commonwealth Investigation department for special duties in the war period. He was attached to the Commonwealth Investigation department for 15 years.

From the *Argus*, 13 May, 1931, page 17:

DEATH OF JOURNALIST

Coroner's Qualified Finding

On April 25th the body of Embrey William Crawford, aged 28 years [*sic*], was found in the scrub at Upper Ferntree Gully. Crawford was last seen alive on January 20, when he left his room in the building of the Young Men's Christian Association. The acting City Coroner (Mr T. B. Wade, P. M.) held an inquest into the death of Crawford yesterday.

Charles Victor Grainge Biggs, chemist, of Moreland Road, East Brunswick, said that he found the body in thick scrub. Replying to Mr Krerouse (who appeared to watch the proceedings on behalf of the relatives of Crawford), Biggs said that it would have been possible for anyone to have tripped in walking through the thick undergrowth.

Victoria Beckingsale, journalist, of Landsdowne Road, East St Kilda, said that she met Crawford at the *Argus* office about five months before his disappearance. He was of a shy and reserved temperament. About eight or nine days before his disappearance he told her that he had lost his

The boatshed painting, oil on plywood, 15 x 30.5 cm (after cleaning).

The reverse of the boatshed painting, photographed by the author during the Joel's auction viewing (on the floor).

John D. Banks' The Road to the Beach *(1924), oil on canvas, 41.2 x 45.7 cm, signed and dated lower left.* The Art Gallery of New South Wales.

Margaret Preston's Edward's Beach, Balmoral *(circa 1929), woodblock print, 30 x 22.4 cm, signed in image lower left, showing red-roofed harbourside houses.*

Roland Wakelin's Synchromy in Orange Major *(1919), oil on cardboard, 30 x 40 cm, signed and dated lower left.*

Roy de Maistre's Boatsheds Berry's Bay *(1919), oil on board, 38 x 23 cm, signed and dated lower left.*

Lloyd Rees's Coolangatta *(circa 1916-19), oil on canvas on board, 22.2 x 25.4 cm, signed lower right.*

Lloyd Rees's Near our Flat, Cremorne *(Christmas 1920-21), oil on canvas on board, 28 x 23 cm, signed with initials lower left, inscribed and dated on the reverse.*

283

Lloyd Rees's The Red House *(circa 1921-January 1922), oil on canvas on board, 29 x 41.5 cm, signed lower right and inscribed with title on reverse. Sold (unrestored) at Sotheby's 28/11/95 (photographed at the viewing by the author). Exhibited at the Art Society of Tasmania, February, 1922 (No. 53 NFS) and probably at Burdett's New Art Salon, December, 1922 (No. 6, seven guineas).*

Lloyd Rees's The Hill Top, Old Cremorne *(circa 1918-20), detail, oil on canvas on board, 29.4 x 39.2 cm, signed lower left.*

Lloyd Rees's Old Boats, Wollstonecraft Bay *(circa 1921-22), oil on canvas on plywood, 25 x 30.5 cm, unsigned.*

Lloyd Rees's Afternoon Sunshine, Sydney Harbour *(1921), oil on board, 22.4 x 33.8 cm, signed and dated lower left.*

Lloyd Rees's Parramatta River *(1922), oil on canvas on board, 18 x 24.5 cm, signed and dated lower left.*

Lloyd Rees's Cornish Coast *(1923), oil on board (?), 29.2 x 37.5 cm, signed and dated lower left.*

Lloyd Rees's Old Barn, Parramatta *(1924), oil on canvas on board, 45.7 x 33 cm, signed lower right.*

Lloyd Rees's The Bay *(circa 1926), oil on canvas on board, 26 x 36.8 cm, signed lower right. Exhibited Gainsborough Gallery, Brisbane, 1928 (No. 5. fifteen guineas).*

Lloyd Rees's Balmoral *(1926-27), oil on canvas on plywood, 27.5 x 28.5 cm, signed lower right.*

Lloyd Rees's The Café at the Spit *(1927), oil on canvas on board, 33 x 39.5 cm, signed and dated lower right.*

position, and that he thought that he was a failure. She received a letter from Crawford, which was written in a despondent tone.

Dr C. H. Wollison, who made a post-mortem examination, said that a bullet wound in the head would have been sufficient to cause death. It was possible, if Crawford had been examining the mechanism of the small pea rifle, for it to have gone off accidentally. The situation of the wound was as consistent with accident as with deliberate intention, provided that Crawford were leaning forward at the time the rifle was discharged.

Constable G. M. Thomas, of Ferntree Gully, who found the body after being informed of its whereabouts by the witness Biggs, said that there were signs on the trees as if Crawford had been practising shooting. There were some empty bullet cases near the rifle.

The acting coroner said that if it had not been for the letter, one would have been forced to the conclusion that it was a case of accident, but he could not get past the letter, which began: 'Just this farewell note' and which referred to Crawford 'having failed indeed.' He was afraid that, in view of the letter and the medical evidence, he must return a finding that Crawford shot himself. Crawford seemed to have taken his dismissal from the *Argus* very seriously indeed, and it appeared to have preyed on his mind. He would qualify the finding to that extent.

I cross-check the Melbourne *Age* from 25 April to 14 May, 1931, looking for references to either Crawford or Sainsbury but there is no reference to Crawford's demise nor an obituary for Sainsbury. There are however, three death notices for Sainsbury. The first is in the 8 May edition.

SAINSBURY. On the 7th May, at the Police Hospital, St Kilda Road, Melbourne. Herbert William Sainsbury (Senior Detective), of 147 Riversdale Road, Hawthorn. No flowers, by request. Private interment.

This is followed directly by:

SAINSBURY. On the 7th May. Herbert William, eldest son of Mrs Sainsbury and the late A. G. Sainsbury, ex-Commissioner of Police, brother of Annie, May, Ernest, Evelyn, George (deceased), Myrtle and Harold.

'After life's fitful fever
He sleeps well.'

On the following day, 9 May, there is a further death notice.

SAINSBURY. On the 7th May, at the Police Hospital, St Kilda Road, Herbert William Sainsbury, eldest son of Margaret and the late A. G. Sainsbury, ex Chief Commissioner of Police, father of Geoffrey, Sybil and Alan, children of the late Esther Daley Sainsbury (nee Pole), interred family grave Brighton Cemetery.
Father and mother united.

'His sword is in its sheath, his cross laid down.'
Inserted by his affectionate sisters.

Embrey's body was taken to the city morgue. Therefore, it is fairly certain that Florence Sainsbury's father, the Dandenong undertaker, did not attend to the funeral arrangements, and could not have come by the boatshed painting in this way and passed it to Florence. The evidence suggests that Crawford was not living in the Dandenongs immediately prior to his death, but at the YMCA in South Melbourne. Senior-Detective Herbert Sainsbury (together with his wife Florence—unless they were estranged) was living in Hawthorn, on the other side of the city. And yet Embrey Crawford and Florence Sainsbury are still possibly connected (perhaps romantically) through the boatshed painting.

What were Herbert Sainsbury's relations like with his wife, Florence? She had been remembered 'as a very difficult woman', by Robert Blain, her executor. A little information is perhaps forthcoming in the death notices for Herbert.

The first death notice has, I think, a terse note to it. 'No flowers, by request. Private interment.' Also, it is the only notice where Bert's home address is given. My guess is that it was written and placed in the *Age* by his wife Florence Sainsbury. It suggests she was living at the same address (and, therefore, not estranged). But the tone also suggests that perhaps the relationship was not a loving one. On the other hand, perhaps the brevity is due to grief. The second notice has been placed, I think, by, or on behalf of, Herbert's mother. There is an emphasis on Herbert's father, the late A. G. Sainsbury, and his title of Commissioner of Police—the sort of emphasis Herbert's mother would give. She, herself, is referred to only as 'Mrs Sainsbury' without Christian names or initials. Is she emphasising pride in the role of faithful partner, faithful even after death? Is the implication 'faithful, unlike Florence'? I read this death notice again. Florence, Herbert's wife, is not mentioned. The lines 'After life's fitful fever/He sleeps well' suggest a mother's anguish and regret that he did not live a happier life.

It is intriguing to note that these two death notices do not employ the word 'loving' or 'beloved', as do virtually all other death notices in the *Age* for that day! I think about this as I go off to find a dictionary of quotations to check the source of 'After life's fitful fever'. I find that it is from *Macbeth* and the full quote is 'After life's fitful fever he sleeps well; Treason has done his worst; nor steel, nor poison, Malice domestic, foreign levy, Nothing can touch him further.'

Malice domestic!

In the single notice for Herbert Sainsbury the following day, the word 'affectionate' is used: the notice was 'inserted by his affectionate sisters'. The family grave at Brighton is referred to, suggesting that this is where the Sainsbury family was centred, and perhaps Herbert had lived there before Hawthorn. 'Father and mother united' suggests that (quite naturally) they felt Herbert's marriage to his first wife was of greater significance than his second marriage to Florence, of whom there is no mention by the 'affectionate sisters'. Was Florence 'on the outer' for reasons other than simply being a second wife? Perhaps she was not considered a good wife ... was not considered a faithful wife. It may be worth checking to see if any of Herbert's children are still living to see whether they can throw light on the nature of his relationship with Florence, and on his death.

Will it be possible to trace Victoria Beckingsale, the journalist on the *Argus* who had known Embrey for five months before his disappearance? It is not a common name. I wonder what her relationship with Embrey was like. Victoria had lived in Landsdowne Road, East St Kilda, and St Kilda was a hunting ground for Florence Sainsbury. Could Embrey have given Victoria the boatshed painting and could it have later ended up in a St Kilda antique or junk shop to be found by Florence Sainsbury? I wonder whether the letter that Embrey wrote to Victoria, 'Just this farewell note' etc, was tabled in the

Coroner's report. Might it make mention of any belongings, including the boatshed painting?

If Victoria is still alive, her information could be crucial. Would she remember any place where Embrey lived, and whether there was a painting on the wall? Was Embrey settled in Melbourne, prior to his move to the YMCA? I hope so, because the boatshed painting would have needed a home while he was off on his hunting trips. He would be unlikely to have carried it around with him if he was a drifter. Would Victoria know of a lovers' triangle?

I am completing a final cross-check for information in the *Australasian*, trying to close the unwieldy 1931 volume, when my eye catches a familiar name. It is on a page from the 2 May edition. The name is Harry McClelland. He was the artist whom Jon Dwyer at Joel's thought could have painted the boatshed painting. The article reads:

> Mr Harry McClelland, an artist who resides for many months of the year at Frankston (V.), is instituting a campaign for the establishment of a gallery of Australian art there. Frankston is a well patronised bayside resort, and many Melbourne people have built homes there and near by. In all probability the project would meet with ready support. The suggestion that the gallery be built of logs, with a shingle roof, however, seems scarcely in keeping with its purpose. The rustic log cabin is appropriate for the bush, but a building more dignified and with some architectural qualities, no matter how simple, seems indicated in this case.

I had already checked McCulloch's *Encyclopedia of Australian Art* to discover that the McClelland Gallery was established in 1961 under the terms of the Nan McClelland bequest as a memorial to her brother, Harry McClelland (1884–1951). The McClellands must have persevered with the idea for thirty years until their deaths. I could not find out much else about Harry. I found a reference somewhere that he had trained at the National Gallery School but could not find him in the list of students.[1] He may have been what used to be termed 'a Sunday painter'.

I have never been to Frankston but the words 'bayside resort' are a bit of a worry. Is it a Frankston boatshed in my painting? Was Frankston regarded as suburban back then? The McClelland Gallery would have paintings by Harry McClelland. I should get around to sending a photograph of the boatshed painting to the director, asking whether he thinks the painting is by Harry, and whether he can identify the scene. But I might leave it for a while. My current line of investigation is proving too interesting.

Monday, 13 September

I walk down Macquarie Street to the Probate Office of the Supreme Court beneath ominous rainclouds. The details of Embrey's death still weigh heavily. Was there a lovers triangle? I wonder.

The Supreme Court is directly opposite the beautiful, Georgian, St James's Anglican Church, commissioned by Governor Macquarie and designed by the convict Francis Greenway. The sight of it always manages to cheer me up. I remember the thrill, twenty-five years ago, of discovering a reference to the fact that, down in the crypt, was a mural

painted in 1929 by a fascinating collection of m̶
ernist sympathisers who called themselves th̶
Turramurra Wall Painters. The group was led by
Ethel Anderson, wife of the secretary of the then
Governor, Brigadier-General Sir Dudley de Chair,
and various other women artists including the wife
and daughter of Dudley de Chair. They were assisted
by Roy de Maistre and Roland Wakelin. When I first
saw this wonderful mural it had been neglected
almost totally for decades and was in a terrible
condition, but today it is in the process of being
restored and its significance will soon be fully
revealed.

It is titled, incidentally, *I Saw Three Ships Come
Sailing By*. (I must stop seeing symbolism in
everything!)

In the Probate Office I check the records.
Embrey Crawford did not make a will in NSW. My
hopes rest now with the Melbourne Probate Office.

Tuesday, 14 September

I call the Melbourne Probate Office to see if they
have found Embrey's will as requested. As it turns
out, they have found his file, but he did not leave a
will. There are, however, various other documents
including a statement of assets. I ask whether
this includes belongings at the time of death and am
told that it does! The fee is $27.60. I send off a
cheque.

Friday, 17 September

The list of assets of Embrey Crawford arrives from
the Victorian Probate Office. The sum total of
Embrey's assets is £553 8s. All but £10 of this is

oceeds of a life insurance policy
h, and constitutes the entire value
onal effects left at his room at the
ossessions are not itemised. Could
a painting included in the personal
en   y's estate was authorised to go to his
next of   his parents. It feels like I've gone
around in a circle.

Thursday, 30 September

I take the boatshed painting to Alan and Jan
Rees again—they have not yet seen it in its cleaned
state.

Alan and Jan are as welcoming as ever. We sit
on the balcony overlooking the Harbour on a stunning, Sydney spring morning. Their response to the
painting is still gently optimistic. They have recently
been shown four fakes purporting to be by Lloyd
Rees and they found these easy to establish as not
being by 'Dad'. The boatshed painting is, however, a
different proposition, but they still share my need for
concrete proof.

So, is the handwriting in Lloyd's early letters the
same as the inscribed title on the frame of the
boatshed painting? They look at it carefully. They
think that it is possible but cannot be sure. Alan
makes the point that the inscription is not only
written on wood (as opposed to paper in the letters)
thus making comparison difficult, but whoever wrote
the inscription on the frame would have had to have
held their hand in the air rather than rest it on a
support such as a writing table. This is because even
if the frame was resting on a surface, the back of the
frame would have been raised about three
centimetres from that surface. This could explain the
slight clumsiness of the inscription as opposed to the

more uniform writing in the letters. There is nothing about the inscription that definitely excludes the possibility of 'Dad' being the inscriber. They agree that if Lloyd wrote the inscription then it would be proof enough that he painted the painting. They strongly suggest I pursue the Police Department's Document Examination Unit to obtain an expert opinion.

Comparing the boatshed painting again to other 1920s oils in the family collection confirms that, if it is by Rees, it is most likely to have been painted around 1918–1922. The pigments are similar to those in *Balmoral, 1927* but not identical. There is an interesting thing about *Balmoral* though. It is signed neatly in pencil on the surface of the paint which means that it could not have been signed while the paint was still wet. It must have been signed sometime later. In fact, as Alan looks at the painting, he realises for the first time that the signature may not in fact be by his father, but added later by someone else. In other words, *Balmoral* may have left Rees's hands unsigned. Like the boatshed painting?

In Renee Free's book we also note the reference to an oil titled *Near Our Flat, Mosman* painted at Christmas 1920–21. It is not illustrated and is worth tracking down for comparison with the boatshed painting since it is one of the few works from the early 1920s which appears to be dated accurately.

Alan and Jan promise to try to track down handwriting samples of Lloyd's friends Wal Taylor and Basil Burdett. They know that they don't have any by Rubery Bennett since they are not aware of any connection or dealings with him.

Saturday, 2 October

Dear Catherine Ives,

Enclosed are the press reports from the *Argus* relating to Embrey. I also scanned the *Age* and other publications of the same dates, but could find no other references.

I have managed to obtain the probate documents, which are enclosed. I hope this material is of interest and not too distressing. It seems that, apart from the letter from Embrey to Victoria Beckingsale, the Coroner would have been forced to the conclusion that his death was an accident.

The material does not provide any evidence of a link to Lloyd Rees's circle of friends and associates. I am wondering whether it is possible that any of Embrey's articles or letters might refer to the names or places I have uncovered in my research. Would it be possible for you to tell me how much of his writing you have, and whether I could peruse it or obtain copies sometime later?

Hoping to hear from you.

Yours sincerely,

Stephen Scheding

Friday, 15 October

Dear Stephen,

Thank you very much for sending the newspaper reports of my uncle's death in 1931. It is such a sad story, but I am far enough removed from the events not to be too upset by it. The place where he died, One Tree Hill, is quite close to where we live in the Dandenongs. It is a beautiful, but isolated, forest area. If it had not been for your investigation of the picture and my subsequent conversation with my mother, I may never have known so much of the story. It was never a subject that was discussed in our family, although I do remember my mother telling me about the unresolved questions that remained in everyone's minds after his death. I did not know about the loss of his job or letter to Victoria Beckingsale. I also looked up the *Age* newspapers of the time at the State Library of Victoria but found nothing. I do have difficulty using microfiche readers however, not being a particularly technical person!

I have a folder with a few of Embrey's articles, some of which were written under the name of John Embrey. They are from the *Australian Sporting and Dramatic News* (14/12/1929; 30/11/1929; 5/10/1929; 31/8/1929; 16/11/1929; 7/12/1929), *Illustrated Tasmanian Mail* (26/2/1930) and the *North Queensland Register* (15/2/1930). They are mainly articles on 'the outdoor life': a lot of hunting, fishing and shooting. My mother says that he worked for a time as a freelance journalist in the country near Orange and travelled by boat to North Queensland writing about his experiences. He was born in 1901 by the way. I'm not sure if I mentioned that when I spoke to you on the phone. I also have a couple of letters that he wrote to his American grandparents just prior to his disappearance and some written by them, trying to reassure his parents during that period. They believed he would turn up at any moment—possibly in America.

I wonder if you have made any progress with the handwriting investigations?

I will be in Sydney at the end of this month for a long weekend. If you like I could bring the writings, letters etc for you to look at. You could peruse them over that weekend if you wish.

Thank you again for sending the newspaper reports. I'm sorry I have been such a slow correspondent.

Yours sincerely,
Catherine Ives

I phone Catherine to tell her how grateful I am for this letter. She tells me that she will be arriving in Sydney on Thursday, 28 October and we agree to meet that evening. This means that I will be able to see Embrey's writings and to get more of 'a sense' of him. Then I intend to fly to Melbourne to tidy up the Melbourne end of my research, a trip which just happens to coincide with the next Joel's painting auction. Catherine tells me again that until she had received the press cuttings from me, she had not known that Embrey had died at One Tree Hill, not far from where she lives. Not only is it a truly beautiful spot but it has also held for her a strange fascination and, even, a sense of foreboding. Now, she feels, she understands why. She would like to know more.

The name also has an effect on me. It is the name used by Lloyd Rees to refer to Mount Cootha which overlooks Brisbane. He was raised within sight of it and he refers to One Tree Hill in the very first paragraph of his first autobiography.

Monday, 18 October

To further prepare for the Melbourne trip, I send off a letter to the librarian at La Trobe Library.

Dear Librarian,
I am currently researching an unsigned oil painting and trying to identify the artist and establish its provenance.

The reverse of the painting has a handwritten number, 8930, which is almost certainly a Sydney telephone number from 1917–1927. But I need to eliminate the possibility that it could have been a Melbourne number.

The painting may have been owned prior to 1931 by an Embrey Crawford. Crawford (b. 1901) was a journalist who moved from Sydney to Melbourne in about 1927. He wrote for the *Australian Sporting and Dramatic News*, the *Illustrated Tasmanian Mail* and the *North Queensland Register*. He was working for the *Argus* up to 1931 when he died tragically.

I am wondering whether the Library has any reference to him. He also wrote under the name 'John Embrey'.

I will be in Melbourne from the 1st to the 4th of November.

I look forward to hearing from you.

Yours sincerely,
Stephen Scheding

Wednesday, 20 October

I decide to make contact with Robert Blain again, the executor of Florence Jane Sainsbury's estate. He had been unable to recall how and when she had come by the painting.

Dear Robert,
Thank you for talking to me about Florence Jane Sainsbury.

I have written to the other friends of Mrs Sainsbury mentioned in her will enclosing a photograph of the boatshed painting, but they were not able to tell me how she came by it.

It is possible that the painting was originally

owned by an Embrey Crawford, a journalist
(aka 'John Embrey') who moved from Sydney
to Melbourne before dying tragically in the
Dandenongs in 1931, the same year, incidentally,
as the death of Mrs Sainsburys husband, Herbert.
I think that in 1931 the Sainsburys were living in
Hawthorn. As a matter of interest, would you
know how Herbert died?

You mentioned that Mrs Sainsbury was one of
those ladies who used to poke around second-
hand shops in St Kilda, Prahran and Windsor in
Victoria, and later in the Dandenong Ranges and
when living at Ferny Creek, looking for what she
and her friends called 'treasures'. I agree that it is
most likely that this is how she came by the boatshed painting. However, would you know whether
she ever purchased things from auctions? Or was
given things by friends?

I hope these questions are not putting you to
too much trouble. I will be in Melbourne in the
first week of November and may phone you then,
unless you wish to contact me before this at the
above address.

Yours sincerely,
Stephen Scheding

Thursday, 21 October

I phone Joe Petroni at Westmead Hospital who was
recommended by Ernie Hughes of the Australian
Institute of Radiography as a good person to X-ray
the boatshed painting. He tells me he is most
interested in doing it.

Friday, 22 October

I arrive at the vast Westmead Hospital and find my
way to the X-ray Department. At the reception desk
I am met by Joe Petroni and Fred Payne, his assistant. Joe regrets that he has another appointment so
he hands me over to Fred. Fred is a jovial, bearded
chap of about my age and expresses great interest in
the project. He leads me to his work area, telling me
casually that it is located in the morgue. Joe and Fred
do a lot of forensic work. At the entrance to the
morgue are two, large, shiny aluminium doors with
signs saying 'no entry' and with painted hands held
up in halt mode. I am taken through and past a neat
row of other, smaller aluminium doors embedded in
the wall, behind which are, well, I'd rather not think.

Fred's work area is clinically pristine. He is
explaining that they often have to X-ray corpses to
discover where bullets are located. I casually ask
whether X-rays would have been used for this
purpose in Melbourne in 1931, but he says he
doesn't think so. There are some large colour
photographs lying on a table on the other side of the
room of a naked body, presumably dead. To distract
myself I tell Fred that I am exploring the possibility
that the painting is by Lloyd Rees. Perhaps I
shouldn't have said this. Too late.

We go over to a tall, silver machine in the shape
of a slimline refrigerator—a Hewlett Packard
Faxitron, model A43805N. Fred takes the painting
and places it against a special red envelope and lays
them together flat onto the floor of the machine, as
if he is placing a pizza into a microwave, and then
locks the door. He tells me that it is the first time he
has ever done this. I have a sudden panic attack and
ask him if the X-rays can do the painting any damage.
He reassures me. After one minute he takes the
painting and envelope out and repeats the process

with another envelope, resetting the machine to a different contrast. Then, with both envelopes, we head off along a corridor to the Dental Laboratory to have the X-rays developed in the darkroom. In just minutes we take the developed plates back to Fred's work area and place them on a backlit display screen.

The effect is dramatic. It is the same image but there is so much new information to look at. The X-ray looks spookily like a Rees lithograph from the early 1980s.

The general indication is that there is definitely not another painting underneath. The artist worked from the beginning on the main forms where they are found in the finished painting. There is little re-working, although the artist may have considered putting a triangular gable on the house but changed his mind. Perhaps it would have made the composition too busy. I think of Rees, the non-topographical artist, working at getting the comp-osition right at the expense of architectural accuracy.

The X-ray has picked up the texture of the plywood and also lumps and streaks of paint on the reverse of the panel. Flat areas are not as detailed as the rough areas because X-rays only pick up depth. We check to see if any fingerprints have been reveal-ed. I have already looked for fingerprints on the painting itself but found only smudges that are vaguely possible. There is no new evidence in this direction. This is unfortunate, because finding finger-prints could prove to be conclusive. Meanwhile, I vainly look for a signature, which might have been painted over for some reason, but find nothing promising. I realise that it would probably take years of looking at the two X-rays, for me to be able to 'read' them properly.

But Fred is the expert. He is mumbling about some letters in the top right-hand corner. I can't see them. So he turns the plate over so that the reverse image is showing and points to the same corner, now the top left-hand corner of the X-ray. There is something there but, as I have discovered before, the paint has been applied in such a way as to hint at many letter shapes. There have been times when I have seen 'Rees' written all over the painting.

Now Fred is adamant that he can clearly see the word 'Rees' in the top right-hand corner of the painting! Except it is in reverse. Which means that, if it is, in fact, there, it is probably written on the reverse of the painting's plywood support, in the top left-hand corner, underneath the strip of book-binding tape. Or, alternatively, impressed into the tape as if the word was written firmly on a piece of paper which was resting on the tape. But since there is no obvious impression on the tape, any signature is likely to be written under the tape. As complicated as this initially seems, it actually makes perfect sense. Lloyd Rees may have signed the painting on the reverse, a not uncommon practice, and the person who framed it could have covered the signature with the tape. Perhaps the signature was faint and not noticed by the framer. And the signature has remained hidden until picked up today by the X-ray.

We undertake a delicate operation. Carefully, we remove the piece of tape covering what might be the word 'Rees', to reveal ... bare board.

'It is a mystery!' says Fred. He takes another couple of X-rays for his own interest. There is no mention of payment for the service and he offers to help with any other paintings I have. After chatting on for a bit, I bid farewell. As I drive home, I wonder about the power of suggestion. Did I make Fred find a signature?

At home, I place the X-rays on my own light box and look again at the corner of the painting that has the inscribed 'signature' in reverse. I can still see it quite clearly. It is the right size for a signature only back to front. Then the phone rings. It is Fred. He has X-rayed the piece of bookbinding tape and has found nothing: the 'signature' was not in, or on, the piece of tape. But he has shown his X-ray plates of the whole painting to other radiographers working in his section and they have all been able to read 'Rees' where he has found it! Admittedly Rees usually used capital letters in his signature, but what the heck ...

Now, me finding a signature is understandable— I have probably become so obsessed with my quest that I am reading anything into anything, but Fred is a professional radiographer who knows how to read X-rays. However, if this phantom signature is not on the back of the painting, then it would mean that the letters are in reverse, in paint, on the top right-hand corner of the painting underneath the surface paint.

The only explanation is that the letters are accidental. A fluke, unless Rees signed his name in reverse and then painted over it. And why would he do that? He couldn't have expected some obsessed nutter like me to have the painting X-rayed seventy years later! That would be too weird for words.

Monday, 25 October

I get a telephone call from Judy McDonald of the Research Section of the La Trobe Library. She tells me that she has found no trace of Embrey Crawford or John Embrey in the library. She does tell me that the library holds copies of the Melbourne Telephone Directory from the 1920s, and the good news is that she has already browsed through some, and can find no telephone numbers without prefixes. I will have to check this, but if it is true, then 8930 is not a Melbourne telephone number.

Thursday, 28 October

4.00 pm: I take a trip down to the Parker Gallery with the painting on the off-chance that ninety-year-old Clarrie Parker, nephew of S. A. Parker, might be there. I meet his son, Lindsay, who tells me that Clarrie's health has deteriorated lately and he no longer drops in.

Lindsay Parker is a most pleasant person. He listens patiently to the story of my search and is particularly interested in my question about whether the size of the frame could have been a stock frame size in the 1920s. He picks up the painting and lovingly caresses the frame, turning it over and peering into its corners and crevices. He names the wood used, a South American pine, and notes that while it is bronzed, it has also been lightly gilded with gold leaf along the outer edges. But it is a less expensive style of frame than the Parker frames from the 1920s that were wholly gilded. The most expensive were carved entirely out of wood, while the boatshed frame has been made with gesso moulded onto wood.

His conclusion is that it is almost certainly a stock frame. The size 6" x 12" is the main indication since stock frames increased in size by six or twelve inch increments. For example, 18" x 24" was a common stock frame size. As well, since the painting was put into the frame while it was still wet, and since the painting was not cut down, the implication is that, before painting it, the artist knew there would be a frame to fit it and may even have had one close by. When I tell him that Penfolds, the stationers, did not sell a stock 6" x 12" frame he merely shrugs. Even if the frame was not a stock size, it is of the type that would have been relatively inexpensive for Parker's to make up in the 1920s. It would have taken two to three weeks to arrive from the time of ordering, perhaps still a short enough time for the paint to adhere to the frame if the painting had been pressed in firmly enough. Lindsay feels that this frame was very possibly prepared by S. A. Parker.

6.00 pm, home: Catherine Ives arrives with her archive. It is contained in an old foolscap tax folder which bears a printed label: McGovern Radiology (the company name of William Charles Crawford). There are items relating to William Charles and the articles written by Embrey, predominantly on sporting subjects. Some are illustrated by the black and white artist Will Mahony, the son of the famous *Bulletin* artist Frank Mahony, and some are illustrated with photographs taken by Embrey. There are a couple of photo spreads of North Queensland life also photographed by Embrey. Catherine points to a photograph which depicts a young woman sitting on a giant turtle. She comes out of this ludicrous pose with her obvious good looks intact. Catherine has discovered from her mum that Embrey had a thing going with this young woman. There are two letters written by Embrey to his grandmother in America shortly before his death, and some letters by the grandmother to Embrey's father shortly after, referring to the family's concern over Embrey's disappearance. The archive is not vast.

Catherine allows me to have the material to photocopy and I offer to return it to her later. In fact, I could deliver it next week since I am considering going to another Joel's auction, which is on then.

This is all good timing. And the coroner's report has arrived today by mail.

Tuesday, 2 November

I am in Melbourne, holed up in my motel room in South Yarra with the photocopies of the Embrey archive. I now have time to look at it thoroughly. Before going through it, I make a call to Robert Blain, Florence Sainsbury's executor, to see if he is able to give me the information I have requested of him in my letter. Robert is as cheery as ever, still amused by my quest. He tells me, firstly, that unfortunately he does not know how Florence's husband, Bert, died. Florence certainly never discussed it. He tosses me a question about why I wish to know about the nature of Bert's death, but I sidestep it.

I explore how Florence may have acquired the painting. Robert thinks she might have purchased paintings at auction. It was the sort of thing she would do, if they were cheap, but he can't be sure. He again conjures up the image of Florence Sainsbury as a magpie pecking around in second-hand and antique shops. But this time he adds a cigarette sticking out of the corner of her mouth.

'Did she smoke?' I butt in. He tells me that she smoked at least a packet of cork-tipped red Capstans a day up until six months before she died. *This* must be the cause of the tobacco smoke staining that had accumulated on the boatshed painting, rather than the pipes of W. C. Crawford whom I had first (wrongly it seems) accused. So Florence was still smoking at the age of 96! She must have been tough. I wonder what *did* keep her alive in the face of her suicidal smoking.

Robert continues: 'She was a very secretive person, almost paranoid. She played her cards very close to her chest so nothing would surprise me about her past. I have a lot of her personal photographs and there are a lot of people in them, but few are named. It was a salutary lesson for me when I looked at them—I went and annotated my own photographs.' I ask him if he could look at Florence's photos and check for the names Embrey Crawford and Victoria Beckingsale. He offers to do this. In fact he tells me that he hadn't got around to throwing them out yet. I haven't the courage, right at this moment, to ask if I can have them.

As an afterthought I ask whether he knew the addresses of Florence Sainsbury when she was living at Ferny Creek in the Dandenongs and at East St Kilda. Without hesitating he says that she lived at Old Belgrave Road, Ferny Creek, for quite some time before the Second World War and after the war had also purchased a house at 10 Deakin Street, St Kilda, which she let out before eventually moving there some time later. I tell Robert that Florence's husband, Bert Sainsbury, is listed in Hawthorn at the time of his death in 1931. Does he know whether Florence was living in Hawthorn with Bert at the time? He says he does not know, but he does add that she and Herbert might have had two houses at that time. One in Hawthorn and one in the Dandenongs. He is certain about the house in the Dandenongs.

Time to go through the Embrey archive. First, there are some bulletins and memorabilia from the Motor Yacht Club of N.S.W. which had been kept by William Charles Crawford. The Commodore of the Club in the years around 1920 was Frank Albert of the music family which owned Boomerang House in King Street. This would explain why William Charles

Crawford, who was a committee member of the club prior to 1917, moved to rooms in Boomerang House around that date. An Old Boys network. Maybe he even got a favourable rent.

In 1918–19 W. C. Crawford was a member of the Transportation Committee of the Motor Yacht Club and used the Automobile Club of Australia to help with the club's transport needs. Thus, there is, again, a possible tantalising link between Crawford and the advertising man, George Patterson, who was a member of the Automobile Club[1] and who was closely associated with Syd Ure Smith for whom Lloyd Rees worked. But, apart from leading to this speculation, the information relating to W. C. Crawford is not helpful.

Then, promisingly, there is another connection with the advertising world in the poignant letter written by Embrey to Victoria Beckingsale which, amazingly, is included in the coroner's report. The letter has been handwritten on pieces of sub-editors' copy paper and is dated Tuesday Morning, 20/1/31. The letters YMCA are scrawled across the top. The envelope has also survived: Victoria's address is 'Reno', Landsdowne Rd, St Kilda. The value of the stamps amounts to four pence. The handwriting is not the same as the inscription on the reverse of the boatshed painting.

Dearest Tora:
    Just this farewell note. I must go. You have been a dear friend to me and I have returned your friendship churlishly enough, I am quite aware.
    When a man fails even in spite of the [word obscured, possibly 'help'] of loyal and sincere friends, then he has failed indeed.
    Bart has been my guiding star for the past four years. His cheery courage and good sense have stuck to me. Whatever small achievements I have

had, I have carried delightedly to him for his approval and criticism. I wanted, more than I can explain, to have something worthwhile to show him eventually, and my job at the *Argus* seemed to be that opportunity. Having [failed?] there I cannot go on.

I do not ask you to forgive my base characteristics. That they exist is manifest. So why harp on them?

I have finished up on a 'high spot' at any rate, in the office. At half past twelve last night I was reading Bagot [?] a proof of his [?] re the [?] and it is comforting to my vanity to see the job in the centre of the leader page this morning.

It would be quite impossible for me to endure the mental anguish which would attend my returning to the obscurity of a wharf-labourer or drover of sheep and cattle after having been elevated for the short glorious spasm ['of' crossed out] to [sic] comparative importance. Introspection would win hands down. I am too thin-skinned to stand humiliation.

That's about enough of me: however, after all, this is an explanatory letter.

I have left my 'Corona' portable [typewriter] with a label carrying your name, in my locker in the reporters' room. It's in a bottom, wooden one, about four from the left. I should like you to have it.

Should you ever go to Sydney you might care to look up Bart: L. V. Bartlett, c/o A. H. White Ltd, Advertising Agents, London Bank Chambers, Martin Place, Sydney.

Good bye, old friend.
All my love,
Embrey

'Bart' appears to have been Embrey's mentor. It would now seem that it is entirely possible that

Embrey had mixed in Sydney in advertising circles.
He may have been introduced to Patterson through
his father, or through Bart or the A. H. White agency
and through these connections may have come
into contact with Lloyd Rees. I will have to check
whether the A. H. White company had dealings with
Patterson's agency, or better still, with Syd Ure
Smith's businesses. And I will have to find out, if
possible, who exactly L. V. Bartlett was.

   Is Embrey's letter a suicide letter? Does one
write one's address on a letter if one is contemplating
suicide? If one is not intending to return to that
address ever again?

   In the Coroner's report are various statements
from witnesses. From G. M. Thomas, the mounted
constable who was the first to inspect Embrey's
body:

> There was a small Winchester pea rifle between
> the legs, partly covered with the left arm, some
> pea rifle bullets were found alongside the corpse
> and a shell of a rifle bullet also [There seem to be
> two different types of ammunition implying two
> rifles] ... A haversack containing a gents blue
> gabardine coat was found partly under the corpse,
> and a gents grey felt hat near the head bearing the
> maker's name (ie) 'Akubra', 'Made expressly for
> J. Richardson and Co. Pty Ltd. Armadale' ... I
> found four-and-a-half pence in coppers, and a pair
> of gold sleevelinks with the raised initials F. L. T.
> on them, and on examining the pea rifle I found a
> discharged cartridge in the bore.

What does F. L. T. stand for? And where did the shell
of the rifle bullet come from? A rifle is not
mentioned by Mounted Constable Thomas. Nor by
Charles Biggs, chemist, who actually found the body.
Biggs testifies that his walking companion, Miss

Leah Price, saw what she thought was 'a boot with a stick in it' and drew his attention to it:

> I immediately went to investigate and ... saw the remains of the body of a man fully clothed lying face upwards. I did not notice any other object lying near the body ... The scrub was fairly thick at this spot. It would have been possible for any-one to have tripped while walking through there.

The report of the post-mortem examination by Dr C. H. Wollison does not speculate on the specific calibre of the battered bullet found in Embrey's skull, although he notes that the bullet wound was three-tenths of an inch in diameter and that the bullet found could have been fired from the gun produced. *Could have*. That doesn't sound absolutely positive, which is odd given that only one gun, the pea rifle, appears to have been found with the body. If a pea rifle uses a .22 calibre bullet then I think this means .22 of an inch. Would a three-tenths of an inch wound require, say, a bullet fired from a .303 rifle? If so, what happened to this rifle? Wollison's general conclusion was that the wound was equally consistent with an accident as with the deliberate intention to take his life.

The possibility of murder is not mentioned by the doctor.

Constable Francis John Purcell, who searched the clothing of Embrey at the morgue before he was identified, found a bunch of keys which led him to the YMCA building and to an identification. He also reports that: 'I found writing in a book called *Caravan* [by John Galsworthy?]. The writing also helped to identify Embrey.

What other evidence is there about Embrey's state of mind in January, 1931? Victoria Beckingsale testified thus:

I knew the deceased Embrey Crawford. I met him at the *Argus* office about five months prior to his disappearance. I saw him on the average once a week. He visited my home on several occasions. He was of a shy, reserved temperament. About eight or nine days prior to his disappearance he told me that he had lost his position as a reporter at the *Argus* office and thought that he was a failure. He gave me the impression that he had lost interest in things and was going to drift. He never at any time mentioned that he contemplated suicide. On the 20th day of January 1931, I received the letter produced, from him. This letter was of a despondent nature and thinking that the letter indicated a more serious trend than I would expect I called at the *Argus* office and showed the letter to the persons in charge who reported the matter to the police. The letter is in his handwriting.

Ellen Dowling, Matron at the YMCA, testified that when she last saw Embrey on 19 January, he was 'in good health and spirits' as he had been for the two months prior. She had 'never heard him say or suggest in any way that he was tired of life. He had no financial worries' to her knowledge. She had seen his room after he left the YMCA and 'the condition of his room was consistent with the deceased's intention to return. He was always cheerful and bright'. Embrey's father, William Charles Crawford, also testified, not surprisingly, that Embrey was of a happy disposition and that he had never indicated in any way that he would take his own life. According to W. C. Crawford, his son was not in financial difficulties as far as he was aware, and he had informed Embrey that he would help him financially at any time if it was needed.

What do the two letters from Embrey to his grandmother in California reveal about him? The first is dated 19/10/30. It begins: 'It seems that I never have time to write to you; I certainly have less time as a newspaper reporter than I have been used to in various other avocations, but this is a Sunday morning, and although I am in the office, I am "ahead of the job" for the day.' He describes himself as one of the shipping reporters for the *Argus* and relates that he has just had a minor 'scoop' reporting about a stowaway on an American ship which has just arrived in Melbourne. He discusses the Depression and its world-wide effects, revealing his politics to be a confusion of vaguely conservative and angrily humanist views. Despite professing to being anti-Socialist (most of the governments in Australia were Labor at the time), he attacks those who maintain a high standard of living, particularly politicians with 'good, "cushy" jobs'. And then he writes:

> People all over the world, I imagine, are just beginning to realise that you can't shoot away countless billions in a world war without feeling the after effects of such wastage.

This sentiment is similar to my wild theory that the Depression was really a result of the bottling up of grief following the war.

An attitude towards the city starts to creep in when he suggests that the 'starvation of the city populace may force parasitic sections from the cities ... back to the land'. In his angry humanist mood, Embrey sounds like he may have got on well with Lloyd Rees, although the latter was, from about 1915, firmly to the left, despite having come from a politically conservative family, as did Embrey.

Of Melbourne, Embrey writes:

> ... a very charming place to live and work in ... although having been used to the wonderful surf

beaches round Sydney I find it difficult to please
myself in spare hours now that summer is arriving.
[Prophetic words?] [But] It is an extraordinarily
beautiful city, nevertheless, and has tree-lined
boulevards and numerous parks and botanical
gardens which leave Sydney far behind. And it is
in less of a hurry, a little less Americanised, if I
may say so, than Sydney. People are inclined to be
a little more conservative, and relish the more
solid things of life, paying not so much attention
to 'having a good time' as invented in your own
Hollywood. Very often I find myself wishing to
be back in the marvellous surroundings of the
North Queensland Barrier Reef, or out in the hills
on a good pony in New England. I look forward
to my first vacation, whenever it shall be. We are
only allowed three weeks in each year and as that
is not nearly enough for me to get back to my old
haunts, I am thinking of letting my holidays
mount up for two or three years, so that I can
have a real vacation somewhere up North again.

He signs off this letter with 'Your loving grandson'.
The second letter, sent just before Christmas, 1930,
is less prosaic and shows him trying hard to display
his talent as a writer. He refers to sending his
grandparents a pair of serviette rings 'made of
Australian mulga timber', and elaborates:

Most poets and novelists who have attempted to
portray the Australian bush rarely fail to make
mention of the good old Mulga. It grows in
clumps, towering in high, spindly trunks above
the sweeping plain country, and its leaves, which
are silver-coloured on one side, continually
twinkle in the breeze, like catspaws coming over
the surface of a lake. The leaves, though hard and
dry and bitter, are in drought time, a wonderful

standby for starving sheep and cattle ... When cut and polished the wood is quite ornamental, and the old-timer bushman takes a pride in carving beautifully grained stockwhip handles. As often as not he will be known, in the verses of poets at least, as 'Mulga Bill'.

He then makes mention of his Dad from whom he has just received a letter—William Charles has been suffering from high blood pressure and business worries are mentioned. Perhaps it is this information that leads Embrey to believe, a few weeks later, that his father could not help him out financially. He comments on a suggestion that his father has made, some time ago, to write some Australian stories, of the same type that appear in the *Saturday Evening Post* under the name of Hal Evarts: 'I had one published here in Melbourne recently, written around that queerest of creatures, the platypus, and Dad was very pleased with it ...' One gets the impression that Embrey is becoming more confident and directed in his writing.

As Catherine Ives had warned me, the articles which Embrey managed to get published, mainly in the *Australian Sporting and Dramatic News* in 1929, are a bit on the bloodthirsty side. But they occasionally rise above the boys' own adventure style of writing, particularly in the descriptive passages:

Gawkish brolgas stalked down to the edge for crayfish, throatily passing the time of day to one another, preening their slate-blue plumage, and with the gorgeous orange-red mask about their eyes, forming beautiful reflections in the water. Pure white spoonbills and white cranes prodded

their bills in the mud, in search of luckless frogs.
Red-legged waterhens darted into the reedy
branches of the lignum, and circumspect emus
came to water.

But the next sentence is: 'It was a sportsman's
paradise.'

It is difficult to excuse the hunting and shooting
mentality when there is the absence of any compen-
sating expression of subtler themes: the shooting
is presented as predominantly a sport—not as a metaphor for an internal struggle or an opportunity for
self-analysis, or consideration of life apart from the
sport. However, there are hints that Embrey may
have been trying to 'work something in'. In the
article from which I have quoted, the author's quest
is to capture a young eagle as a gift for his
unsuspecting girlfriend who has expressed interest in
wild birds. The author is attacked by a male eagle
who is guarding the nest. He eventually manages to
shoot it with his 'Colt' and it flies off:

> One of his legs hung limply, indicating an
> abdominal wound. Higher and higher he rose,
> and then set his wings in a long volplane which
> carried him far out of sight, gradually nearing the
> ground. I found him later, after a long search,
> crumpled on a tussock of cane-grass, his six-foot
> wings spread majestically over the ground in their
> last rest. Of his mate there was no sign.

No further mention is made of the proposed gift.
One wonders if there is some veiled symbolism here,
some dark reference to Embrey's perceptions of
relationships. If Embrey had not died, would he have
developed these fledgling themes?

In the 1920s, the large-circulation *Bulletin* regularly carried full-page advertisements for guns and sporting guns were sold in department stores.

In *Peaks and Valleys* there are references by Lloyd Rees to the shooting of wildlife:

> I raised the rifle and aimed at the bird. I heard the crack of the report and then, to my astonishment, I watched the bird tumble to the ground. All three of us were silent and a terrible sense of shame came over me. It was the third time I had shot a fellow creature but not the last. There had been the duck I wounded at 'Mobolon', and the poor sparrow that I killed with that most evil of toys, the air gun. I was over thirty years of age when I killed deliberately again and had no childish sense of ignorance to protect me. It was a slim lizard, some twelve inches long, sunning itself on a horizontal branch above the water in a quiet corner of the river in the Burragorang Valley, long before it was dammed. The creature was a deep golden brown, a little darker than the golden branch on which it lay.
>
> One of our number carried a gun, and with a sense of bravado I asked if I could have a shot. It was quite a distance from me and once again I doubted my capacity to hit it—but again, I did. It fell into the clear water and slowly sank some three feet to the sand below. It lay there, its golden underbelly beautiful against the richer colour of the sand and from it flowed its blood, which shimmered in the ripples of its own fall. I stood there feeling I had shed my brother's blood, which indeed I had, for the conviction had already grown within me that all life on earth is akin to our own.[2]

The date must have been around 1926. The members of the 'party' are not named. I can't help wondering whether Embrey was present.

There are three letters written from America by Embrey's grandmother in 1931 after she has been informed about her grandson's disappearance. They are addressed to her son, William, and family. The first includes these words of hope:

> When he was in Queensland he wrote me that I need not be surprised to have him walk in on me anytime in the far distant future and that he would catch a packet boat and come very leisurely ... He wrote that he wanted to expand his knowledge of writing and the opportunities were so limited in Australia, that he felt to make a success of himself ... to meet some of the world's renowned writers ... He wrote to me about some money I sent him asking me what he should do with it. I told him that was up to him ... I am surprised that he did not tell you that he was intending to go, but he is old enough and has been away from home for such a long time ... Taking his camera was to get some pictures for his articles en route ...

The second letter of three pages, written a couple of weeks later, does not refer at all to the disappearance of Embrey. But the third letter is quite interesting. After repeating the reassurances of the first letter she adds that 'when he left the ranch [in Queensland?] he wrote me he did not tell them he was leaving, just got up and left without thinking what they thought ...' Then this eighty-year-old grandmother reports on a visit to a fortune teller.[3] The fortune teller apparently intones:

> I see two young men, one a light complexion fellow, the other a dark young fellow. They are

travelling together. The first one is a writer, the other a doctor or a dentist. They are on their way over here. They live across the water. They are coming very leisurely on a boat which will touch many places. They may not get here for six months but don't be surprised for they will be here. [There is a] young girl ... and [she and one of the young men] have been in love with one another and he asked this girl to marry him but a woman came between them and was the cause of a broken engagement ... This ... young man and this young girl will get married even if it is against the wishes of the party who separated them ...

When Grandma Crawford learned that Embrey was missing, she also got out the letters he had recently sent her, and analysed them, searching for the clues that he was intending to turn up unannounced in California. She made notations regarding these clues in the margins of the letters and sent them to William Charles Crawford and his wife Dorothea so that they could see for themselves. There are references in Grandma Crawford's letters to other letters received from Embrey which were not sent back to the family. Perhaps from these other letters Grandma Crawford was able to glean some information about him. A male friend? In one or two of his articles Embrey refers to adventuring with a mate. Trouble with women? Embrey may have hinted at something—his letters to his grandmother suggest he was close to her. Then she must have discussed Embrey with the fortune teller. Or perhaps the latter just picked the likeliest details: that he had a good mate and, being young and unmarried, also had women in his life.

Is it really possible that Embrey could have been involved with Florence Sainsbury? I borrow the motel's Melbourne street directory and look up the name of her street in the Dandenongs, which Robert Blain has told me was Old Belgrave Road. Old Belgrave Road ends virtually at the Upper Ferntree Gully railway station on the edge of the Ferntree Gully National Park. A walking track begins at the station and winds up the centre of the Park to One Tree Hill, only a couple of kilometres away.

Could Embrey have travelled by train to meet with Florence Sainsbury before continuing on his (their?) way towards One Tree Hill, the scene of his death? When Embrey eventually arrived at One Tree Hill, did he then commit suicide? Was it an accident? Was he murdered? I read carefully over all the documents contained in the Coroner's report again.

And there I find it, buried in the testimony of Constable George Matthew Thomas.

Perhaps I blocked it out on the first reading because of the horror of it. Now I take in every chilling detail. To me it is proof beyond doubt that Embrey committed suicide. It renders irrelevant any possible inconsistencies to do with the type of gun, his financial circumstances or state of mind. Constable Thomas reports:

> About six feet away from the body I found at the height of four feet six inches, half of a pair of spectacles tied to a tree. Above this were two holes that could have been made by bullets fired by the deceased. On the other side of the tree I found the other half of the spectacles ... There was no broken glass that I could see. The portion of the spectacles that was behind the tree could have been attached to the tree and then shot away.

Embrey must have played a ghastly version of Russian Roulette. If he shot the string and saved the spectacles, he would live. If he could not save the spectacles by this means, he would take his life with the last bullet.

At least two shots missed the string (hitting the branch above). And then, a shot bisected the spectacles, passing cleanly through the bridge. Perhaps this was unexpected. He still had bullets left (they were found by his side) but he had lost his goal. An even more pessimistic interpretation is that he was aiming for the spectacles and by blasting them away he had achieved his aim. Either way, he made no attempt to retrieve the spectacles. The next shot must have entered his brain.

The symbolism of the spectacles is dreadfully sad. If Embrey was shortsighted, then without his glasses on, he was making it very hard for himself to shoot accurately at such a target. Also, if he was shortsighted, the spectacles would have represented his means of seeing forward. If he was longsighted then the spectacles would have been necessary for reading and writing—they would have been linked inextricably with his ambition to be a writer.

Wednesday, 3 November

In the La Trobe Library, a study of the Melbourne telephone system from the 1920s onwards confirms librarian Judy McDonald's view that all numbers in Melbourne required a prefix. 8930 is definitely not a Melbourne telephone number. Embrey Crawford is not listed in any of the Melbourne telephone directories around 1930, and neither is his 'guiding star' L. V. Bartlett—in fact, nowhere in the library is there any trace of L. V. Bartlett. Victoria Beckingsale, around 1930 is living with her father, H. Beckingsale, at 5 Landsdowne Road, St Kilda.

Thursday, 4 November

Telephone calls to the Beckingsales in the current phone books reveal that Victoria Beckingsale died about fifteen years ago. She had remained unmarried throughout her life. She is remembered by family as 'a good person'.

I take a one-hour train trip from Melbourne to the McClelland Gallery at Frankston. I have sent the Director, Simon Klose, a letter and a photograph of the painting. When I arrive he welcomes me with coffee and then shows me to the store room.

He has been doing some research of his own since he received my letter. Initially he had thought that the boatshed painting could be by Harry McClelland and that the subject might be a Frankston scene. 'Harry did do some early works which were quite good before his work deteriorated,' he says. But then, he had shown the photograph to a trustee of the Gallery who had lived in the Frankston area all his life and who knew Harry and his work intimately. This trustee's word was 'gospel' in terms of Harry's oeuvre. And this trustee was certain that the painting was not by Harry McClelland. The style is not close enough to Harry's, he had said, although he did agree there was some similarity. Also, the subject was not one that was identifiable around the Frankston area, and, to cap it off, Harry never framed pictures without signing them.

We look at Harry's paintings in the store room. They seem to be the work of an enthusiastic amateur.

There is some similarity in the vigorous brushwork of the backgrounds, but his attempts to depict specific form are almost invariably clumsy. It seems that Harry's real talent lay in his ability to organise and support other artists working in, or visiting, the area around Frankston. Years after his death his enthusiasm culminated in the McClelland Art Gallery.

I am now reasonably convinced that the boatshed painting is not the work of Harry McClelland. But I wonder about the painting that Jon Dwyer from Joel's had seen: the one that made him think that the boatshed painting was by McClelland. What was it like? Could I ever find it? Just to make sure.

Tuesday, 9 November

Back in Sydney, I head for the State Library, to search for traces of L. V. Bartlett, a.k.a. 'Bart'. There is nothing in the indexes of printed or published material, nor in reference books such as the *Australian Dictionary of Biography* or the annual *Who's Who in Australia*.

But, in the Mitchell Library's Manuscript Index I find something astonishing. It is Leonard V. Bartlett's First World War diary! Additional information in the index states that 'L. V. Bartlett served as a signaller on a troopship at the landing of Gallipoli and as telephonist at the evacuation with the 4th Battalion. Later he served in France as a Lieutenant with the 56th Battalion'. As I am waiting for this treasure to be brought out, I ask who donated the diary to the library, in the hope that it was a relative who is still alive. The librarian tells me that, following the war, the Mitchell had a Soldier's Diary Call and Bartlett was one of those whose diary was purchased as a result.

I find a desk in a quiet corner of the library and

settle down for a good read. Unfortunately, only two
volumes survive: 1915 and 1918. The volumes for
the middle two years do not exist. They may have
been lost by Bartlett during the war. On the back of
one volume he has summarised his service: 'Egypt,
Gallipoli, France/Enlisted 1st September, 1914/
wounded Bullecourt, May, 1917/Gassed Villiers
Bretonneuse April 1918/Discharged February
1919.' The two volumes are tiny, with minute
handwriting. It is certainly not the handwriting of
the person who wrote the inscription on the boatshed painting. Each day has been recorded for 1915
and 1918 and there is a lot of reading for me to do.

Reading, I discover, is something that Bart did a
lot of. A wide range of books and fashionable mag-
azines were obviously borrowed, swapped or
bartered in the trenches so that Bart's reading list is
probably that of many other young, intelligent
soldiers caught up in that disaster. In Egypt on
Saturday, 10 April, 1915, he is reading *Gate of the
Desert* by Oxhenham. He arrives at Gallipoli on 31
May within weeks of the initial landing of 25 April.
On 16 June he writes 'Reading *Rodin's Corner* by
Merriman. Would that I were in Sydney and be done
with this sordid war.' I wonder if *Rodin's Corner* is
about the sculptor and whether Bart's reading of it
reflects an interest in art. A month later he is 'sorry
that the *Dornford Yates* yarns have finished'. He also
reads *The Shulamite* by Askew.

20 July: 'My first day on intelligence staff. I shall
be a reporter if I come thro' all right.' He reads *The
Importance of Being Earnest* and on 27 July writes:
'Got a *Cassels* magazine. Great Luck!' On 5 August:
'On Major de Maistre's staff for the day.' I wonder if
this is a brother of artist Roy de Maistre who will
later be linked professionally to Lloyd Rees. Could
Bart have met Rees in the 1920s through the de
Maistres? The next day: 'Perfect Hell until well into

the night. I shall be an advocate for peace after this war ... Fed up with war ...' Bart describes the general stench and degradation in the trenches. By this stage he hasn't washed for weeks. And there are rotting bodies of enemy troops close by. On 19 August he gets the flu and a couple of days later he calls on the Indians for 'a feed of curry'. On 6 September: 'Leave LONE PINE trenches for what we hope will be the last time.' But this is not to be. His butter runs out and also his maple syrup, but still 'Plenty to read'. He reads *The Beloved Vagabond* by Locke, 'quite an interesting little book'. I think of Embrey in 1931 reading *Caravan* on One Tree Hill.

I take a break from the diary and check information about Lone Pine. It was the scene of the most bloody and intensive fighting that Australian forces had ever experienced. Over 2,000 Australians and 7,000 Turks were killed when the Anzacs took Lone Pine over a few days in early August, 1915. During one hour in the early morning of 7 August, 234 Light Horsemen fell dead in an area 'no larger than a tennis court'.[1] The Turks had previously cut down all the pines on the ridge they were defending, to use the wood for roofing for their trenches and for firewood. The skyline was reduced to a single tree and during the battle this lone pine was blasted to a stump.[2]

In October Bart gets ill again with the flu and dysentery and writes: 'Totally fed up with this whole caboosh.' And days later: 'It's a year since we left the Queen City and I'd love to be back. My opinion is changed muchly on sodgering [*sic*]. I'd give anything to enter The [Sydney] Heads today.' He reads *Sophie of Kravonia* by Hope. On 10 November: Twenty-four today. What a birthday in what a hole.

Cooked some pancakes and read *Double Bed Dialogues*.' So, Bart must have been ten years older than Embrey. 27 November: 'Read Leroux's *Phantom of the Opera* … Mud everywhere … My God I'm fed up with these conditions.' Bart is not inclined to state the bleeding obvious. Only occasionally does he refer to the death all around him during this year.

In the 1918 volume, he is still reading voraciously. For example, *Broad Highway* which he describes as 'one of the best books I've ever read. Nearly made me weep.' For part of the year he is convalescing. On 3 November: 'Did some painting in the morning.' This is mildly interesting. It may mean that he was interested in painting beyond its benefits as occupational therapy, but since he is not recorded anywhere as an artist in the 1920s, he probably never seriously took up the activity.

He turns twenty-seven on the day before Armistice when 'Everyone was mad'. On 16 November, he embarks for home. On the way the ship stops at New York: 'Not an ounce of beauty in the city or harbours … The people couldn't do better than to stop their hustle for five minutes and remember they only die once.'

The diary ends before he sails through The Heads.

I remain seated in the library, thinking about the Gallipoli legend. When I was at school, the standard version had been along the lines that Gallipoli marked the birth of the Australian nation. The baptism by fire. The reckless, fearless, bronzed Aussie prepared to die in the name of country for the first time. In Bart's diary there is not a trace of any of this. In fact in Bart's diary the Anzac at Gallipoli is diligent, anti-war and *bookish*.[3] Why does the idea of Gallipoli resonate still? Perhaps it is to do with the taking on of a totally impossible task, directed by a

force beyond control. Trying to climb up a bloody
hill against all the odds, facing almost certain defeat.
A life and death struggle but one which, if survived,
will forge an identity. But an identity more likely to
do with failure rather than victory. Perhaps
Australians, for some perverse reason, are more
interested in failure than in success.

Is this perversity the reason I have taken on such
an impossible task? Creating a mountain of
information in the weird, unlikely hope that I can
prove who painted one small, unsigned painting?

My reading of Bart's Gallipoli diary, and then my
brooding, has taken a couple of hours and I need to
check other information in the library before it
closes. In his letter to Victoria Beckingsale, Embrey
had given Bart's address as the A. H. White advertising agency. It has to be A. N. White, which is listed
in Sands' under Advertising Contractors. It is a large
entry which states that they are 'Interstate, New
Zealand and South African Press Representatives' on
the sixth floor, London Bank Chambers, Martin
Place, Sydney. The entry is larger than the one for
Catts Patterson, who describe themselves: 'Advertising–Counsel Service' at 375 Kent Street. One
gets the impression from the entries that the two
firms were rivals. I cannot remember any mention of
A. N. White in George Patterson's autobiography.

Now to the alphabetical listing in Sands' to see
where Bart lived in Sydney after the war. I decide to
begin with the year in which Embrey died, 1931. I
find an address quickly. It is 8 Etham Avenue,
Darling Point. I flick through the microfiche to the
suburban directory listing for the same year, which
will tell me who else was living here. Number 8, I
find, is a block of flats. Bart is in flat number 5 with

two others. One is a W. A. Nunnerly and when I see
the name of the other occupant, I am floored.

It is John Banks. Oh, wow! Oh no! Is this
leading to evidence that it is Banks, not Rees, who is
connected to Embrey and that Banks may have
painted the boatshed painting? On stylistic grounds I
am fairly positive that the boatshed painting is not by
Banks. Nevertheless, it is now a most critical question. I am slightly reassured by remembering that it
was Banks who had first encouraged Lloyd Rees to
move from Brisbane to Sydney. At least there is a
whiff of a link between the Bart/Embrey friendship
and Lloyd Rees, since Rees knew Banks who was
living with Bart in 1931. But is this John Banks really
the *artist*? I will have to check it out.

I head home to digest all this.

Wednesday, 10 November

The issue of whether Banks might have painted the
boatshed painting is still lurking and I can't
concentrate on the other information until I can rule
Banks out. I need to put my painting against a Banks
and study them together. I try phoning various
contacts at the Art Gallery of NSW to see if someone
will take me down to the vaults today to see their
Banks, *The Road to the Beach* of 1924. Finally, Linda
Slutskin of the Education Department agrees to take
me down.

When we reach the Banks, hung amongst scores of
other paintings on one of many huge wire screens, I
whip the boatshed painting out of an envelope.
Linda is nonplussed. But when she sees the painting
she forgets that I have broken a rule by not declaring

a painting before bringing it in. She can't take her eyes off it. She is not interested in looking at the Banks which, I note, is quite wishy-washy in comparison to the intensity of the boatshed painting. While she admires my painting I take a closer look at *The Road to the Beach*. A group of gowned women are strolling beneath tall trees towards the beach. The paint is thin and the painterly effects are all on the surface. It has a feathery feel to it and seems slightly out of focus. Having seen other paintings by the artist, I am beginning to see how much each one is done to a formula. There is a lack of personal dedication by the artist, beyond his purpose of pleasing.

There is a superficial similarity between the two paintings which owes something to Corot, the great French painter. But Banks has cheapened the lessons of Corot by producing something that reeks of commercial sensibility. I'm probably being a bit tough on poor old Banks, but the point is, I doubt whether he could have painted the boatshed painting. Linda, when she finally gets to look at the Banks, agrees. But I need to see more.

I mention to Linda that on the way out of the gallery I intend to drop into the de Maistre Room which has been recently opened. The murals, sold to the gallery by Frank McDonald, have been grandly incorporated into a room which is adjacent to another room furnished with paintings, prints and objects from the 1920s.

'Oh,' says Linda. 'Have you heard that Professor Joan Kerr stood up during a gathering of gallery guides and stated that the murals were not painted by de Maistre, but are, in her view, by the wife and daughter of Admiral Sir Dudley de Chair?'

'Golly,' I say. I did know that Sir Dudley, the ex-Governor of NSW, and his wife had commissioned the murals, and that Lady de Chair and her daughter had been members of the Turramurra Wall Painters, but this is a bit of a bombshell. I had had contact with Joan Kerr recently. She had asked me to write a couple of entries for her book on Australian women artists, to be published in 1995, one theme of which is the 'history of neglect' suffered.[1] She did not mention the mural. I wonder whether she has evidence, or whether she is working up some publicity for the book.

Upstairs, I find that the murals are splendid, but I have to say that I would not have ascribed them immediately to Roy de Maistre. Their style seems atypical of de Maistre's known work of the late 1920s and early 1930s. But I do not have time to think about this new mystery now.

Across the Domain, in the Mitchell Library, I check John Banks's exhibiting history in the 1920s. He begins exhibiting in 1914. He exhibits annually with the Royal Art Society as well as regularly at Rubery Bennett's various galleries.The works from the 1920s which are illustrated in the catalogues, albeit in black and white, look much the same as *The Road to the Beach*. However, in the earlier catalogues there are some small oil sketches listed, with titles such as *Bradley's Head* (5 guineas in 1917) and *The Beach* (5 guineas in 1918). Unfortunately these early oils are not illustrated. It is hard to imagine that he could change his style, not to mention his sensibility, so dramatically in such a relatively short time—but it is possible. Perhaps sudden commercial success of the later 'chocolate box' works led him to replicate them exclusively, at the expense of an earlier, subtler talent? I decide to check Banks's address or addresses through the 1920s looking for other clues, connections, cross-references ...

Banks's residential addresses are listed in the Sands' Directory. There are no listings of a residential address in any of the telephone directories.[2] He may not have had the phone on at home in the 1920s or 1930s. In the R. A. S. catalogues only one address is given for Banks in the alphabetical list of exhibitors section of each catalogue—16 Spring Street, Sydney—which must be his city office. This is confirmed in Sands' which gives 16 Spring Street as the office of his insurance and commercial broking business, his 'day job' which he never gave up.

What I am looking for now is proof of a relationship between the artist John Banks and Embrey's friend Bart, around the time that the telephone number 8930 existed. That is, of course, prior to October 1927.

I can only find addresses for Bart between 1923 and 1926, when he is in outer suburbia in Boundary Road, Pennant Hills. In 1925 he is also listed in Sands' as the Manager of Profitable Publicity at 5 Macquarie Place. Then, he is not listed again until 1931, at the Darling Point address, with John Banks. He may have been travelling the outback with Embrey from 1927 to 1930, since, in January, 1931, Embrey refers to Bart as being his 'guiding star for the past four years'. Their travels may have been sporadic and perhaps they had a base to return to in Sydney. Perhaps, also, Bart moved to Melbourne with Embrey and stayed there with him for a time before returning to Sydney.

I find that from 1917—the date Lloyd Rees arrived in Sydney—until 1931, John Banks's private address is in Prince Albert Road, Mosman. Then, in 1931, he is listed in Etham Road, Darling Point with L. V. Bartlett.

Up until 1927, Sands' lists Banks at number 66 Prince Albert Road, and from 1928 to 1930 he is ten doors up at number 86. What prompted that odd move? Then, I notice something equally odd. Listed under Artists in Sands' is a Miss V. Bartlett. In 1927 she is at 74 Prince Albert Road, Mosman. By 1930 she has moved to number 98. Playing leapfrog with John Banks? My guess is that Miss V. Bartlett is related to Leonard V. Bartlett. The fact that Banks and Leonard V. Bartlett knew each other by sharing the same address in 1931, together with the fact that Banks and Miss V. Bartlett were close neighbours and both artists (they must have known each other), supports my supposition that Leonard V. Bartlett and Miss V. Bartlett may be related.

I thought I knew the names of most artists working in Australia in the 1920s! Who is this mysterious Miss V. Bartlett?

The electoral rolls for Mosman in the late 1920s tell me that the full name of Miss V. Bartlett was Violet Artah Bartlett and her occupation is, again, listed as artist. 'Artah' is a most unusual name. It does not appear as a surname in the Sydney Telephone Directory. Nor is it a word listed in the index to the *Encyclopaedia Britannica*. I can find no mention of a Violet Artah Bartlett in any Australian art books, catalogues or directories in the art reference section of the Mitchell Library. There is absolutely no record of her ever exhibiting in Sydney. But in the *Dictionary of British Artists 1880–1940* there is a Miss Violet A. Bartlett, exhibiting at the Royal Institute of Oil Painters in England between 1898 and 1905. This is almost certainly she. In which case she must have been a competent painter at least. I am hoping that copies of wills for both L. V. (Bart) and Miss V. Bartlett will show my speculation about a connection between the two to be correct.

Could this mysterious artist, Miss Violet Artah Bartlett, have painted the boatshed painting? It would be ironic if the painting was by one of those

lost female artists who were my special interest
before I began this quest.

Thursday, 11 November

At the Probate Office, finding John Banks's will
proves easy. Since I know that he died in 1945, I go
straight to that year and record the probate number
to retrieve it later. Then I start looking for evidence
of Leonard V. Bartlett's will.

I begin with the year 1931, the last year in
which I have a record of him, and work carefully
through the microfiches. When I am up to 1982, I
pause. Bart would be 91. I remember he was wounded and gassed in France. Would he have made 91?
My eyes scan down the list of Bartletts on the
microfiche screen. And at the precise moment that
they reach Leonard Victor Bartlett, a very spooky
thing happens.

I hear 'The Last Post'.

I look up from the microfiche screen, warily.
The room is crowded with people, who, moments
ago, had been discussing bankruptcies, court orders,
appeals, and so on, and every single person is now
frozen. The office is totally silent, except for the
eerie sound of a muted trumpet.

And then I realise. It is 11.00 o'clock on the
eleventh day of the eleventh month. Armistice Day.
'The Last Post' is followed by a brief news item on
the interment of the Unknown Soldier at the War
Memorial in Canberra.

Is this some sort of omen?

There is no will for a Violet Bartlett. Perhaps she
married and her name changed. Or more probably,

she returned to England and died there. And Bart's and Banks's wills are an anticlimax.

Bart's will mentions a friend, a Mrs Anne Ross of Queen Street, Woollahra, and two daughters, Anna Wendy Moore and Mary Blanche Bartlett. But there is little other useful information other than that he was a retired company director living in Orange when he made the will in 1981. I remember that Lloyd Rees painted at Orange in the late 1940s, and also that he drew in the Pennant Hills area around 1930. Bart's address was Boundary Road, Pennant Hills in the 1920s. Is this significant?

John Banks's will describes him as 'Insurance Company Manager'. The will also mentions Banks's interest in various properties but no addresses are given. There is a reference to his wife, Elizabeth. There appear to be no children although children of his siblings are mentioned. The Testator for his will is a nephew, Gordon Drummond Banks. There is little else. I need to contact the people mentioned in these wills in the hope that someone will be able to link Bart to Lloyd Rees.

I find I am becoming more interested in this Miss Violet Bartlett. It seems extraordinary that she is listed in the Sands' Directory and electoral rolls as an artist but is not recorded anywhere else as having exhibited in Sydney. As far as I know, none of her work has ever emerged in Australia. What is her story? What was her work like?

Saturday, 13 November

In the current Sydney Telephone Directory there is a G. D. Banks listed in Mosman. I write this person a letter, seeking more information on the artist, John Banks.

Tuesday, 16 November

I had previously asked Alan and Jan Rees if they could find any newspaper cuttings of reviews of exhibitions by Lloyd Rees which included *The Bay*, the painting exhibited in 1922 with the catalogue number 22. My hope is that *The Bay* might be described in a review and that the description tallies with the boatshed painting. We make contact again and Alan tells me that they have found some reviews. Also, Jan has just received a letter from the Queensland State Library which includes copies of Miss Jeanettie Sheldon's account books from the Gainsborough Gallery. Jan tells me that when a painting by Rees titled *The Bay* was exhibited in Brisbane in 1928 it was sold. The purchaser was ... a Mr Smith.

Now, if I could track this painting down and find that it resembles, or is even another version of, the boatshed painting ... But Smith! The name is a researcher's nightmare.

Saturday, 20 November

I call Catherine Ives to thank her again for showing me her archive, and to bring her up to date. Far from being traumatised by the confirmation of her uncle Embrey's suicide, Catherine appears to express relief upon knowing the exact truth. And not only relief: she tells me that hearing actual details about Embrey's friend, Bart, sends tingles up her spine. Maybe Bart kept diaries in the 1920s, she says excitedly. She urges me to contact the people mentioned in Bart's will. To find out whatever else I can.

When I phone the Mrs Ross mentioned in Bart's will, who is still at the same address in the current

Sydney Telephone Directory, she is extremely helpful. She offers me the name and telephone number of
one of the daughters, Mrs Wendy Moore of Orange.
She feels that Wendy should be able to help me.

Wendy Moore does not seem too surprised by
my call. L. V. Bartlett, 'Bart', her father, left a small
collection of paintings done in the 1920s, and he was
generally interested in art. When I press her for an
example of something in his collection, she refers to
a Sydney Ure Smith etching! This is terrific, given
Smith's connection to Rees in the 1920s. She says
that in the 1920s Bart had worked for the *Bulletin*
and *Smith's Weekly* (run by Joynton Smith) and had
mixed with writers and artists in Sydney. In the mid
1920s, he established his own advertising agency
which was later called L. V. Bartlett Advertising.

Bart had married a nurse whom he had met in
the war and they had three children before separat-
ing and divorcing in the late 1920s. His first wife
returned to England with the three children. In
1930 Bart married again to Mary, Wendy's mother.
Interestingly, one of the three children from Bart's
first marriage, (another) Mary Bartlett, Wendy's
step-sister, visited Australia a few years ago and
met with Wendy to ask for details of her father. I
remember that this Mary was the other daughter
mentioned in Bart's will.

Bart was a great one for moving. The family
moved twenty-five times in fifty-two years. He left a
shoe box full of letters. Wendy does not remember
any letters referring to Lloyd Rees nor to any of the
other names I mention, but she says she will check.
There are some photographs of Bart and friends—
one shows them leaning against a car, holding guns.

I tell her about the war diary written by her
father and she is most interested. She did not know
of its existence. In fact, she expresses great regret
that her father had never ever discussed the war. I

offer to send her my notes of the diary and some
other information, including some questions, to see
if any of it makes sense to her. Wendy says she would
be more than happy to look it over.

Wednesday, 1 December

Wendy Moore phones. She has listed the paintings
from her father's collection. The etching by Sydney
Ure Smith is titled *Gore Bay, Sydney*, and inscribed
'original series no. 78'. Wendy has given this to her
daughter who lives in Yass. But she remembers it as
being about 4" x 4". There is a Sid Long etching,
The Lake, Avoca, 1926, number 17 of an edition of
60. A watercolour by J. W. Tristram is also dated
1926. There are also works by Alf Fischer, G. K.
Townshend and Elsie Dangerfield.

Wendy tells me that most of the works have
been re-framed at some time in their lives, so unfortunately there is little information on the backs. The
Alf Fischer is a watercolour country scene with cattle
under trees. Wendy remembers her mother saying he
painted it for her on top of a hatbox lid, perhaps on
a picnic, and thinks it must date from 1928 onwards,
when her parents first knew each other. Seems like
around this time Bart is going on picnics with artists.
There are four drawings by Low, the *Bulletin*
cartoonist, still in original frames and these have
framer S. A. Parker's labels.

Wendy tells me some more about her father:

He was born in the little village of God-
manchester, Harts, England, where his father ran
the local pub. He was obviously well educated but
I never knew where, but he used to tell how he
sang in the choir of St Paul's, London ... As he
ran away to Australia at about fifteen, it is hard to

get the years exactly right, I know he put his age forward to get into the Australian Army in 1914 ... I think he worked more on advertising in the *Bulletin* than on writing articles ...

As we chat on I explore the probable connection between Bart and Rubery Bennett, but Wendy has no knowledge of where Bart bought his artworks. I ask Wendy whether she has heard of a Violet Bartlett. Wendy thinks that Violet may have been the name of Leonard Bartlett's first wife. She was ten years older than he. None of the other names mentioned in my letter to Wendy ring any bells with her. She has no knowledge of a link between her father, Bart, and Lloyd Rees other than the fact that Bart obviously knew of him. Wendy is able to give me the name and address of one of the daughters of Bart's first wife, the step-sister who had visited her from England seeking information. Her name is Mary Blanche Bartlett. Perhaps she may be able to solve the mystery of Violet Artah Bartlett.

The date that Bart began collecting (and mixing with artists?) judging from the dates of the paintings, would seem to be about 1926. This would make sense because he established his advertising business in 1925. It was probably successful since he stayed in advertising until he retired. In 1926 he was probably spending some profits on art. The odd one out, in terms of its date, is the Syd Ure Smith. In *The Etchings of Sydney Ure Smith* it is recorded as being etched in 1918.[1] The measurements are given as 7⅛" x 7⅛". Wendy had said hers measured 4" x 4". However, in the catalogue of an exhibition at Josef Lebovic's gallery in the 1980s, I find the following item listed which might explain the discrepancy:

'Reproduction for Christmas Card of Ure Smith's 1918 etching *Gore Bay*'. On it is printed 'Ure Smith Original Etching Series No 78'. It is approximately 4" x 4". Therefore, it would seem that Wendy's work is actually a Christmas card rather than an original work collected by Bart. I hope she will not be too disappointed. However, if it is a Christmas card, it may have been given personally to Leonard Bartlett by Ure Smith and could prove that Ure Smith and Bart were colleagues or friends. I wonder what the greeting might be on the back of the card?[2]

While Bart's Ure Smith was almost certainly not purchased from Rubery Bennett's gallery, it is almost certain that the Sid Long was. Sid Long's work had been handled almost exclusively until 1921 by Adolph Albers, Sydney's first successful art dealer. But in 1921 Long had taken Albers to court because he believed he had been 'shortchanged' by his dealer. Long did not return to Albers until the 1930s.[3] During the estrangement, Long is known to have had an exhibition of his recent etchings with Rubery Bennett at 139 King Street in 1926, which is the date of the etching Bart owned. It is also possible that the Tristram was purchased from Rubery Bennett. Tristram did not have a solo exhibition with Bennett until 1930 but Bennett had advertised Tristrams for sale in 1925. His work was popular and it is likely that a 1926 work would have sold immediately or soon after. Tristram did, however, exhibit with other dealers in the 1920s. The cartoons by Low may also have been purchased from Rubery Bennett since Bennett is known to have sold newspaper illustrations by the *Bulletin* artists from the 1920s on. In 1924, Bennett's gallery was situated at 219 George Street, diagonally opposite the *Bulletin* building where Bart worked. Since Bart was buying art from Bennett, surely it is likely that his friend Embrey may have purchased at least one

painting from Bennett. The boatshed painting? In
which case I still have to find a connection between
Rubery Bennett and Lloyd Rees. Or, if the boatshed
painting is by Violet Bartlett, I need a connection
between Bart (and Embrey) and Violet.

Friday, 3 December

I compose a letter to Wendy Moore's step-sister,
Mary Bartlett, in West Sussex, UK. West Sussex is, of
course, to the south-west of London, and Stansted,
Essex, where Violet A. Bartlett is recorded as living
from 1895–1905, is to the east.

> Dear Miss Bartlett,
>   I am researching an unsigned painting from the
> 1920s in an attempt to identify the artist who
> painted it. I enclose a photograph of the painting.
> It is in oils, measures 6" x 12" and is painted on
> plywood.
>   I have been in contact with Wendy Moore
> who kindly gave me your address in the hope that
> you may be able to provide me with some
> information.
>   One of the owners of the painting may well have
> been an Embrey Crawford who was a friend of
> your father from around 1927 to 1931. Another
> owner was a Florence Jane Sainsbury. One pos-
> sibility as the artist of the painting is a Violet
> Bartlett who exhibited in England at the turn of
> the century and appears to have worked in Sydney
> in the late 1920s, but nothing more is known
> about her at this end.
>   I am wondering if Violet Bartlett was related to
> Leonard Bartlett and may have joined him in
> Sydney in the 1920s? She is listed as living in
> Prince Albert Road, Mosman. Violet may have

mixed in the circle of artists living in Mosman which included Lloyd Rees, Wal Taylor, Peter Templeton, John Banks and Rubery Bennett.

In the course of my research I have come across the First World War diary of Leonard Bartlett which is in the Mitchell Library in Sydney. If you are interested, it may be possible to obtain a copy of this by writing to The Manuscripts Librarian, Mitchell Library, Macquarie Street, Sydney, 2000. I made some brief notes from the diary when I viewed it and enclose these for your interest.

I look forward to hearing from you, if you can help me with any information.

Yours sincerely,
Stephen Scheding

Tuesday, 7 December

I keep searching for signs of Violet. She is not in McCulloch's *Encyclopedia of Australian Art*,[1] nor in any other book on Australian art as far as I can see. She is not in the press clippings folder for the name 'Bartlett' in the Mitchell Library, nor in any indexes in the Mitchell.

Searching 'offshore', I cannot find her in any of the other standard books on British art. And she is not listed in Benezit's ten volume *Dictionnaire des Peintres*[2] nor any other international dictionaries of artists, such as the thirty-seven volume Thieme-Becker published in 1927.[3] I cannot find her appearing in auction records from anywhere in the world from the 1970s until now. I decide to write to some institutions in England who might have a record of Violet. I check the *International Directory of Arts* published in Germany.[4] There is no listing for the Royal Institute of Oil Painters at which Violet is recorded as having exhibited two oils and I suspect it

is long defunct. But the librarians at the Tate Gallery
and Courtauld Institute may be worth writing to.
Their libraries are bound to be the most extensive on
British art in general.

The *International Directory* lists public
museums and art galleries by country. Under Great
Britain, each museum or gallery is listed alpha-
betically under city or town with the county follow-
ing in brackets. In Essex, where Violet was living
from 1898 to 1905, there are a number of institu-
tions, mainly specialising in local history, archeology
or ethnography. There is also the Beecroft Art
Gallery, Westcliff-on-sea which is linked to the
Southend Museum Service, and the Colchester and
Essex Museum which has a museum resource centre.
I send letters requesting information to the two
Essex institutions as well as the Tate and the
Courtauld.

Thursday, 16 December

There is a message left on my answering machine
from a Genevieve Banks, saying that she is the
daughter of G. D. Banks, nephew of the artist John
Banks. She has left her number for me to call.

When Genevieve answers the phone, she greets
me as an old friend! I had known her years ago.
I knew her by her married name, which is why I
did not make the connection. In fact, I remember
now that she was related to the artist and that the
family had paintings by John Banks on their walls.
It's odd that I have forgotten this. Perhaps my
current obsession has detached me from the real
world. Like me, Genevieve is surprised that I had
written unwittingly to her father, Gordon Banks.
Sadly, Gordon passed away back in September, as he
was approaching his ninety-third birthday. My letter

was forwarded to her from his address and she has it in front of her. She is able to confirm that John Banks was living at Etham Avenue, Darling Point in 1931. I *have* got the right John Banks!

Her father left her a book which was possibly presented to John Banks by his artist-colleagues. It includes an original example of the work of each of them and there is a work by Lloyd Rees included. She will look through the book thoroughly for works by the other artists mentioned in my letter, including Violet Bartlett. There is also other material which she offers to search through. She invites me over to her house on Sunday morning which means that I also have the chance to look at a range of other paintings by Banks.

Sunday, 19 December

Genevieve lives in a large, renovated Victorian house overlooking a park on the foreshores of the Harbour. Paintings line the walls. When I see the album, there is no indication of how it came to exist. It is not known whether the works were given at one time or swapped or collected by Banks over time. Included are the works of most of the well-known artists of the first decades of this century: A Parisian sketch by Lambert (circa 1901), a Norman Lindsay drawing, a Lawson Balfour oil, a James Muir Auld, an early James R. Jackson oil, a B. E. Minns watercolour ... about forty works in all. And of course the Lloyd Rees. It is a delicate ink and watercolour drawing dated January, 1917, of Princes Bridge, Melbourne. Because of the date, it was possibly a gift from Rees to Banks when Rees arrived in Sydney in 1917. There are no works by Violet Bartlett.

We sift through a suitcase of newspaper articles and memorabilia but find no references to Rees or to

any of the other characters I have come across in my
search. Then I peruse the numerous paintings by
John Banks around the house, finding a couple of
unsigned early ones. There are some similarities in
the grittiness of the paintwork, especially in the
foregrounds, a feature which I have noted before.
But the overall feel is still very different. The boatshed painting has a depth of mood which is nowhere
evident in any of Banks's works of the 1920s. More-
over, Genevieve has seen numerous Banks' paintings
and cannot actually recall a building in any of them.
There are several large works from the mid-1920s.
Banks was extremely popular and the larger works
sold for up to 200 guineas—an enormous sum for
the time. It is unlikely, however, that those values
have kept pace with inflation, although his work
often sells for four-figure amounts at auction today.
In the 1920s, Rees's work rarely sold for more than
25 guineas. His oils now fetch five-figure amounts.

      I discover that Banks's father, James Banks, was
a crusty old sea captain who was most interested in
the arts while instilling in his seven children the need
to have a secure job before pursuing artistic endeav-
ours. The family feels that this is the reason that John
Banks never gave up his day job. The oils on the wall
still seem to be 'demand driven'. There is no
doubting their overt attractiveness, and the kimono-
clad women have inured them from becoming old-
fashioned, but they are primarily designed to please
an audience. The fame they achieved in their time,
paradoxically, may have helped to hold back Banks's
development—in much the same way that fame for
Streeton in the 1920s may have helped him as a
painter (his technique became all important), but
not as an artist.[1] In relation to commercial success
impinging on art, Lloyd Rees has been quoted as
saying:

Had I got high prices for my paintings at a time
when I needed money, I might have had an
inclination to keep painting in a mood that was
acceptable. I devoutly hope not, but this is a
matter in which you can subconsciously delude
yourself.[2]

If the boatshed painting is by Banks it would have to
be very early, but this is unlikely since Banks was
trained and influenced by Lawson Balfour around
1915. We know Banks's work in the 1920s shows an
affinity with Balfour's, but Balfour probably influenced Banks's style from the very beginning.
Indeed the early Banks paintings in the family's
collection confirm this assumption. I am now convinced the boatshed painting is not by John Banks.

Amongst the other material left by John Banks is
a book by P. Neville Barnett titled *Japanese Colour
Prints*.[3] This book, and others privately printed by
Barnett, has always been highly sought after. The fact
that Banks had a copy underscores his interest in the
Orient, as it was known then. This interest was wide-
spread in Sydney art circles in the 1920s. It is not
surprising that Admiral Sir Dudley de Chair,
Governor of NSW, and his wife in the 1920s chose to
commission a mural in the fashionable oriental style
in their London flat when they returned home.

The Banks family also owns a couple of oils by
Rubery Bennett. One appears to be an early work
from the 1920s. I had been looking for an early one
just to make certain that the boatshed painting is not
an early Bennett. I think I can now say that it isn't.
This early work by Bennett is similar to his better-
known, later work except that it is more tentative
and the paint surface is much drier.

Genevieve does not have any knowledge of W.
A. Nunnerly who resided with John Banks and
Leonard Bartlett at 8 Etham Avenue. Nor do the

other names mentioned in my letter to her late father mean anything.

I hand over my file on her family: wills, illustrations of Banks's exhibited works and other material and thank her. On the way home I drive past 8 Etham Avenue, Darling Point. It is a large, square, brick apartment block, probably built circa 1930. I would love to know how Bartlett, Banks and Nunnerly ended up here in the same apartment together in 1931.

There is only one Nunnerly in the Sydney Telephone Directory. My call to the number, in Vaucluse, brings an interested response from Mr Nunnerly who tells me that he is from South Africa. As far as he knows there are no other Nunnerlys in Sydney. He can tell me that all Nunnerlys come originally from Shropshire.

Thursday, 20 January, 1994

The letters from institutions responding to my request for information on the artist Violet Bartlett have all arrived. Despite extensive searches by the diligent librarians and curators, no additional information on Violet is forthcoming.

Thursday, 27 January

In today's edition of the *Australian Financial Review*, Terry Ingram has broken the story on Professor Joan Kerr's opinion that the mural in the de Maistre Room at the Art Gallery of NSW (which are unsigned) were not painted by de Maistre. He repeats her claim that Lady de Chair and her daughter Elaine had contributed substantially to the mural and may have even painted all of it. There is the cheeky piece of information that the mural had been sold to the Art Gallery by Frank McDonald for $220,000 having been purchased at Christie's in London for a good deal less.

Frank McDonald is on the phone. I think he is checking to see if I had anything to do with the breaking of the story—I assure him I didn't. But I remember the dissimilarities between the murals and de Maistre's known work. De Maistre's oils of the period in which the murals were known to have been painted tend to radiate outwards with energy. They are bold and dynamic. The murals, on the other hand, seem to droop inwards: they are languid and decorative. Frank assures me that the de Chair children have no doubt that de Maistre was commissioned to do them. The son, Somerset, had put them into Christie's as de Maistres and daughter Elaine would know if she or her mother had helped, and she has certainly not claimed this. But could someone else have helped de Maistre after he was given the commission? Frank agrees that this is possible but in no way detracts from the value of the work. Many important artists used assistants on major works.

I remember that in the early 1930s, de Maistre was collaborating with the English painter Francis Bacon who was at the time designing furniture and interiors before achieving his great fame. I suggest half-jokingly to Frank that perhaps Bacon helped de Maistre on the murals. If this could be proven then the de Maistre/Bacon room could be worth a million or so. I also tell Frank that the murals remind me of the work of the artist Frank Weitzel. Weitzel exhibited with de Maistre in Sydney in the late 1920s at an exhibition patronised by the de Chairs.[1] He then followed de Maistre to London and was working there until his untimely death in 1932. His known work is extremely rare. I offer to hunt out reproductions of the one or two drawings that I think show the resemblance.

This has been an interesting conversation. I find I have suddenly become very interested in the story of a large, unsigned painting. It's not just to test Frank but to test provenance. Is proof by provenance infallible? I settle down to compose a letter to the Keeper of the Department of Documents at the Imperial War Museum, London.

Dear Sir or Madam,

I am currently researching the provenance of some Australian artworks. One of these works is a mural which was in the London apartment of Sir Dudley and Lady de Chair. Sir Dudley, following his war service, was a Governor of NSW from 1923 to 1930 when he returned to England. The mural was completed sometime after.

De Chair's autobiography, *The Sea is Strong*, is almost exclusively about the First World War and thus there is no information on events after 1919. However, the entry by Chris Cunneen in the *Australian Dictionary of Biography* refers to the fact that his unpublished memoirs are in the Imperial War Museum. It is most likely that these are also exclusively about official matters. However, I am eager to know whether they make mention of anything of an artistic nature. Lady de Chair was an enthusiastic patron of the arts.

The mural was purchased by the Art Gallery of NSW last year, and the various sections of it have been incorporated into a room known as 'The Roy de Maistre Mural Room'. Although it is unsigned, it is ascribed to de Maistre, the expatriate

Australian painter who is known to have exhibited in the early 1930s with Francis Bacon who was designing furnishings and interiors at the time. The attribution is largely based on the recollections of members of the de Chair family.

Recently, it has been suggested, by a Professor of Fine Arts, Joan Kerr, that the mural may have been painted by Lady de Chair and her daughter. I enclose a copy of an article to this effect published in the *Australian Financial Review*. Personally, I feel that this is unlikely, although they may have assisted. If the murals are not primarily by de Maistre, then another possibility is the artist Frank Weitzel who was associated with Lady de Chair in Sydney and travelled to London at about the same time, only to die tragically of tetanus at the home of the writer David Garnett in 1932 at the age of twenty-six.

I would be most pleased if you could indicate whether Sir Dudley de Chair's unpublished memoirs are of the kind that would be likely to mention the mural, Roy de Maistre, Francis Bacon or Frank Weitzel, and whether it would be worth my while having someone go through the memoirs at greater length.

As you can imagine, the issue of authorship of the mural is most intriguing and I am hoping to discover any information which could prove conclusive.

Hoping to hear from you soon,
Yours sincerely,
Stephen Scheding

Monday, 7 February

At last, the letter from Mary Bartlett arrives.

Dear Mr Scheding,

Your letter of 3 December, 1993, came at a very busy time for me, and over the Christmas and New Year period everything seems to grind to a halt. All that is by the way of explaining why you have not heard from me until now.

I have not been able to help you in spite of my enquiries. I rang a cousin—our fathers were brothers but did not keep in touch with each other. She has no recollection of a Violet Bartlett even though her mother, now deceased, was the one who was interested in all branches of the family.

The assistant Curator of Worthing Art Gallery gave me a little information by telephone, so I then went to Worthing Library—much bigger and better than our village library. In the reference section in the *Dictionary of Artists 1880–1940* by J. Johnson and A. Greutzner, there was only the following: 'Miss Violet A. Bartlett—Exhibited 1898–1905, *The Thatch,* Stansted, Essex, ROI 2'. If you have a copy it is on page 45, but I expect you already know that! I am sure Violet was not related to my father.

I do want to thank you very much for the notes you were able to extract from my father's diaries. I wish he had told Wendy [Moore, Mary's step-sister] or me about them on the many occasions that I visited Australia after the 1939–45 war.

You might be interested in a very old catalogue connected with an exhibition by Norma Bull at Australia House in London in 1947 entitled *Two Hemispheres.*

As you can guess your letter prompted me to start turning out—very necessary when you are over 70.

Yours sincerely,
Mary B. Bartlett.

My letter back to Mary:

Dear Miss Bartlett,

Thank you very much for your letter of 23 January and for the research which you have done.

My research, which began as a mystery about who painted the boatshed painting, is becoming a bit of a mystery about the artist Violet Bartlett. The lack of information on her is certainly puzzling. I had been hoping that Violet was perhaps a relation of your father who looked him up when she arrived in Australia in the 1920s. It does seem likely that she might have met him then because of their mutual connection with the artist John Banks.

I am wondering if you could help me 'round off' a section of my research regarding your father who was a friend of Embrey Crawford who may have owned the boatshed painting. Your father resided in about 1931 with an artist by the name of John Banks. Banks was previously a neighbour of Violet in Prince Albert Road, Mosman. I don't suppose the name John Banks rings any bells?

I understand that your mother was a nurse in the First World War. If you could possibly tell me her name, I could trace her addresses in Sydney to see if it leads me anywhere. Would you know when and why she returned (?) to England. The briefest family information would be most adequate.

You mentioned a catalogue of the work of Norma Bull. I would be most interested in having a copy of this. As part of my work I have developed an extensive research library on Australian art and any additions are cherished.

I hope my requests are not putting you to too much trouble. I will let you know if I discover anything further at this end.

Yours sincerely,
Stephen Scheding

Tuesday, 15 February

A short response from Mary Bartlett:

> Dear Mr Scheding,
>   I am enclosing the Norma Bull catalogue. Please keep it. I hope it will compensate you for the fact that I am unable to help you any more with information concerning my parents, or Violet Bartlett.
>   Yours sincerely,
>   Mary Bartlett

This end to our correspondence seems a little abrupt. Does she know more? Or does she simply feel she has offered as much as she can? After all, I guess I can't expect everyone to join the quest to the extent that I have.

I decide to have one final go at discovering who Violet was. Even though she is fading fast in terms of a possible connection to Bart and Embrey, I am interested to know about her anyway. What could be the story of a woman who was exhibiting paintings in the Royal Institute of Oil Painters in 1898–1905 and then living in obscurity in Sydney in the late 1920s? I phone Emma Hicks, a London researcher who does research for Australian institutions. I first met her years ago when she was living in Australia and researching for Frank McDonald. Emma agrees to do some spadework for me and I tell her I will send an outline of the information I have on Violet.

Wednesday, 16 February

I have been working on developing a catalogue of all the known Rees oils from about 1918 to 1928. My main purpose is to locate oils from the period, in particular those known to be circa 1920–22, and compare them 'in the flesh' to the boatshed painting.

So far the catalogue includes about 150 oils that are known to have been exhibited between these dates, but, of course, not all of these have been located. I can find only about fifty oils from the period that are locatable. I have made a separate list of these. Many of the fifty correspond to paintings in the list of works known to have been exhibited. This leaves at least 100 Rees oils from 1918–28 which have yet to be located! That is, if they have not been destroyed. And many would not have been. Rees may have destroyed or painted over early work which he considered unsuccessful, but it is less likely he would have destroyed work he considered good enough to exhibit.

In the past couple of weeks I have located *Old Boats, Wollestonecraft Bay* in the Art Gallery of NSW which is said to be dated circa 1920 (but which I think could be 1921–22) and *Near Our Flat, Mosman* in a private collection and which is dated Christmas 1920–21. I have discovered that Sotheby's have in recent years sold *The White Horse* (which I believe to be circa 1922), *The Red House* (a painting of this title was exhibited in 1922) and *Near Old Cremorne Wharf, Mosman Bay* (this is similar in style to *Near Our Flat* and therefore probably dates to 1920–21). Joel's have sold *Parramatta River* which is dated 1922. I will write to the auction houses asking them to forward my letters to the owners in the hope that I may be able to examine these oils. And not just the oils, but their frames—I'm also looking for signs of green bookbinding tape, or stickers with serrated edges, or even identical frames.

In fact, one way towards solving the mystery of whether Lloyd Rees painted the boatshed painting might be to organise an exhibition of works by Rees which are known to have been painted between 1918 and 1928 and to include the boatshed painting where I think it might fit chronologically if it is by Rees. Then everyone could have a go at working it out on stylistic grounds.

Thursday, 17 February

As part of this search for early Rees oils, I take a trip to the Manly Art Gallery which owns *An Old Barn, Parramatta, 1924*. While this oil is a bit later than the period on which I am focusing, I remember that after it had been stolen and then recovered some years ago, a photograph of it appeared in the *Sydney Morning Herald* (28.3.85) which showed the frame. Although the photograph was in black and white, the frame appeared to be very similar to the one on the boatshed painting. I have the original catalogue for the Manly Art Gallery, published in 1930. It lists *An Old Barn* as having been presented by the artist. Many other artists are recorded as having presented a work to the gallery. In the front of the catalogue, under a list of all the patrons and office bearers of the gallery is the information: 'City Receiving Depot: Mr S. A. Parker, 219 George Street, Sydney.'

Will the frame on *An Old Barn* be a Parker frame and identical to the frame on the boatshed painting? Will it have bookbinding tape or a serrated-edge sticker?

I will never know. I discover that the original frame, since its appearance in the photograph in 1985, has been removed from *An Old Barn*, displaced by a new frame. Since I phoned the Curator, Phillipa Charley, about viewing the painting and the frame, she has been madly searching for the original frame. She even went to the Manly Council Depot where the gallery stores some old frames. She has also waived the cost that the council now charges the public for such bizarre demands. But the original frame, perhaps crucial evidence, has mysteriously disappeared.

But look! this is exciting. There is an inscription on the reverse of *An Old Barn* unmistakably in Lloyd Rees's handwriting, stating that the [original] frame for the painting is to be supplied by Rubery Bennett. At last! Evidence of a relationship between Rees and gallery owner Rubery Bennett, beyond merely the fact of their knowing of one another. Indeed, supplying a frame in such circumstances is surely something that a dealer might have done. I feel my research to this point has suddenly been vindicated: Bennett could well have been Rees's dealer or agent in 1924.

The gallery also has a letter by Rees written from 'Bondo', Parramatta to the Hon. Secretary of the gallery on 21 November, 1924 which pertains to the delivery of the painting. Rees writes that the painting can be collected on Monday or Tuesday but adds '… please don't bother about sending a motor here [to Parramatta] specially … I can easily leave it at an address in the city one day next week.' Was this a habit of Lloyd's? I recall my earlier speculation that, because of the telephone number 8930 on the reverse of the boatshed painting, Rees may have organised to deliver it to a city address so that it could be collected.

One other thing: *An Old Barn* has an incised signature. That is, it was scratched on after the paint had dried. It is almost certainly in Rees's hand, but it may mean that the painting left his hands *unsigned* and was later signed on request.

Saturday, 19 February

I spend some time in the Mitchell Library, reading *Art in Australia* and *The Home* through the 1920s,

looking for clues. The advertisements for the various
art galleries are interesting since they often name the
artists exhibiting. In 1925, Rubery Bennett, while at
219 George Street, lists thirteen Australian artists
and thirteen British. There is no reference to Lloyd
Rees. In fact, by 1925 there are no artists from the
Bennett stable who had a close relationship to the
Ure Smith circle, despite Bennett having previously
advertised Ure Smith etchings. Instead there are big-
selling names such as Streeton, Sidney Long, the
Lindsays, Gruner and Hilder.

It would appear that Bennett's direction,
by 1925, was towards representing the popular
artists of his time. He does not appear interested in
up-and-coming artists nor those whose work does
not fit an accepted mould. It is difficult to imagine
him selling works by Wakelin, de Maistre or Lloyd
Rees. But did Rubery Bennett represent Rees in
1924? Rees's inscription on *An Old Barn* suggests
that he might have. L. V. Bartlett may not have
purchased paintings from Bennett until 1926 or
1927, but Bennett may have kept the odd Rees in
the stock room while exhibiting the more lucrative
artists in his galleries. Bart's friend Embrey may have
purchased the boatshed painting from Bennett
around this time.

A 1925 advertisement for the Grosvenor
Galleries, run by Wal Taylor, refers to an exhibition
by 'Eight Young Painters' including Lloyd Rees.[1] This
raises the possibility that the boatshed painting, if
by Rees, could have been with his friend Wal Taylor
(to be sold to Bart or Embrey?). Despite the fact
that Rees held a major one-man show with Basil
Burdett in 1922, there are no mentions of Lloyd
Rees in the advertisements for Burdett's galleries
after Burdett moves from 219 George Street to the
corner of King and Phillip Streets and then, in 1925,
to the Macquarie in Bligh Street. And the lists of

exhibitions at the Macquarie Galleries which were published in 1975 do not show Rees having a one-man show until 1931.[2] However, it is difficult to imagine that Burdett did not sell the odd Rees work between 1922 and 1931 (the dates of Rees's solo exhibitions with Burdett) given Burdett's association with Lloyd.

While L. V. Bartlett may have bought the Tristram watercolour and the Sid Long etching from Rubery Bennett, it is likely that he, with Embrey, would have frequented other galleries, especially those exhibiting works by artists in the Ure Smith circle, given Bart's connection to the advertising world, and probable connection to Ure Smith (because of the Christmas card). So Bart or Embrey could have bought the boatshed painting from Wal Taylor or Basil Burdett—as well as from Bennett.[3]

If the boatshed painting was at some time with one of these dealers, it may not have been sold, but stayed instead in their collection. If it stayed in Burdett's collection, it might explain how the painting had ended up in Melbourne. I am assuming Burdett's things were in Melbourne at the time of his death in 1942—he moved there in 1931. Was there an auction of his estate? If so, might the catalogue refer to a painting identifiable as the boatshed painting? It is worth checking.

Friday, 4 March

Photocopies of the newspaper reviews of Rees's exhibitions, which include paintings titled *The Bay*, have arrived from Alan and Jan Rees. The package also includes handwriting samples of 'Dad's' friend, Basil Burdett. I am most interested to compare Burdett's handwriting with the *Suburban Scene* inscription on the boatshed painting, particularly remembering Burdett's introduction to Rees's 1922 book where he writes: 'Mosman was the *scene* of the first tentative efforts in oils, but the essentially *suburban* atmosphere proved so limited ...'[1] (My italics again.) In other words, Burdett may have added the title *Suburban Scene* since that is how he saw Rees's pre-Parramatta work. There do seem to be some similarities between Basil's handwriting and the inscription, but I will need to find more samples of his writing to see if this is worth exploring.

Neither of the reviews of the 1922 Rees exhibition (in the *Bulletin* 14/12/22 and *Daily Telegraph* 7/12/22) refers specifically to a painting titled *The Bay* which was catalogue number 22 in that exhibition. However, Alan and Jan have also included a review of Rees's exhibition at the Gainsborough Gallery in Brisbane in 1928 which also included an oil titled *The Bay*. This was the painting which was purchased from the gallery by a Mr Smith. Since there was more than one painting with the title *The Bay*, it is not known whether the 1928 painting is the same work as the one exhibited in 1922. But the description of it in the review is most interesting: 'In *The Bay*, an admirably treated oil, there is a real poetic feeling and a spirit of mystery. It is the most attractive picture in the show.'

A 'spirit of mystery'! I must track down the actual painting.

Saturday, 5 March

In the Mitchell Library, I find two more samples of Basil's handwriting, also with similarities to the *Suburban Scene* inscription. But there are also problems, particularly with the 's's. One of the letters by Basil Burdett is to George Lambert, asking him to accept a reduction of price for a drawing. It is dated

12 February, 1925, and notes that some unsold
drawings by Lambert which had been exhibited
before Christmas have been held at Burdett's gallery.
This confirms that Burdett engaged in the practice,
common to galleries, of holding unsold works for
later sale. In this case, holding Lambert's drawings
may even have occurred during a change of address
as indicated by the altered letterhead.

The Mitchell also has a letter by John Young,
Burdett's partner in the Macquarie Galleries, to Tom
Roberts in March, 1929, but his handwriting is not
similar to the boatshed inscription. There are no
original documents in the Mitchell Library by the
other suspects, Wal Taylor and Rubery Bennett, both
of whom were educated in Brisbane. I will find a way
of getting samples of their handwriting as well.

In *Australian Art and Artists to 1950—A
bibliography* published by the Library Council of
Victoria, there is a list of articles by, and about, Basil
Burdett.[1] Most interesting is the information that the
State Library of Victoria holds a copy of the auction
catalogue of paintings from the estate of Burdett,
sold at Joel's in February 1943! Now, what if
Burdett had handled the boatshed painting and it
stayed with him until his death? Could *Suburban
Scene* by Lloyd Rees be listed in this 1943 auction
catalogue? I organise to obtain a photocopy of the
auction catalogue.

Tuesday, 8 March

Dear Alan And Jan,
    Thank you for your letter the other day. Your
ongoing input is greatly appreciated.
    Enclosed is a checklist of Lloyd's oils from
1915–32 which I have printed out to help me
get a sense of titles, his movements, etc. Also a

draft chronology to begin to cross check the information I have so far.

I am about to write to the Arts Unit at the State Library of Queensland to see if they can locate a firmer link between Rubery Bennett and Lloyd Rees and to seek a sample of Bennett's handwriting.

The plot thickens. I like to think that the connections are more than coincidences.

What I now need to know is this:

(1) Do you know of any oils (other than those in my checklist) painted circa 1921–22 with which I could compare the boatshed painting? It is possible that paintings from this period may have exhibition stickers, inscriptions, even bookbinding tape (!) etc. In particular it would be good to locate other oils from Rees's 1922/23 exhibition at 219 George Street.

(2) You discovered that a painting titled *The Bay* was bought by Mr Smith of Brisbane in 1928 from Miss Sheldon's gallery. Do you know who she was? Could this be A. H. Smith of Brisbane who is listed in Renee's book on Rees as owning a number of Rees oils in 1972, including a second version of *An Old Barn*? Her oils seem to have passed to J. D. and G. D. Smith. Do you know what happened to the Smiths or their oils? I will also ask the State Library of Queensland if they know anything of the Smiths. (It is a rotten name as far as research goes!)

(3) Would you have any samples of the hand-writing of Wal Taylor?

I think you will agree that there are enough reasons for my pressing on to solve the mystery of the boatshed painting. I will keep sleuthing and let you know of any more clues. Please let me know if you have any ideas.

Best wishes,
Stephen Scheding

Wednesday, 9 March

I have received a response from diligent researcher, Emma Hicks, re Violet Bartlett.[1] Her letter begins:

> Dear Stephen,
>   You might have had cause to hope that the lengthy gap in communications might mean that I had finally managed to turn up some small snippet of information on Violet Bartlett ... but I'm afraid she's proved as elusive as ever.

Emma has been exhaustive in her search for Violet. She has checked masses of sources to no avail. At the end of her letter she notes that 'the Bartlett name does seem to crop up more regularly among American artists'. She has chased up a couple without any luck.

There is not much joy in her letter. Unless ... If Violet was a wandering American artist, could she have come into contact with the American Crawford family when she was in Sydney in the 1920s?

Could Embrey have purchased one of her paintings? The boatshed painting? Or is Violet destined to remain infuriatingly in obscurity? Even though I think the boatshed painting was probably done by a male artist, I would love to locate some of Violet's work for comparison. To be thorough. Given my enthusiasm for 'lost' female painters, Violet has now become, for me, the epitome. Hang on. I was supposed to have given up these enthusiasms.

Thursday, 10 March

I write back to Emma asking her if she could do some research on certain aspects of the de Maistre mural.

Friday, 1 April

The 1943 catalogue of paintings from the estate of
Basil Burdett has arrived from the State Library of
Victoria. In it, there are eighty paintings listed for
sale. The surprise is that at the time of his death,
Burdett owned no paintings at all by Lloyd Rees, let
alone one with a promising title. I find this
astonishing. It seems impossible that Burdett,
reportedly a close friend and supporter of Lloyd
Rees, and a collector, would not own a Rees work!
What was the reason for this? Did Lloyd and Basil
have a falling out? If so, it certainly has not been
recorded. However, number 58 is *Landscape* by
Unknown Artist. It is the only work in the auction
catalogue where the artist is not known. Could this
landscape be a Rees? The unsigned boatshed
painting?

Many of the titles in the catalogue are putative,
that is, the auctioneer has titled works, often giving
them the most cursory title, rather than the artist's
title. For example, a work by Margaret Preston is
simply titled *Flowers*—her titles were usually more
specific than this. Of the eighty works in the
catalogue, seventeen have the title *Landscape*. There
are eight called simply *Nude*. Thus, if the Unknown
Artist's *Landscape* is the boatshed painting, it is not
surprising that it does not have its inscribed title:
Suburban Scene.

Number 57 is *Landscape* by Griffiths. This is the
only entry in the catalogue where just the surname of
the artist is given. It is possibly Harley Cameron
Griffiths. Florence Sainsbury owned a Harley
Cameron Griffiths. Did she purchase it from the
Burdett sale? And the boatshed painting as well? I
wonder if Joel's have a copy of the Burdett catalogue
with annotations relating to the purchasers of the
paintings? I will find out.

The auction catalogue of the Burdett collection has a note which states that the collection had previously been exhibited at the National Gallery of Victoria. Perhaps the catalogue of that exhibition might include Rees paintings which somehow did not make it to the auction. But a call to the NGV reveals that no catalogue exists today! The library does have a review of the exhibition but there are no references in the review to Rees paintings. The paintings listed in the auction catalogue show Burdett to have been an extraordinary collector. There are works by Roberts, Withers, McCubbin, Bunny, Gruner, John D. Moore, Wakelin, Preston, Shore, Vassilieff, Drysdale, Dobell and Arthur Boyd. There is also a work by the all but forgotten Australian modernist, Mary Cecil Allen.

Monday, 2 May

A sample of Rubery Bennett's handwriting arrives from Joan Bruce at the State Library of Queensland. It does not really resemble the inscription *Suburban Scene* on the boatshed painting. Joan has been unable to discover any other link between Bennett and Lloyd Rees in the library's holdings.

Tuesday, 3 May

A sample of Wal Taylor's handwriting has been unearthed by Alan and Jan Rees. They have sent me a photocopy. I phone Alan and tell him that I now have so many handwriting samples of Lloyd, Basil, Wal and Rubery that I will take them all to the Document Examination Unit of the Police Department and ask them for a verdict.

Monday, 9 May

An interesting letter has arrived from the Imperial War Museum:

> Dear Mr Scheding,
>   I forwarded your letter of 2 January to Admiral Sir Dudley de Chair's family and I have now received a reply from his daughter to this effect:
>   *I can tell you that the mural done for my mother was definitely by her friend Roy de Maistre, and was ornamenting a flat in London that she occasionally used, but frequently let. It would not be mentioned in our father's memoirs* The Sea is Strong.
>   I can confirm the statement in the last sentence as we have the typescript draft of the book among our collection of the Admiral's papers and it contains no reference to the mural. I hope that this information is of some value to your investigations into the process of art research.
>   Yours sincerely,
>   Roderick Suddaby
>   (Keeper of the Documents)

So, at this stage, it seems that the mural in the Art Gallery of NSW will remain ascribed to Roy de Maistre. The provenance will ensure this. The mural had been consigned to the Christie's auction in London by the de Chairs' son, Somerset de Chair, as being by de Maistre, and the ascription is now confirmed by the de Chairs' daughter, Elaine. The son and daughter would probably have been teenagers in the 1930s when the mural was commissioned by their parents. They may not have remembered the mural being commissioned and painted, but no doubt there is a strong family story that it was done by de Maistre.

  But is that the end of it? What if de Maistre, as

a close friend of the de Chairs, had organised the commissioning and painting of the mural, but handed over the bulk of the painting of it to another artist? An artist such as his friend Frank Weitzel, ten years younger, unknown, but gifted in design. Weitzel would have been acceptable to the de Chairs as they would have known his work which was exhibited in the Burdekin House exhibition in Sydney in 1929 of which they were patrons.[1] Weitzel had designed the wall decorations for a 'man's study'. The study was arranged by Weitzel and Henry Pynor and the furniture was made by Anthony Hordern's. De Maistre had designed a 'man's bedroom' in the same exhibition. Weitzel died in 1932 and he was quickly forgotten. Could he have been dropped from the de Chair family story regarding the mural? Particularly as de Maistre's reputation increased in England.

Thursday, 19 May

At the Art Gallery of NSW, inside the de Maistre Room, a number of items have stealthily materialised. Three de Maistre oils and some drawings. The gallery's obvious intention of placing them there is to show, by stylistic comparison, that de Maistre painted the adjacent mural. This is the gallery's response to the recent conjecture. An attractive brochure about the mural is available for sale with illustrations and an essay. It begins:

> The murals in The Roy de Maistre room were executed in the 1930s in London by the expatriate, Roy de Maistre ... de Maistre's mural consists of six panels in oil, and gold and silver paint on linen. They were painted as a commission for the de Chair London apartment in Carrington House, Hertford Street, and are thought to have

hung in the dining room. Lady de Chair lived in her London apartment for several months in the early 1930s ... It was probably at this time that the murals were completed.

Do the works now placed adjacent to the mural prove the case? The oils appear to be more dynamic and angular than most of the mural with its largely rounded, drooping design. There is a 1926 design by de Maistre, in gouache, for a wall painting. But this looks even less like the de Chair mural. There are two preliminary drawings for the design of a screen. These are almost certainly by de Maistre and do have the languid feel of the mural. Another drawing, titled *Study for Mural,* depicts an oriental-like structure in a landscape. One of the features on the building has a distinctive design resembling snake scales. This design is also found in the mural. It is unusual enough to indicate that the drawing is probably by the same artist as the artist of the mural. On the gallery card next to it the drawing is stated to be by Roy de Maistre, from a private collection, but the drawing itself is unsigned. Its ascription to de Maistre is also based on provenance. The card also, significantly, stops short of claiming that the drawing is a preliminary sketch for the de Chair mural.

There is no hard evidence here, such as a contemporaneous newspaper article about de Maistre working on the mural, or a letter discussing the fact. Nor a drawing signed by de Maistre which is obviously a preliminary sketch for the mural.

Monday, 6 June

Dear Alan and Jan,
Enclosed are photocopies of some material relating to Lloyd that I have come across in my

search—mostly from *The Home* and *Art in Australia*.

Any luck on the Smiths of Brisbane and *The Bay*?

Yours sincerely,

Stephen Scheding

Thursday, 16 June

I am both clutching at straws and endeavouring to be thorough as I write once again to Robert Blain, the executor of the estate of Florence Sainsbury, previous owner of the boatshed painting:

Dear Robert,

I am just writing to let you know that I am still working on my research about the unsigned painting, previously in the possession of the late Florence Sainsbury.

I am currently working on a theory that the unsigned painting may have been purchased by Mrs Sainsbury from the Joel's auction of the collection of Basil Burdett. The sale took place in February 1943. Burdett was a well-known figure in Australian art circles.

Last time we spoke, you mentioned that you had some papers, photographs, etc, that had belonged to Mrs Sainsbury, and that you would probably get around to throwing these out. If you have not already done this, I am wondering if I might be able to have them. It may be that the material will contain nothing helpful to me, but in the interests of my research I feel I need to be absolutely thorough.

Could you please let me know if this material is still available?

Best wishes,

Stephen Scheding

Monday, 27 June

Dear Mr Scheding,

I am sorry I was not able to reply to your letter dated 16 June, 1994, earlier as I wished to confer with the joint executor of Mrs Sainsbury's estate.

He agrees with me that all documents associated with the estate have been passed to her solicitor and all personal photos have been destroyed as Mrs Sainsbury was a very secretive person and we are sure she would not wish for her personal documents to be made public in any way at all.

Yours sincerely

Robert Blain

My charm must be wearing out.

Tuesday, 28 June

An interesting response arrives from Emma Hicks about the de Maistre mural.[1] Again her research has been exhaustive. She has meticulously tracked the de Chairs' movements in London in the 1930s. But she has been unable to obtain proof or otherwise that de Maistre painted the de Chairs' mural. She has, however, discovered that Carrington House was not built until circa 1938. Her letter concludes:

If you can be sure that the mural was a commission specifically for the flat at Carrington House, it would appear to date from the *late* not early 1930s.

Thus, while the mural may remain ascribed to Roy de Maistre, Frank McDonald and the Art Gallery of NSW will have to rethink either the period of its execution or the residence for which it was painted.

Of course, if it was done in the late 1930s, Frank Weitzel could not have had anything to do with it since he died in 1932.

Sunday, 14 August

In April I had written to Jon Dwyer at Joel's to see whether the company still had the auctioneer's catalogue for the Basil Burdett collection and, if so, whether it was annotated with the names of the purchasers. I have not heard from him but, since I am in Melbourne anyway at another Joel's art auction, I ask Jon about it. He hasn't found it, despite a good search and asking other members of the firm whether they had borrowed it. But, so I can double-check, he lends me his office and brings all of the old Joel's catalogues from the 1930s to the 1950s to me in folders.

It takes me about two hours to go through them but there is no trace of their copy of the Burdett catalogue. And yet Joel's records appear, otherwise, so complete, with most catalogues having neat, pencilled annotations relating to purchasers. I wonder darkly whether someone might have stolen the Burdett catalogue and forlornly hand over my un-annotated copy to complete their archive.

I will never know whether Florence Sainsbury purchased paintings from the Burdett collection. Was her Griffiths lot 57? Was the boatshed painting purchased as lot 58, 'Artist Unknown' and is it in fact by Rees? It was a long shot anyway.

At Joel's auction I buy a couple of paintings to cheer myself up.

Thursday, 1 September

Out of desperation I had begun to write to all the Smiths in the Brisbane telephone directory hoping to locate one that was related to the Smith who owned *The Bay* in 1928. I'm hoping to find this version and discover that it is another version of the boatshed painting. There are thousands of Smiths in Brisbane. I had started by sending letters to the Smiths with initials J. D. and G. D. since I knew that a J. D. and G. D. Smith had owned 1920s oils by Rees in the 1960s.[1] I had received numerous letters back but, despite some intriguing responses—one Smith took the trouble to tell me politely that she was not interested in books or paintings—no-one had any oils by Lloyd Rees.

Then, today, the phone rings. It is Alan telling me that he has had a call, out of the blue. The caller had said 'Hello, my name's Smith'. It turned out that he was the owner of *The Bay* and was phoning to let Alan know he had it, and some other oils, and would Alan be interested in seeing them. Alan was. He had seen them. *The Bay*, alas, was not similar in subject to the boatshed painting.

Christmas 1994–95

People have been recommending books to me over the past two years. As I tell them about my research they tell me about books they think might relate to it. I have now read numerous thrillers on the theme of tracking down art, usually some 'great' work. In these, the hero is invariably successful. Non-fiction has also been recommended. The book that has interested me most so far is *The Quest for Corvo—An Experiment in Biography* by A. J. A. Symons.[1] Apart from being a remarkable exercise in researching the life of the elusive writer Baron Corvo, the book also works, according to Symons' brother in the introduction, as an autobiography of A. J. A. Symons himself. I have also read *The Infanta Adventure and the Lost Manet* by Andrew W. Brainerd who subjects an unsigned painting found in a Paris junk market to various scientific and quasi-scientific tests in an attempt to prove that it is a copy by Manet of Velasquez's *L'Infante Marie Marguerite*.[2]

Some time back, Elizabeth Ellis, Curator of Pictures at the Mitchell Library, had particularly recommended *The Search for Gainsborough* by Adrienne Corri which sets out to prove that a particular unsigned painting is by Thomas Gainsborough.[3] I set off to seek out Corri's book for what I anticipate should be a good read for my holidays. Adrienne Corri tries to prove that a painting is by Gainsborough by going through eighteenth century banking records. Banking records! It makes sense: someone pays Gainsborough for a portrait. Gainsborough banks the money. The payee and the payer are recorded in bank ledgers as receiving and giving the same amount of money at the same time. Two hundred and fifty years later Adrienne Corri identifies the sitter in the portrait and matches up the sitter's family and Gainsborough with the entries in the bank ledgers. Her research takes about eight years.

For me, the implications are terrifying! What if detailed records of banking in Sydney in the 1920s actually exist somewhere? Would I have to spend eight years searching through them looking for references to a financial transaction involving the sum of x guineas and the artist Lloyd Rees, the gallery director Rubery Bennett and fledgling collector Embrey Crawford for example? Of course, the boatshed painting might have changed hands for cash, but if Rubery Bennett's Australian Fine Art Gallery was involved, a cheque was probably obligatory.

Over a few days, via phone calls and letters, I manage to find out a lot about where all my main characters might have done their banking in the 1920s. I had previously asked Alan Rees who might have extracted his Dad's teeth, so of course I have no compunction about asking in which bank Lloyd might have deposited his money. Alan tells me that he probably would have banked with the Commonwealth Bank for political reasons. While Lloyd had obtained his housing loan from the Rural Bank (now the State Bank) in 1934, Alan feels he would have stayed with the Commonwealth for his ongoing banking. On the other hand his family back in Queensland was associated with the Bank of NSW (now Westpac).

Mrs Violet Bennett, Rubery's widow, responds tolerantly, providing the information that Rubery would have banked with the Queensland National Bank on the corner of Hunter and Pitt Streets. This bank eventually disappeared into the National Australia Bank. I am unable to discover the banking histories of the other art dealers, Basil Burdett and Wal Taylor. Catherine Ives consults with her mother and finds that William Charles Crawford and probably his son Embrey banked with the E. S. & A. (English Scottish and Australia Bank, now the ANZ).

I make calls to the archive departments of the four major banks, Westpac, Commonwealth, ANZ and NAB, to find out whether they have kept records which are specific enough to provide the information I am after. The bank archivists are fascinated by my question, but the general consensus is that, by the 1920s, the explosion of information that banks had to deal with (compared to Gainsborough's time) meant that only minimal information would have been recorded. Graeme Bird, the Commonwealth's archivist, believes that in the case of 1920s cheque account records, only the date, the last three digits of the cheque number and the amount would be recorded. Not the payee. However, he doubts that even this information would be around today. Judy McArthur of Westpac thinks that records were kept for seven years before being destroyed. She tells me that the Bank of NSW kept the first current account ledger of each branch for the Bank's archives, so unless my characters were banking at newly opened branches there would be no record at all of what I am after. She also doubts whether the records, if they did exist, would be full enough to give me the information anyway. The story is the same at the ANZ and the NAB. Records are unlikely to exist and, if they do, are unlikely to give me the information I want. To make absolutely sure, I will follow up my telephone enquiries with a detailed letter to the Archivist of each bank.

But, meanwhile, back to the holiday. My wife is working, in this case, directing a children's television series in New Zealand, while our six-year-old son and I look on, be extras, potter around, or go travelling. I am resting, not only from my full-time job as a psychologist in schools but from my other (night) job of this research. For almost two years it seems I have been holed up at night in the attic with the family asleep below, bent over my books and notes, into the early hours of the morning. In addition I have written and illustrated three childrens' books.[4] I feel a bit worn out.

I really need to resolve this soon. The problem is that my provenance is shaping up to be circumstantial at best. Is there any other way of proving the painting is by Rees? Or by any other artist?

Wednesday, 1 February, 1995

I fly home.

I wonder whether further technical examination of the boatshed painting would be of any use. I suspect it won't, but I phone David Stein, the painting's restorer, to make absolutely sure. David agrees with me. Firstly, there would be little sense in attempting to date it using scientific methods since these would not be nearly accurate enough to date it more precisely than the 1920s.[1] I already know it was painted in the 1920s. Such scientific analysis is most useful when trying to date paintings which are well over a hundred years old, where precise accuracy is not required; and when artists used pigments which they ground themselves and which may have been unique. In the 1920s, most professional artists chose from the same ranges of commercially available products, most often Winsor and Newton. Infra-red examination would also not be helpful in the case of the boatshed painting since the surface has too much depth. Infra-red rays pick up 'hidden' marks, such as pencil lines, when the surface is comparatively flat.

Friday, 3 February

The responses from the banks have all arrived and, predictably, confirm the information given by the archivists over the phone. A letter from the ANZ Bank reads as follows:

Dear Mr Scheding,

Regrettably we cannot help with your enquiries regarding the Lloyd Rees painting.

'Modern' banking records do not contain sufficient detail to allow the sort of research you propose. Apart from this, we do not retain records relating to customers' accounts simply because of the huge bulk they would comprise and the difficulties in permitting research in what are, in effect, confidential records. I think you will find that this situation pertains with the other banks' archives too.

Interestingly, Lloyd Rees worked as a junior officer at the Brisbane branch of one of our predecessor banks, the Union Bank of Australia Ltd from 21 April 1911 to 29 February 1912. He is recorded as resigning to take a position with the Bank of New South Wales.

Yours sincerely,
T. J. Hart

Monday, 6 February

At Sotheby's, I see *Flowerpiece* by Roy de Maistre, circa 1926, to be sold at their next auction in May. Behind the flowers, as part of a wall hanging, is a design I have seen before. It runs horizontally and resembles the scales of a snake. It exists in one of the panels of the de Maistre mural in the Art Gallery of NSW. It is so distinctive that it makes the connection between the mural and de Maistre virtually conclusive! De Maistre must have had a hand in painting the mural.

Flowerpiece is referred to and illustrated in Heather Johnson's book on de Maistre (opposite *Gerberas,* a still life which has the same scale-like design). Heather comments that de Maistre may have brought the material for the wall hanging depicted in *Flowerpiece* back from France in the mid-1920s. 'Or,' she writes, it could have 'come from Frank Weitzel' who engaged in 'fabric printing using batik methods'.[1] De Maistre may have unconsciously incorporated the 'snake scale' design in *Flowerpiece* and *Gerberas* (dated 1926) into his mural of circa 1938. Or, the mural may have been designed in 1926 in Sydney, to be executed when his patrons, the de Chairs, returned to London. If this is the case, then de Maistre's colleague, Frank Weitzel, may perhaps have been involved.

When I phone Heather Johnson to discuss all this, she is most interested.[2] She had not noted the design appearing in both the still lifes and the mural. When I bring up the subject of provenance, of how, until now, the attribution of the mural depended almost solely on the word of the de Chairs' daughter and their son Somerset, who had sold the mural at Christie's in London, Heather laughs.

'But did you know Somerset was a bit of a rogue?' she asks.

So much for provenance.

It seems that even if I could establish what seemed like a perfect provenance for the boatshed painting it would be possible for someone to come along in the future and cast doubt on it. What a depressing thought.

The de Maistre mural has provided an interesting sub-plot to my investigations of my small unsigned painting, the de Maistre being, of course, a huge, unsigned painting.

My wife thinks there is more to it than this. She sees the whole thing as an oedipal battle with my one-time mentor Frank McDonald. But that's all Greek to me.

Tuesday, 7 February

Senior Constable Debbie Battersby of the Police Department's Documents Examination Unit meets me in the foyer of Police Headquarters and whisks me to her office, collecting her boss Peter Eastman

on the way. After all this time she has kindly agreed
to see me at short notice. Crime must have slackened
off. I have the boatshed painting, with the inscription on the frame, and a bundle of handwriting
samples by Lloyd Rees, Basil Burdett, Wal Taylor,
Rubery Bennett and also by Rees's Brisbane friend
Peter Templeton for good measure.

I tell them something of my research and they
become interested, asking detective-like questions
along the way. Debbie, a painter herself, loves the
boatshed painting. Peter does not think it very good.
But they both seem to enjoy the story. We spread the
handwriting samples out on a large desk. They ask
me not to reveal any of their methods that would be
of advantage to forgers. Peter gets out one particular
reference volume that is both a researcher's and a
forger's dream come true.

Together they pore over the inscription and
handwriting samples. There is no quick, impulsive
decision. They just keep looking for about fifteen
minutes. Then they both focus mainly on a Lloyd
Rees letter written to Mr Gill in 1933. They are
conferring together on the similarities that I had
noted months ago, in particular the 's' beginning the
words 'Suburban' and 'Such', the 'n's, the 'r's and
the 'e's with their tails staying down. They make
promising noises. They look through the handwriting of the others, noting the 'class' similarities
which are no doubt due to all suspects having been
taught writing at around the same time in the same
State. But slowly, and systematically, they reject each
sample and return to Lloyd Rees's handwriting.

I must admit that over the last few months I had
swung around to thinking that Basil Burdett was a
prime candidate for having written the inscription,
not only because of the similarities I had noted
between his writing and the inscription, but his use
of the words 'suburban' and 'scene' in his article on

Rees. I subtly push Burdett's handwriting samples back in front of Debbie and Peter. They look at them quickly but then reject them. They do not think the inscription is by Basil.

Back to Rees's 1933 letter to Gill. I hadn't looked at this letter for a while but now I feel the excitement that I had felt when I first compared it to the inscription. And the experts are pointing to more similarities. They are also taking into consideration that the inscription was written in pencil on wood and we are comparing it to ink on paper. They also note, as Alan Rees had worked out, that the inscription would have been written without the writing hand being supported, since the surface of the frame would always be above a writing surface. The main difficulty is that the inscription is so short. If only there were three or four 'c's for example, instead of one, it would be possible to be more certain about the similarity of the little loop the inscription-writer puts at the beginning of the 'c' in 'scene' which seems to be the same as most of the 'c's in the letter.

They note that Rees's handwriting changed after about 1924. Debbie and Peter are surprised that someone would change their style so much in just a few years. Peter Eastman, perhaps jokingly, puts it down to the writer being an artist, more likely to experiment with his style than a non-artist. They conclude that if the inscription on the frame is by Rees, it is closer in time to the 1933 samples rather than the pre-1924 samples. They discuss other problematic factors such as the mood the writer of the inscription might have been in, or if it was written late at night: it may not be in the writer's normal style. I tell them that Lloyd Rees had suffered a breakdown from 1928 but by 1933 his life and career were back on track.

We sit back and talk things through some more.

They are able to say that they can be reasonably
certain that the inscription is not by Burdett, Wal
Taylor, Rubery Bennett or Peter Templeton. But,
there is a very strong possibility that the inscription
was written by Lloyd Rees. Given the shortness of it,
however, they cannot be absolutely certain.

Tuesday, 14 February

I go over the facts. Embrey's final letter to Victoria
Beckingsale, dated January, 1931, strongly suggests
that his relationship with Bart began four years
previously, around 1926. This was the year Bart
appears to have been buying paintings from Rubery
Bennett, when Bennett has his gallery in Boomerang
House. Embrey's father, William Crawford, was also
in Boomerang House. The handwriting on the frame
of the boatshed painting is very possibly by Lloyd
Rees, and if so, it would have been written sometime
after the circa 1924 change to his handwriting style.
It could have been written at the moment in time
when the painting was about to change hands.

Rubery Bennett did not advertise works by
Lloyd Rees after 1925 but he was probably selling his
work in 1924 from his gallery at 219 George Street,
given Rees's inscription on the reverse of *An Old
Barn, 1924* which says that the frame for the painting
is to be supplied by Bennett. The frame for *An Old
Barn* was almost certainly made by S. A. Parker. Why
wouldn't Lloyd go directly to Parker for the frame
on *An Old Barn*? The only reason I can think of is
that Bennett was Rees's agent in 1924, that Rees had
works on consignment with Bennett.

Bennett had followed Basil Burdett, Rees's
friend and agent (at least around 1922), into the
premises at 219 George Street when Burdett
vacated. Rees's other friend, bookbinder Wal Taylor,

remained at 219 George Street during 1924 with Bennett. Rees had exhibited with Burdett at the end of 1922 and then gone overseas in early 1923. When he returned in 1924 there were probably unsold Australian paintings still at 219 George Street with his friend Taylor and Rubery Bennett. In the Royal Art Society catalogue of 1924, Rees lists his contact address as 219 George Street. Out of Taylor and Bennett, it is Bennett who seems to have been the dealer. Taylor did not run his own gallery until he established the Grosvenor in 1925 after Bennett had moved out.

I have been to visit the site of 219 George Street a few times in the past couple of years. I am not sure what I was looking for but I didn't find it. It had been located in a row of small but beautiful art nouveau buildings on the corner of Grosvenor Street. The row had, in the last decade, become a victim of 'facadism', that is, a skyscraper had been erected on the land leaving only the facades of the previously existing buildings. Unfortunately the facades that remain do not include number 219 since that building, further down the row, was demolished completely. For me, the remaining facades are not enough compensation for the loss of 219 George Street.

Wednesday, 15 February

I decide to contact Violet Bennett, the widow of Rubery Bennett. I had previously written her letters, but now I feel more confident about talking directly to people who were part of the art scene seventy years ago. I phone her up and put it to her that Rubery Bennett was Lloyd Rees's dealer or agent in 1924. 'Yes, that is probably quite right,' she says. She tells me that Rubery and Rees knew each other from

Brisbane. She also confirms that after about 1924 they drifted apart, Lloyd Rees mixing in different circles.

She also tells me the reason that Rubery Bennett and S. A. Parker fell out. They had an arrangement whereby Rubery organised for artists to have their work framed by Parker. Parker would frame works left on consignment with Bennett. The problem was that the artists ran up bills. Parker blamed Rubery for this. 'Of course, it wasn't Rubery's fault,' says Violet. I wonder whether Lloyd Rees was one of those who didn't pay. Although I had asked the question in a previous letter to Violet, I ask again whether she remembers clients by the names of L. V. Bartlett or Embrey Crawford. She doesn't—she didn't begin working full-time in the Boomerang House gallery until 1927.

I thank Violet and praise her for her extraordinary memory. 'For some things,' she responds wistfully.

Saturday, 1 April

The research on the boatshed painting is at an end. There seems little point in gathering more information. I still do not know for certain whether the painting is by Lloyd Rees, but I can't help summarising a possible scenario based on the research.

Lloyd Rees may have painted the boatshed painting some time between 1917 and the beginning of 1922, when he was living variously at Mosman, Waverton or Cremorne Point on the Harbour. That is, before he moved to Parramatta where his style became more consistently detailed and atmospheric. The subject could be an imaginary view of Balmoral in Mosman. Balmoral would have been accessible from North Sydney near Waverton, by the tram service which was operating from 1900 to 1958. Or, if Rees was living at Mosman or Cremorne Point when he did the painting, he could have boarded the tram when it passed through Cremorne junction or Mosman. But he would have found it almost as easy to walk to Balmoral from his Cremorne Point home. No other Balmoral paintings from the 1917–22 period are known and the boatshed painting would be a precursor to the known group of Balmoral/ Middle Harbour paintings of 1926–27.

It is impossible to date precisely the oils from this experimental period around 1920. His approach seems to have varied a little unpredictably. And, anyway, only one or two Rees oils from this period bear reliable dates. I am guessing that the boatshed painting (if it is by Rees) was painted after the relatively thinly painted *Coolangatta* which Rees retrospectively dated as 1919 but may be as early as 1916. The boatshed painting may have been painted prior to his three known oils of Cremorne which can be dated, from a contemporaneous inscription on one of them, to Christmas 1920–21. In these three paintings he is using distinctive dabs with a square brush. It certainly seems to be painted before *Old Boats, Wollestonecraft Bay* which, judging by the crisp light and mastery of distance, leads me to think it was painted after the Cremorne pictures, although the artist dated it retrospectively at circa 1920. *Old Boats* seems to be painted about the same time as another Sydney Harbour subject, *Afternoon Sunshine*, which is dated 1921.

Around 1920 Rees would have been preparing for his December, 1922 exhibition which was to raise funds for his overseas trip. (When his friend Roland Wakelin held an exhibition in February, 1922 to fund a trip abroad it included works painted up to seven years previously.) If the subject is a house (albeit imaginary) at Balmoral, then the angle of the shadow of the chimney suggests that it might be a winter painting. *The Cafe at the Spit* of 1927 looks to be a summer painting and this is supported by the fact that the shadow of the cafe's chimney indicates that the sun is more overhead. But if the subject is Balmoral, the house itself is almost certainly imaginary, possibly an idealisation of the sort of place that Rees desired. He was later to build a Mediterranean fantasy near the Harbour foreshore at suburban Northwood. The house in the painting may have represented a place like those convivial abodes of his friends such as the Wakelins, at Waverton. The house appears to be vacant: to be occupied by the artist's own desires?

The boatshed below the house may symbolise a launching place for his career via his upcoming exhibition, or for his planned overseas trip. The painting exudes a sense of nervousness, the house half-retreating, half-emerging, behind the launching place. The 'explosion' of the tree on the left might be a reminder of the way events can affect visions, shatter dreams. There may even be some Freudian-style sexual symbolism implanted in the composition.

When it was finished the painting was framed hastily. The frame appears to be one of S. A. Parker's. Rees may have purchased a stock frame, or had a custom one made by Parker. If the latter, then he could have saved money by putting it into the frame himself. Parker certainly did not do this—it is not put into its frame professionally. Whether a stock or a custom frame, Rees may have used bookbinding tape handed to him by his friend Wal Taylor, to seal the painting in its frame, and then left it with Taylor or Basil Burdett in The New Art Salon above Parker's at 219 George Street. It may have been exhibited as *The Bay* at The New Art Salon in December, 1922, number 22 in the catalogue, and have been one of a number of Rees's early works with this title. The only other exhibited work it could be in the 1922 exhibition (going by the titles) is *Early Spring* catalogue number 15. But this work is listed in the catalogue with Parramatta paintings and is probably a Parramatta subject.

The twenty-five oil paintings in the 1922 exhibition ranged in price from five guineas to twenty guineas. There were five at seven guineas and only two at twenty guineas. *The Red House*, number 6, was priced at seven guineas. A painting with this title, painted prior to 1922, survives today and is 29 x 41.5 centimetres (the boatshed painting is only 15 x 30.5). It is hard to explain away the anomaly in the sizes/ prices if the boatshed painting is *The Bay*.[1] And yet, there is the evidence that the boatshed painting is *The Bay*: the sticker numbered 22 on the frame.[2]

When the exhibition was over, *The Bay* may not have been sold. Perhaps the price was too high. Since Rees travelled overseas almost immediately, *The Bay* would probably have stayed in the gallery waiting to be sold, or for Lloyd's return. But then, the gallery's director, Basil Burdett, moves out and Rubery Bennett takes over the space in March 1924, with Lloyd's friend Wal Taylor still working there at his bookbinding.

In March 1924, Basil Burdett manages Rees's exhibition of twenty-five paintings at Farmer and Co. in Sydney, organised by Eric Collings of Farmer's for Rees's return from overseas. There were no Australian subjects in this show and *The Bay* probably remained at 219 George Street (with Bennett/Taylor). Lionel Lindsay, in the foreword to the catalogue of the 1924 exhibition, writes: 'Finding his work at a standstill Lloyd Rees wisely went away to Europe.' If others felt the same way then this would render any old, unsold, Australian work difficult to sell in 1924. *The Bay* would have remained in

Rubery Bennett's stock room. While it seems Basil Burdett was acting for Rees in March 1924, there is good evidence that by November 1924 Rubery Bennett was acting as Rees's agent. Basil Burdett appears to be unsettled, attempting to establish galleries in Phillip Street and Bond Street before establishing the Macquarie Galleries in Bligh Street with John Young in March 1925. Also, during 1924, he moves out of Lloyd Rees's home in Parramatta to live with his mother in Neutral Bay. An article by Burdett on Rees's recent European work on show in Brisbane following the Sydney exhibition, published in July 1924, is not uniformly glowing. It puts down the pre-1923 Australian oils before concluding that 'Lloyd Rees may yet add lustre to the name of his native city'.[3]

Rubery Bennett, by the end of 1924, had attracted big name artists such as Streeton, Gruner, James R. Jackson and the Lindsays, and seemed to be the dealer on the way up. Rees would have been quite happy for him to hang on to any unsold paintings when he moved from 219 George Street to Boomerang House, 139 King Street in 1925. Especially if the relationship with Basil Burdett was cooling. Rees did not have a solo exhibition in Sydney from 1924 until the early 1930s. He exhibited in a mixed exhibition at Wal Taylor's Grosvenor Galleries, at 219 George Street, in March, 1926, and annually at the Royal Art Society exhibitions which were organised by Rubery Bennett. He could easily have been angling to get a solo show with Rubery Bennett around 1926–27 even if he was not part of his close circle. Rees might even have thought: if Bennett can ask up to 200 guineas for the work of John Banks ...

L. V. Bartlett and his friend Embrey Crawford may have met Lloyd Rees through their mutual acquaintance, John Banks, in 1926 or 1927. Bart was buying works of art from Rubery Bennett's King

Street gallery at this time and Rees might have mentioned that he had some works with Bennett. Embrey may have selected the boatshed painting, perhaps even in the company of Rees in Bennett's gallery.

It might have been difficult for Rees to be in that situation. I can imagine him, shy and awkward, his behaviour verging on gauche. What is his role to be in this situation? Should he be involved in the selling at this point or leave it completely up to Rubery Bennett, the experienced dealer? The situation is saved by Embrey agreeing to buy the boatshed painting. At this stage, it is still uninscribed. The boatshed painting has lost the title *The Bay*. Lloyd Rees takes the painting and inscribes the title *Suburban Scene* on the reverse. Then, imagining that he is sealing the deal, he inscribes Embrey's telephone number—Embrey uses his father's telephone number—on the reverse. He begins to add an address but realises that this is unnecessary, since he knows that William Crawford works upstairs, and, flustered, stops writing before completing 'Boomerang House'. He forgets to, or for some reason decides not to, write his own name.

Perhaps a discussion took place during the appraisal which indicated the twenty-four-year-old Embrey was not well off and needed time to pay before he could collect the painting; or perhaps his father would pay. Perhaps the painting was a gift from his father. Whatever the case, William Charles Crawford's telephone number, written apparently by Lloyd Rees, ended up on the back of the boatshed painting. The title Rees wrote might have subconsciously been triggered by Basil Burdett's 1922 criticism of Rees's work: 'Mosman [above Balmoral] was the scene of the first tentative efforts in oils, but the essentially suburban atmosphere proved so limited that a move to the at least more varied

interest of Bay Road [Waverton] was made.' Perhaps
Rees had argued with Burdett over the criticism and
the title was written in defiance. Or perhaps it was
Rees's ironic acknowledgement of that assessment.

Embrey may have later taken the painting with
him to Melbourne. It could have entered the hands
of Florence Sainsbury because Embrey knew her, or
was even romantically and tragically involved with
her. Or, more prosaically, the painting somehow
ended up in a junk shop to be found by the
fossicking, fag-in-mouth Florence.

Or perhaps the scenario is completely wrong.
Perhaps the boatshed painting is by the lost Violet
Bartlett.

Or perhaps one day, someone, somewhere, will con-
clusively prove that it is by somebody completely
different.

Once again I lay out the photographs of Rees's
work in chronological order, looking to see if and
where the boatshed painting fits in.

And keep looking.

Such is research.

ENDNOTES

Preface
1   *... virtually my entire collection ... up for auction at Sotheby's*
    in Sydney ... Sotheby's, Fine Australian Paintings, Sunday 24
    November, 1991, lots 155–201 and 274–323.
2   *Joanna Mendelssohn once kindly wrote in a* **Sydney Morning**
    Herald *review ...* see *Sydney Morning Herald*, September 5,
    1986, p12.

Friday, 16 April, 1993
1   *My first real find at Joel's ...* Joel's auction, November 1983,
    lot 1127. The lot came from the estate of an H. H. Borbidge.
2   *... incorrectly catalogued as being by an A. M. Moore ...*
    Another lot, also from the Borbidge Estate, titled *The News*
    Boy and dated 1894 was inscribed 'to A. M. Moore from
    E.M.M.' which probably explains the miscatalogue of both
    paintings by Joel's who should have catalogued E.M.M. as the
    artist, not A. M. Moore. The current whereabouts of *The News*
    Boy is unknown.
3   *He ... learnt some home truths that he described as 'pungent'*
    ... I find this reference in Lloyd Rees's first autobiography *The*
    Small Treasures of a Lifetime, 1969, Ure Smith Pty Ltd, p72.
4   *... he heard the President remark 'I hope he doesn't submit his*
    paintings' ... Quoted from Renee Free's *Lloyd Rees*, 1972,
    Lansdowne Press, p42.
5   *... linocuts of Margaret Preston ... (with their distinctive red*
    roofs) ... A number of colour reproductions of Preston's
    woodcuts showing harbourside buildings with their red roofs
    can be found in the wonderful catalogue raisonné *The Prints*
    of Margaret Preston by Roger Butler, Australian National
    Gallery and Melbourne University Press, 1987. *Edward's*
    Beach, Balmoral c1929, is a good example.
6   *... the contours of [Rees's* **The Road to Berry**, *1947] ...*

suggest the female form ... In 1985 Brett Whiteley painted a
homage to Rees's *Road to Berry*. To me, it seems a weak copy
which adds nothing to Rees's idea and, surprisingly, given
Whiteley's fondness for the female form, is nowhere near as
erotic as the Rees work. Both works are illustrated side by side
in the catalogue *Rees/Whiteley—On the Road to Berry*,
Museum of Modern Art, Heide, July–Sept 1993.

Saturday, 17 April

1   ... *something that the art historian Renee Free wrote about ...
     [Rees's] ... intensely meditative method of painting and the
     way it suggests the passage of time* ... See Renee Free's
     introduction to the *Lloyd Rees Retrospective—Souvenir
     Catalogue*, Art Gallery of NSW, 1969. The actual quote is:
     'One value in Rees's method of painting, central to his
     meditative approach, lies in its suggestion of the passage of
     time'.

Tuesday, 20 April

1   ... *Renee Free's excellent 1972 monograph* ... *Lloyd Rees* by
     Renee Free, Lansdowne Press, 1972.

Wednesday, 21 April

1   *The first Australian art book that I ever bought was Bernard
     Smith's* **Australian Painting** ... *Australian Painting—
     1788–1960* by Bernard Smith, Oxford University Press, 1962.
     This has since been brought up to date with additions by
     Terry Smith. The other major history published in 1968 is *The
     Art of Australia* by Robert Hughes, Penguin Books, which
     has been reprinted many times.

2   ... *an incredibly helpful publication* ... **Australian Artists'
     Index**—A biographical index of Australian artists, craft
     workers, photographers and architects compiled by Jan
     McDonald and published by the Arts Libraries Association,
     Sydney, 1986. Jan McDonald has taken 416 standard
     reference works relating to Australian artists and indexed
     them. She has alphabetically listed over 10,000 artists together
     with the publications in which these artists appear. An
     excellent companion to McDonald's index is *Australian Art
     and Artists to 1950—A bibliography based on the holdings of the
     State Library of Victoria*, published by the Library Council of
     Victoria, Melbourne, 1982.

3   ... *students at the Power Institute of Fine Art have written
     approximately 1300 essays and theses* ... See *Handlist of Fine
     Arts Fourth Year Essays and Theses 1971–1988 in the Power*

Research Library of Contemporary Art by Anthony Bradley, Power Institute of Fine Arts Occasional Paper No. 8, 1990.

4   *... of these only a couple of titles [by the Power Institute students] appear to be about authenticating or attributing a work of art ...* These are Robyn Lee's 'A consideration of the Attribution of a *Flight into Egypt* in the Art Gallery of NSW to David Teniers, The Younger' and Bruce Adam's '*Adam and Eve*, attributed to Michael van Coxcie'.

5   *In 1984 the Saleroom Correspondent for the* **Australian Financial Review,** *Terry Ingram, did a devilish thing ...* This episode is reported in *Australian Financial Review*, May 4, 1984.

6   *One could, of course, cite examples of truly brilliant scholarship by curators ...* Since my writing that, Mary Eagle of the National Gallery of Australia has published her analysis of a painting in that gallery's collection (*Spirit of the Drought*) which had been attributed to Charles Conder and later to Arthur Streeton. Following extensive technical and stylistic considerations, Mary concludes that *both* artists were involved in the painting. See *The Oil Paintings of Arthur Streeton in the National Gallery of Australia* by Mary Eagle, published by the National Gallery of Australia, 1994.

7   *A newspaper report of the ... [theft of Rees's* **An Old Barn, Parramatta, 1924]** *... stated ... Dr Brown was not sure ... that it* was *by Rees ... Sydney Morning Herald* article by Susan Wyndham, 28 March, 1985.

8   *... dispute ... [regarding] ... the attribution of ... an 1820s history painting by Augustus Earle ... [titled]* **Trajan Inconsolable after the Battle of Ctesiphon** *...* Nancy Underhill's challenge appears in a review of 'The Great Australian Art Exhibition' which included *Trajan Inconsolable*, etc. The review was published in *Art Monthly*, August 1988. An essay by Ron Radford on the painting appears in *Creating Australia*, the catalogue of the 1988 exhibition, published by International Cultural Corporation of Australia Ltd, 1988, pp74–5. By 1995 Radford had re-attributed *Trajan Inconsolable* to John Lewin. Another painting in the Art Gallery of South Australia, *Boy with Sulphur-crested Cockatoo*, had also been previously attributed to Augustus Earle. In 1988 Earle was flavour of the month but following the gallery's subsequent purchase of Lewin's major *Fish Catch, Sydney Harbour* and research on Lewin, both Earles were re-attributed to Lewin and are thus recorded in *Australian Colonial Art 1800–1900* published by the Art Gallery of South Australia, 1995.

Thursday, 22 April

1   *[Rees] ... is recorded as using plywood to paint on (eg.*
    Geraniums, 1936) *... Geraniums, 1936,* is catalogue number
    11 in the *Lloyd Rees Retrospective Catalogue*, Art Gallery of
    NSW, 1969, where the support is described as 'plywood'.

2   *... and certainly he painted directly onto wooden board in the
    1920s, for example,* **Autumn Mist, Parramatta,** *of 1925 ...
    Autumn Mist, Parramatta,* 1925, is number 7 in the *Lloyd
    Rees Retrospective Catalogue*, Art Gallery of NSW, 1969,
    where the support is described as 'hardboard'.

3   *... some of his works on canvas ... were laid down on plywood
    ...* The support (ie. canvas on plywood) for *Old Boats,
    Wollstonecraft Bay* c1920 and *Balmoral,* 1927, is referred to in
    the 'List of Plates' in *Lloyd Rees—An Artist Remembers* by
    Lloyd Rees with Renee Free, Craftsman House, 1987, p152.

4   *... Roland Wakelin once quoted another friend as saying 'I
    wish he wouldn't work on them after rigor mortis has set in in
    order to solve it' ...* Quoted from *Art Gallery of NSW
    Quarterly* Vol. 11, No. 1, October 1969 (Lloyd Rees Special
    Number), p491.

5   **Afternoon Sunshine, Sydney Harbour** ... It is illustrated in
    Sotheby's catalogue, 27 November, 1989 (lot 211).

6   **The White Horse** ... is illustrated in Sotheby's catalogue
    27 March, 1988 (lot 266).

7   **An Old Barn, Parramatta, 1924** *and* **Coolangatta, 1919** ...
    both are illustrated in Renee Free's *Lloyd Rees*, Lansdowne
    Press, 1972.

8   *His interest in depicting tall trees dates from at least 1915 ...*
    See Sotheby's catalogue, April 19, 1989, lot 280A, pencil
    drawing (illustrated).

9   *Trees may infer ...* The book *Landscape and Memory* by
    Simon Schama (Alfred A. Knopf, New York, 1995) was
    published to great acclaim when I was near the end of my
    research. It gave me a bout of deep humility when I read it
    and I then re-read my analysis of the landscape of the boatshed
    painting.

10 *... a well-known black and white lithograph by the
    distinguished war cartoonist and illustrator Will Dyson
    titled* **Compensation** *...* The lithograph is illustrated in *Will
    Dyson—Cartoonist, etcher and Australia's finest war artist* by
    Ross McMullin, Angus & Robertson, 1984.

11 *... Rees's description of his first glimpse of Sydney in December
    1917 ...* The description is quoted from *The Small Treasures of
    A Lifetime* by Lloyd Rees, Ure Smith, 1969, p45.

12 *Norman Carter ... wrote in 1938: '[Rees's] work is not directly*

painted as a result of momentary impression ...' Quoted in
Renee Free's *Lloyd Rees*, 1972, Lansdowne Press, p50.

13   *Basil Burdett ... wrote ... that Rees has 'a tendency to over-
emphasise intriguing detail at the expense of greater unity' ...*
Quoted from Burdett's article 'The Later Work of Lloyd Rees
(Specially written by Basil Burdett, Sydney)' which appears
under the heading 'Art in Brisbane' by 'Optimum Pati',
published in *The Queensland Magazine*, July 1924, p28.

14   *[Rees:] ... 'my prayer, if I had one, would be to work, work,
work ...'* Quoted in *Pol* magazine, 15 July–15 August, 1980,
p64, article titled 'Lloyd Rees—Australia's Old Master' by Lily
Brett-Lovett.

15   *... 'the small painting entitled* Balmoral *is something of a
mystery to me. I had not the vaguest idea of doing it ...'*
Quoted from *Lloyd Rees—An Artist Remembers*, by Lloyd
Rees with Renee Free, Craftsman House, 1987.

Friday, 23 April
1   *Were ... [the 1920s] ... really 'roaring' as the title of Jack
Lindsay's book implies? ... The Roaring Twenties* by Jack
Lindsay, The Bodley Head Ltd, 1960.

2   *'The Terrible Twenties' ... Humphrey McQueen's chapter
heading in his* Social Sketches of Australia *...* See *Social
Sketches of Australia* by Humphrey McQueen, Penguin Books,
2nd edition, 1991, p94. Another descriptive title is *The
Confident Years: Australia in the Twenties* by Robert Murray,
London, 1978. The 1920s were also described as 'crazy' (see
for example *The Crazy Years—Paris in the Twenties* by William
Wiser, T & H, 1983).

3   *'... the deaths of around 60,000 Australian men' ... Social
Sketches of Australia* by Humphrey McQueen, 2nd edition,
1991, p94.

4   *Wakelin, Roy de Maistre ... [et al] began to understand something about modern art ... The Story of Australian Art* by
William Moore, Angus and Robertson Limited, 1934, Vol. 1,
p107.

5   *Dattilo-Rubbo was using 'divisionist' brushstrokes ...* this was
a technique which was developed in the post-impressionist
periods where paint is applied in short dabs or strokes in
varying colours. The colours are intermingled but not actually
mixed. The colours mix in the spectator's eye at certain
distances.

6   *... [Rubbo's] overseas trip in 1907 ...* For information about
Rubbo's early awareness of divisionist brushstrokes, see
Australian Modern Painting by Mary Eagle, Bay Books,

1990, p31. An actual example of a Rubbo work using such brushstrokes was sold at Sotheby's, 19th April, 1993, lot 55, illustrated in colour. It is titled *Venezia* and dated 1907.

7.   *Rubbo challenged Charles Tindall ... to a duel with pistols, swords or fisticuffs ...* The incident is referred to in *Cav. Antonio Dattilo-Rubbo—Painter and Teacher and some prominent pupils* published by the Manly Art Gallery, 1981, p9.

8.   *The 'Colour in Art' exhibition also included ... perspective drawings ... done by Lloyd Rees ...* See *Australian Modern Painting* by Mary Eagle, Bay Books, 1990, p48.

9   *Rees ... first saw ... 'the first essays in Cubist and Abstract painting ever done in Australia' ...* See *The Small Treasures of a Lifetime* by Lloyd Rees, Ure Smith, 1969, p90.

10   *Rees later wrote ... 'the Wakelin/de Maistre collaboration would sooner or later have to find public expression' ...* See *The Small Treasures of a Lifetime* by Lloyd Rees, Ure Smith, 1969, p91.

11   *... Heather Johnson writes that 'Lloyd Rees remembers the opening ...' [of the de Maistre/Wakelin exhibition] ...* Quoted from *Roy De Maistre—The Australian Years 1894–1930* by Heather Johnson, Craftsman House, 1988, p34.

12   *... the Salon style ...* The Salon style, and the more traditional forms of painting from 1900 to 1940, are analysed in Ian Burn's book *National Life and Landscapes*, Bay Books, 1991, where he argues forcefully for the vitality and importance of such art.

13   *The majority of present-day art historians have gone off with Don Quixote ...* Quoted from *Making Australian Art 1916–1949*, by Nancy Underhill, Oxford University Press, 1991, p223.

14   *... Hera Roberts ... succumbed to depression and committed suicide ...* information from *Cover Up—The Art of Magazine Covers in Australia* by Robert Holden, Hodder and Stoughton, 1995, p127.

15   *Paul Johnson begins his 800-page populist history ...* *Modern Times—The World from the Twenties to the Nineties*, by Paul Johnson, HarperCollins, 1991.

16   *... contracts which read like scientific formulae (A. You will see to it that (1) my clothes are kept in order; (2) That I am served three regular meals a day in my room) ...* A 1914 letter by Einstein outlining numerous conditions which he wanted imposed upon his wife was offered for sale at Christie's, London in November, 1996. See front page article in the *Sydney Morning Herald*, October 31, 1996.

17 *Susan Sontag in her book* ... See *Illness as Metaphor*, by Susan
    Sontag, Penguin, New York, 1987.

18 *... epidemic diseases ... used as metaphors for social disorder*
    ... In 1994, when checking information about the influenza
    pandemic I discovered that an essay on the topic had just been
    published. This was 'The Masked Disease: Oral History,
    Memory and the Influenza Pandemic 1918–1919' by Lucy
    Tasker, published in *Memory and History—in Twentieth-
    Century Australia* edited by Kate Darian-Smith and Paula
    Hamilton, OUP, 1994. Susan Sontag's thesis, in relation to
    the flu pandemic in Australia, is referred to in this essay.

19 *a pamphlet ... titled* **The Two Plagues: Influenza and
    Bolshevism** ... See B. Hoare, *The Two Plagues: Influenza and
    Bolshevism*, Melbourne, 1919. This is also referred to in *The
    Masked Disease: Oral History, Memory and the Influenza
    Pandemic 1918–1919* by Lucy Tasker (ibid).

20 *'We were all badly infected by Freudianism in the twenties'* ...
    quoted in *The Black Swan of Trespass—The Emergence of
    Modernist Painting in Australia to 1944* by Humphrey
    McQueen, Alternative Publishing Cooperative Limited, 1979,
    p79.

21 *Mary Eagle in her book* ... *Australian Modern Painting—
    Between the Wars 1914–1939* by Mary Eagle, Bay Books, 1990.

22 *Lloyd Rees 'left the most extensive personal account ...'* quoted
    from *Making Australian Art 1916–1949*, by Nancy Underhill,
    Oxford University Press, 1991, p36.

23 *'... Smith and Julius ... [was] a focal point for virtually all
    the important artists in the country'*. See *Peaks and Valleys*, by
    Lloyd Rees, Imprint Lives edition, CollinsAngus &
    Robertson, 1993, p124.

24 *... Patterson induced Smith, and the artists George Lambert,
    Thea Proctor, Margaret Preston and John D. Moore to advise
    Ford on car colours* ... See *Making Australian Art 1916–1949*,
    by Nancy Underhill, Oxford University Press, 1991, p152 for
    the advertisement showing Ure Smith, Thea Proctor and
    George Lambert inspecting the 'new colour harmonies in
    Ford cars'.

25 *One [oil painting] did get into* ... See *The Small Treasures of
    a Lifetime*, 1969, Ure Smith Pty Ltd, p72.

26 *... Rees ... learned ... 'pungent' home truths* ... See *The Small
    Treasures of A Lifetime* by Lloyd Rees, Ure Smith, 1969, p72.

27 *But Rees's description of the R.A.S. remains generally correct:
    'their exhibitions ... retained unity'* ... Quoted from
    The Small Treasures of a Lifetime, Ure Smith Pty Ltd, 1969,
    p71.

28   *'... is it beautiful?' To which de Maistre perkily replied: 'I
      think so, Mr Ashton.'* See *The Small Treasures of A Lifetime* by
      Lloyd Rees, Ure Smith, 1969, p93.

29   *The Schools of Rubbo and Ashton trained literally hundreds of
      artists in Sydney* ... See catalogue of *The Sydney Art School—
      Retrospective Exhibition, 1890–1933* held at The Education
      Department's Art Gallery, Sydney, 1–28 March, 1933 and
      *Cav. Antonio Dattilo-Rubbo—Painter and Teacher and some
      prominent pupils,* Manly Art Gallery, December 5, 1980 to
      January 18, 1981.

30   *... the majority of students who went through the art
      schools over the previous forty years were female* ... This
      apparent contradiction is analysed in *Australian Women
      Artists—First Fleet to 1945: History, Hearsay and Her Say* by
      Caroline Ambrus, Irrepressible Press, 1992. Tables showing
      numbers of male and female art students and exhibitors are
      provided.

31   *A Miss Bouffler sold pictures from the Hotel Australia
      Bookstall around 1918 and advertised work by Lloyd Rees* ...
      An advertisement for pictures appears in Ure Smith's *Art in
      Australia* No. 5, 1918 for Miss Bouffler's Bookstall in the
      Hotel Australia, Castlereagh Street, Sydney.

32   *... The Artists' Gallery on the corner of Pitt and Bridge
      Streets also listed Lloyd Rees as one of its artists* ... Thirty-two
      artists exhibiting with The Artists' Gallery are listed in *Art in
      Australia* advertisements of this period.

33   *Anthony Hordern and Sons Art Gallery flourished from 1912
      through to 1961* ... See *Anthony Hordern and Sons Art Gallery
      1912–1961,* unpublished museology exercise by Patricia
      McDonald, 43 pages, 1978, in The Power Research Library of
      Contemporary Art.

34   *Burdett ran his New Art Salon from about March 1922* ...
      The opening of the gallery is recorded in the *Daily Telegraph*,
      4 April, 1922.

35   *... [The New Salon] ... moved in about July to 219 George
      Street* ... See *Art in Australia* advertisement Third series,
      Number 1, August 1922.

36   *... Burdett, distraught, went to Melbourne 'where he joined
      the* Herald *as a journalist'* ... see *Early Sydney Moderns* by
      Jean Campbell, Craftsman House, 1988, p115.

37   *... Jean Campbell describes Burdett* ... See *Early Sydney
      Moderns* by Jean Campbell, Craftsman House, 1988, p59.

38   *Jan Minchin writes that 'those who knew Basil Burdett ...'* See
      Art and Australia, Vol. 17, No. 4, p369.

39   *In an article in* Art and Australia *in 1975 Rees describes*

> *Burdett* ... See 'The Macquarie Galleries—some personal memories by Lloyd Rees' in *Art and Australia*, Vol. 13, No. 1, p40.

40   *Richard Haese quotes one of Burdett's closest friends, Daryl Lindsay* ... See *Rebels and Precursors—The revolutionary years of Australian art* by Richard Haese, Allen Lane (Penguin Books), 1981, p103.

Sunday, 25 April

1   *I was the only living person who knew what the J. H. stood for* ... Ten years later I published an article on James Howe Carse in *Art and Australia* (Vol. 17, No. 1, Sept. 1979).

Tuesday, 27 April

1   *Aletta Lewis is a good example* ... Aletta Lewis was trained in London and came to Sydney in 1927 at the age of 23. She befriended the modernists Adelaide Perry, Wakelin and de Maistre. She spent six months in American Samoa and then exhibited at the Macquarie Galleries in 1928. She left Australia in 1929. See *Heritage—the national women's art book,* edited by Joan Kerr, G & B Arts International Limited, 1995, p390, article by Jacqui Strecker.

2   *Winifred Honey is such an artist* ... Winifred Honey (born 1892) studied at the National Art School, Melbourne, where she won prizes between 1907 and 1911 including the Travelling Scholarship. She left for London in 1912 and did not return to Australia. See 'The Lady is a Honey' by Stephen Scheding, *The Australian Way,* June, 1990.

3   *There are extensive records of artists who trained with the two main schools in Sydney* ... See catalogue of *The Sydney Art School—Retrospective Exhibition, 1890–1933* held at The Education Department's Art Gallery, Sydney, 1st to 28th March, 1933. The Sydney Art School was run by Julian Ashton; See also *Cav. Antonio Dattilo-Rubbo—Painter and Teacher and some prominent pupils,* Manly Art Gallery, December 5, 1980 to January 18, 1981.

4   *The National Gallery School in Melbourne is similarly documented* ... See *Von Guerard to Wheeler—The first teachers at the National Gallery School, 1870–1939* catalogue published by The Victorian College of The Arts Gallery, exhibition 6–21 April, 1978. The catalogue has a supplement which lists 'students who attended the school of art' under 'School of Painting', 'School of Design', and 'Drawing Classes'. It also lists annual prize winners.

5   *An anecdote about Picasso ... is told by Gertrude Stein in [her
     book]* ... I found the quote in *The Faber Book of Art Anecdotes*,
     edited by Edward Lucie-Smith, Faber and Faber, 1992, p438.

Monday, 10 May

1   *Lloyd Rees recounts his 'excitement on discovering ...
     the location of Streeton's* **Cremorne Pastoral**' ... See
     The Small Treasures of A Lifetime by Lloyd Rees, Ure Smith,
     1969, p48.
2   *... [Rees] notes the way [Streeton and Constable] had
     organised the elements of nature* ... See *The Small Treasures of
     A Lifetime* by Lloyd Rees, Ure Smith, 1969, p49.
3   *Manly turned out to be 'an exciting climax with its rows of
     pines'* ... See *Peaks and Valleys*, by Lloyd Rees, Imprint Lives
     edition, CollinsAngus & Robertsons, 1993, pages 117–18.
     Manly was Rees's first glimpse of Sydney through his porthole
     when he arrived by ship.
4   *'there was a jetty ... the proximity of my home to the tram
     service'* ... Quoted from *Lloyd Rees—An Artist Remembers*,
     Lloyd Rees with Renee Free, Craftsman House, 1987, p23.
5   *Rees was living with [his wife] Dulcie in Mosman at the time,
     near her parents' house* ... See *Peaks and Valleys*, by Lloyd
     Rees, Imprint Lives edition, CollinsAngus & Robertson,
     1993, p180.
6   *'I had no hope of living by painting ... A natural source of
     subject matter was the foreshores of Sydney Harbour, which I
     could reach by tram'* ... Quoted from *Lloyd Rees—An Artist
     Remembers* by Lloyd Rees with Renee Free, Craftsman House,
     1987, p13.
7   *'I formed a particular friendship ... typical harbour
     headland with russety trees and golden rocks'* ... See *Lloyd
     Rees—An Artist Remembers*, by Lloyd Rees with Renee Free,
     Craftsman House, 1987, p13.
8   *'... Wakelin was about half a mile away* ... See *Lloyd Rees—
     An Artist Remembers*, Lloyd Rees with Renee Free, Craftsman
     House, 1987, p13.

Wednesday, 13 May

1   *Bert makes it sound almost like a treat* ... Bert Spratt also
     tells me the story of Ray Bostock who established the, mod-
     ern city network in 1945 or 1946. And how prior to the 1956
     Olympic Games, Ivan Gunn, an ex-PMG worker who had
     been on the organising committee, had been instrumental in
     the early introduction of STD dialling which occurred at least
     ten years before the planned time of implementation.

Tuesday, 18 May

1   *It has been something of a mystery ...* See 'Lloyd Rees—
     A Lifetime from Federation to Bicentenary' by Renee Free,
     Art and Australia, Winter, 1989, Volume 26, Number 4,
     p575.

2   *I had a phobia about flake white ... See Lloyd Rees—The Last
     Twenty Years* by Renee Free in collaboration with Lloyd Rees,
     Craftsman House, 1990 edition, p16.

3   *The first major period of depression began in 1923 on the
     first visit to Europe, when Daphne Mayo ... [broke off
     her engagement with Lloyd Rees] ... because of her own destiny
     as an artist'* ... The good news is that she succeeded. She
     is now regarded as one of the most important sculptors
     of the between-wars period. I am reminded of the classic
     story of Dorothea Willis Barclay, whom Daphne Mayo must
     have known. Dorothea's story is the mirror image of
     Daphne's. Dorothea achieved local fame after her sculptural
     studies were exhibited at the Paris Salon in 1910. Back
     home in Australia, her work was favourably reviewed and a
     portrait bust was purchased by the Art Gallery of NSW. She
     showed with the Society of Artists in Sydney. In 1920 at the
     age of thirty-seven she married the watercolourist John
     Eldershaw, a close friend of Lloyd Rees. At which point
     Dorothea abandons her art. As an artist, she was never heard
     of again. See Caroline Miley's article titled 'A Lost Sculptor'
     in *The Australasian Antique Collector,* 31st Edition, Jan–June,
     1986.

4   *The first opalescent vision of Sydney ...* see *Art and Australia
     op cit,* p576.

5   *'Life went on ... to find out what was killing me'* ... See *Peaks
     and Valleys,* by Lloyd Rees, Imprint Lives edition,
     CollinsAngus & Robertson, 1993, pages 183–4.

6   *Novelist William Styron* (**Sophie's Choice,** *etc) has recently
     published a brilliant, illuminating little book ... Darkness
     Visible,* Picador, 1992.

7   *I start with* **The Life and Work of Rubery Bennett** *by
     Katherine Campbell Harper ...* Copperfield Publishing
     limited edition, 1979.

8   *It was at the 1920s Annual exhibition ...* ibid, p24.

9   *It was staggering ...:* ibid, p24.

10   *[He first made his living] ...* ibid, p26–27.

11   *... 'a sleeping partner' ...* ibid, p27.

12   *'May Moore agreed to let Rubery have two rooms' ...* ibid, p30.

13   *In 1927 or soon after ...* ibid, p31.

14   *Wal [Taylor] would mount and frame Lloyd's work* ... see
      Small Treasures of a Lifetime, Ure Smith, 1969, p35.
15   *I check the Mitchell card index for trade catalogues* ... The
      Mitchell holds numerous trade catalogues specialising in
      anything from chemical and scientific apparatus, lathes and
      pumps to fishing tackle and printers' inks. They are mostly
      well indexed and fully illustrated. The Mitchell has a selection
      of stationers' catalogues, including Penfolds, Sands' and
      McDougall and the vast Lasseter's catalogue (Lasseter's sold
      everything including stationery).

Wednesday, 19 May
1   *According to Nick Vine Hall in* Tracing Your Family
      History in Australia ... See *Tracing Your Family History in
      Australia—A Guide to Sources* by Nick Vine Hall, Rigby,
      1985.
2   *... a twenty metre long panorama ... by the amateur painter
      and inventor Muriel Mary Sutherland Binney* ... At the time
      of completing my research, Binney's panorama was on
      permanent display at the National Maritime Museum.
      Unfortunately, when I viewed it, I was unable to find a
      matching house and boatshed depicted anywhere along its
      twenty metre span. And disappointingly, it stops just short of
      Balmoral in Middle Harbour, which is a likely site for the
      boatshed painting.

Saturday, 5 June
1   *... an article by Hazel Rowley* ... The *Australian* (the
      Weekend Review) Saturday, 5 June, 1993, p5. The biography
      by Hazel Rowley is titled *Christina Stead, a biography*,
      published by Heinemann, 1993.

Tuesday, 8 June
1   *'I never claimed to be a topographical painter' [Rees] once
      wrote* ... See *Lloyd Rees—An Artist Remembers*, Lloyd Rees
      with Renee Free, Craftsman House, 1987, p25.
2   *Sydney Ure Smith wrote in 1917: '[Rees] is not a realist ...'*
      Quoted by Renee Free in the *Lloyd Rees Retrospective Souvenir
      Catalogue*, Art Gallery of NSW, 1969, p4.

Thursday, 1 July
1   *I locate some useful articles on Wal Taylor and his
      bookbinding* ... See 'Artistic Bookbinding in Australia', article
      in *The Home*, June 18, 1922, p88; 'The Bookbinding of Wal
      Taylor', article by John Troy in *Art in Australia*, Third series,

No 12, June 1925. 'The Art of the Bookbinder—Wal Taylor and his Work', article in *The B.P. Magazine,* 1st December, 1936.

Monday, 12 July

1   *'The "specialist" was undoubtedly American, for his first words had proclaimed him'* ... [and related quotes following] ... Quoted from *Peaks and Valleys*, by Lloyd Rees, Imprint Lives edition, CollinsAngus & Robertson, 1993, p184.

2   *Lloyd Rees attended the Ithaca Creek School ... which he describes as a wonderful place which 'opened up new vistas'* ... see *Peaks and Valleys*, by Lloyd Rees, Imprint Lives edition, CollinsAngus & Robertson, 1993, p59.

Wednesday, 21 July

1   *Ernie is most helpful* ... Ernie Hughes also tells me that X-rays were discovered in 1895 and that radiography was being used in Australia, in Bathurst, by 1896.

Thursday, 22 July

1   *[The New Art Salon] exhibition is discussed by Jean Campbell in* **Early Sydney Moderns** ... *Early Sydney Moderns—John Young and the Macquarie Galleries,* by Jean Campbell, Craftsman House, 1988, p60.

Wednesday, 11 August

1   *[Hendrik Kolenberg] is the Curator of Australian Prints, Drawings and Watercolours and is also the author of* Lloyd Rees—Etchings and Lithographs ... See *Lloyd Rees—Etchings and Lithographs, a catalogue raisonné* by Hendrik Kolenberg, Beagle Press, 1986. He also curated Lloyd Rees's Centenary Retrospective, Art Gallery of NSW, March–May, 1995.

Saturday, 21 August

1   *Both Fergus and Catherine have spent some time researching* ... Fergus tells me that as a young man, when he was studying law, which he later dropped to become a businessman, he had written a manuscript for a book about characters in early Australian history and it involved researching with his co-writer, George Cassidy, in the Mitchell Library. Catherine has been doing family research. She keeps in contact with the American side of the family and in 1984 she travelled to the States to visit relatives. In the garage of some relatives she discovered an unsigned oil portrait of her great-great-great

grandmother, one Ann Moate, which must have been painted
circa 1830. She was lucky enough to obtain it and had it sent
back to Australia. She sent her parents a telegram which read:
'Ann Moate is arriving on Qantas Flight ...'

Tuesday, 24 August
1   *Jack Lindsay describes [Pelligrini's]* ... See *The Roaring
    Twenties* by Jack Lindsay, The Bodley Head, London, 1960,
    p16.
2   *[Pelligrini's] is referred to in Louis Stone's* Betty Wayside ...
    See *Betty Wayside* by Louis Stone, first published 1915,
    London.
3   *Bernard Hesling ... knew the artist Arthur Murch and
    Jimmy Cook 'around Pakie's Club in the late 1920s'* ... See
    Stir this Stew by Bernard Hesling, Ure Smith, 1966, p142.
4   *Roy de Maistre had decorated Pakie's in 'a daring and
    uncommon arrangement of colours'* ... see *Roy de Maistre—
    The Australian Years 1894–1930* by Heather Johnson,
    Craftsman House, 1988, p80.

Friday, 3 September
1   *I check the* Dictionary of Australian Quotations ... edited
    by Stephen Murray-Smith, Heinemann, 1984.
2   *Hugh Stretton is quoted from* Ideas for Australian Cities ...
    Ideas for Australian Cities, by Hugh Stretton, Georgian
    House, 1975 (2nd ed.).

Wednesday, 8 September
1   *Northwood [was] an 'unknown suburb' to most people in
    Sydney* ... Quoted from *Peaks and Valleys*, by Lloyd Rees,
    Imprint Lives edition, CollinsAngus & Robertson, 1993,
    p204.
2   *[Rees] writes lovingly about his years in the Northwood house*
    ... see *Peaks and Valleys*, by Lloyd Rees, Imprint Lives edition,
    CollinsAngus & Robertson, 1993, p205.
3   *... the introduction which Basil Burdett wrote to* Sydney
    University, The Drawings of Lloyd Rees ... See *Sydney
    University, The Drawings of Lloyd Rees* published by Smith and
    Julius, 1922, introduction (not paginated).

Sunday, 12 September
1   *I found a reference somewhere that [Harry McClelland] had
    trained at the National Gallery School but could not find him
    in the list of students* ... See *Von Guerard to Wheeler—The first
    teachers at the National Gallery School, 1870–1939* catalogue

published by The Victorian College of The Arts Gallery, exhibition 6–21 April 1978.

Tuesday, 2 November

1   *George Patterson, who was a member of the Automobile Club*
... Patterson relates an hilarious incident when he takes a
drunken George Lambert along to the Automobile Club in
the 1920s. See *Life Has Been Wonderful* by George Patterson,
Ure Smith, 1956, pages 54–5.

2   *In* Peaks and Valleys *there are references by Lloyd Rees to the
shooting of wildlife* ... see *Peaks and Valleys*, by Lloyd Rees,
Imprint Lives edition, CollinsAngus & Robertson, 1993,
pp68–9.

3   *Then this eighty-year-old grandmother reports on a visit to a
fortune teller* ... Interest in fortune telling, and psychic
phenomena in general, was rife at the time. For example, when
the Lindbergh baby was kidnapped in 1932 the services of
psychics were both offered and sought to help solve the crime.

Tuesday, 9 November

1   *During one hour in the early morning of 7 August, 234 Light
Horsemen fell dead in an area 'no larger than a tennis court'*
... see *The Broken Years—Australian Soldiers in the Great War*
by Bill Gammage, ANU Press, 1974, p75.

2   *this lone pine was blasted to a stump* ... A Sergeant Keith
McDonald of the 45th Battalion souvenired a pine cone from
this tree and carried it around for the rest of the war. When he
returned to Australia, seeds from the cone were planted by his
aunt. Information obtained from a letter to the *Sydney
Morning Herald*, April 23, 1995 from a Jonathan Graham of
Double Bay.

3   *... the Anzac at Gallipoli is diligent, anti-war and* bookish
... Bill Gammage's brilliant book, *The Broken Years* (ibid)
quotes from other Gallipoli diaries and numerous letters from
Anzacs. Bart's diary is not referred to. It could well be the
only evidence that Anzacs were reading so extensively in the
trenches.

Wednesday, 10 November

1   *[Joan Kerr's] book on Australian women artists, to be
published in 1995, one theme of which will be the 'history of
neglect' suffered* ... The book was published in 1995 under
the title of *Heritage—The National Women's Art Book, 500
works by 500 Australian Women Artists from Colonial Times to
1995,* published by G + B International, An Art & Australia

Book. My entries were on Winifred Honey and Annis Laeubli.

2   *There are no listings of a residential address in any of the telephone directories* ... There is obviously a lag between the time a person moves to an address and the time it is listed in the Sands' Directories which were published annually. Such a lag is probably even more pronounced in the Electoral Rolls, since people often delayed changing the entry after moving address. It was probably easier voting absentee than going through the process of applying to change rolls. For this reason, I have not used the Electoral Rolls much, except for double-checking information from the more reliable sources. However, sometimes they can provide a smidgin of additional information. Telephone directories are the most up to date in terms of information because there is a need on the part of the subscriber for the information to be current. For professional people, income depended upon the entry being correct and up to date. The Sydney Telephone Directory was published twice a year in the 1920s and early 1930s.

Wednesday, 1 December

1   *The odd one out, in terms of its date, is the Syd Ure Smith* ... See *The Etchings of Sydney Ure Smith*, Introduction by Hal Missingham, Ure Smith Miniature series 6, 1950, plate 8.

2   *I wonder what the greeting might be on the back of the card?* ... When I finally saw the card by Ure Smith it was framed so nicely I did not have the heart to ask Wendy's daughter to remove it from its frame. I do not know whether or not a message was written on the back of the Christmas card.

3   *In 1921 Long had taken Albers to court because he believed he had been 'shortchanged' by his dealer. Long did not return to Albers until the 1930s* ... See *The Life and Work of Sydney Long*, by Joanna Mendlessohn, Sydney, 1979, p82.

Tuesday, 7 December

1   *[Violet Bartlett] is not in* McCulloch's Encyclopedia of Australian Art ... See *Encyclopedia of Australian Art* by Alan McCulloch, Hutchinson, 2 vols, 1237pp, 1984. This work is an extraordinary achievement by an obviously obsessive person. I wrote a review of this edition for the *Sydney Morning Herald*, December 1, 1984. The encyclopedia has since been revised by McCulloch's daughter, Susan.

2   *[Violet Bartlett] is not listed in Benezit's ten volume* Dictionnaire des Peintres ... See *Dictionnaires, critique et documentaire des Peintres, Sculpteurs, Dessinateurs et Graveurs* by E. Benezit, 10 vols, published by Librairie Grund, 1976.

3   *[Violet Bartlett is not listed in] the 37 volume Theime-Becker*
     ... See Theime-Becker, *Algemeines Lexicon der Bildenen
     Kunstle*r, 37 vols, Leipzig, 1927.
4   *I check the* International Directory of Arts *published in
     Germany* ... See *International Directory of Arts* 17th edition,
     Germany, 1985–6.

Sunday, 19 December
1   ... *fame for Streeton in the 1920s may have helped him as
     a painter (his technique became all important), but not
     as an artist* ... I must admit that there is debate over this
     point and Streeton's late work often sells for as much as
     his early masterpieces. Similarly, not everyone would agree
     with me that Rees's late paintings of the 1980s are
     masterpieces.
2   *'Had I got high prices for my paintings at a time when I
     needed money, I might have had an inclination to keep
     painting in a mood that was acceptable ...'* Quoted in *Pol*
     magazine, 15 July–15 August, 1980, article titled 'Lloyd
     Rees—Australia's Old Master' by Lily Brett-Lovett.
3   *Amongst the other material left by John Banks is a book by
     P. Neville Barnett* ... See P. Neville Barnett, *Japanese Colour
     Prints* (Sydney, 1936).

Thursday, 27 January, 1994
1   ... *an exhibition patronised by the de Chairs* ... The Burdekin
     House Exhibition, see catalogue, October 8–December 21,
     1929, published by the exhibition committee.

Saturday, 19 February
1   ... *an exhibition by 'Eight Young Painters' including Lloyd
     Rees* ... The other seven were Norman Lloyd, H. C. Gibbons,
     H. R. Gallop, Robert Waden, Gordon Esling, Robert Johnson
     and Erik Langker.
2   ... *the lists of exhibitions at the Macquarie Galleries which
     were published in 1975* ... The lists of all Macquarie exhibitors
     were published in the catalogues accompanying the five
     exhibitions titled *Fifty Years of the Macquarie Galleries*. Each
     exhibition covered a decade from 1925 to 1975. They were
     held from March to July, 1975.
3   *So Bart and Embrey could have bought the boatshed painting
     from Wal Taylor or Basil Burdett* ... Gayfield Shaw continued
     to exhibit a cross-section of artists through the 1930s
     including the occasional Rees. Shaw had sold Rees's work
     from 1917—but this was mainly work on paper.

Friday, 4 March

1   *[Basil Burdett] writes: 'Mosman was the* scene *of the first
    tentative efforts in oils, but the essentially* suburban
    atmosphere proved so limited ...' Quoted from *Sydney
    University, The Drawings of Lloyd Rees* published by Smith and
    Julius, 1922, introduction (not paginated).

Saturday, 5 March

1   *In* Australian Art and Artists ... *there is a list of articles by,
    and about, Basil Burdett ...* See *Australian Art and Artists to
    1950—A bibliography based on the holdings of the State Library
    of Victoria* published by the Library Council of Victoria,
    Melbourne, 1982.

Wednesday, 9 March

1   *I have received a response from diligent researcher, Emma
    Hicks, re Violet Bartlett ...* The complete text of the letter is
    as follows:

Dear Stephen,
     You might have had cause to hope that the lengthy gap in
communications might mean that I had finally managed to
turn up some small snippet of information on Violet Bartlett
... but I'm afraid she's proved as elusive as ever.
     Her second R.O.I. exhibit was in the 23rd Exhibition,
1905, and was no. 113 'Phlox', 12 guineas; once again she
exhibited from the same address, The Thatch, Stansted, Essex.
In view of the fact that she used the same address over a seven
year period, it seemed safe to assume that this may have been
the family home. So last time I was in the Public Record
Office I tried to chase the household through the 1891 census
but frustratingly I could find no mention of it amongst the
Stansted returns. I also had been waiting for a proper reply
from the Saffron Walden library, but when they finally replied
by phone it was only to say they could find nothing; their only
glimmer of hope was a family of doctors from Saffron Walden
called Bartlett, but they had died out some years ago. I also
checked the International Genealogical Index (the 'Mormon
Microfiche') for any entries from parish records but again
failed to turn anything up. As far as 'Artah' [Violet's middle
name] is concerned I am wondering whether it is a strange
version of 'Arthur' as I did notice in the I.G.I. that there were
families called Arthat or Artar.
     I looked at copies of *The Year's Art* in case it gave any
further information but again with no luck. I have also by now

checked wills from 1932 until 1984, and although the occasional Violet/Violet Annie/Violet Alice Bartlett turned up none of them seemed likely candidates.

I have written on the off chance to an English water-colourist, Charles Bartlett RWS (b.1921), since he exhibited Essex scenes from the 1950s and is now living there, but so far he has not chosen to reply.

The Bartlett name does seem to crop up more regularly among American artists. I did come across the will for a Josephine Hoxie Bartlett who died in London in 1910; I take it she must be the same person as the artist exhibiting from Edinburgh 1887–1899, since the name is unusual. The will mentions that she had lived in Edinburgh, but that she came originally from Staten Island, New York; she bequeaths her estate to a sister and niece in America. Not a Violet in sight …

On my 'rounds' I must have checked masses of sources for any clues, but to no avail. Should anything further turn up, I will of course let you know. In the meantime, apologies for such a disappointing reply.

With all best wishes,
Emma.

Monday, 9 May

1   *[Weitzel's work] was exhibited in the Burdekin House exhibition* … See catalogue, October 8–December 21, 1929, published by the exhibition committee.

Tuesday, 28 June

1   *An interesting response arrives from Emma Hicks about the de Maistre mural* … The full text of the letter follows:

Dear Stephen,
Re: The ? Roy de Maistre mural and the de Chairs.
    Not much luck with this either …
    I see from the *Dictionary of National Biography* that Admiral Sir Dudley de Chair retired as Governor of NSW in 1930, and that he lived most of the rest of his life in London; however, Carrington House was not some substantial man-sion, so much as a substantial mansion block of flats that went up in Hertford Street (off Park Lane, by Shepherd's Market) in c1937. The first residents according to the ratebooks, had moved in by September 1937, but the de Chairs were not amongst them. It seems that they were living at 4, Ennismore Gardens, South Kensington in 1936, according to the street and court directories. This had been the home of Lord Bellew.

I never found the de Chairs listed at Carrington House in the street directories or residents lists, but they did finally turn up in the voters lists of 1938, 1939, 1940–41 as residents at Flat 411, Carrington House. There were no electoral rolls during the war years and the de Chairs are no longer listed at Carrington House in 1945. So it appears they moved into their flat in c1938 and perhaps only stayed there a few years. By 1938 about 100 people were listed as voters at Carrington House, and one of the apartments was a small embassy (Chilean, I think). Their son, Somerset, always kept his name listed amongst the residents in Kelly's street directories (this section had been called the court list—ie. professional classes and above), but Sir Dudley did not, which makes it a more onerous task to find out where he was living, but he reappears in Kelly's in 1954 as resident at 11 Campden Hill Gate in Kensington. He seems to have lived there until 1957, after which I think they moved to Rottingdean, on the coast near Brighton, where Sir Dudley died the following year.

This is none of it very helpful, except that if you can be sure that the mural was a commission specifically for the flat at Carrington House, it would appear to date from the *late* not early 1930s. I found a photograph of the outside of Carrington House but have not found anything about the decor inside, and in view of the fact that the address was only an apartment, albeit quite likely rather a grand one, I was not really expecting to.

With all best wishes,
Emma Hicks

Thursday, 1 September

1   *... I knew that a J. D. and G. D. Smith had owned 1920s oils by Rees in the 1960s ...* This information is recorded in the catalogue section of *Lloyd Rees* by Renee Free, Australian Art Library, Lansdowne Press, 1972.

Christmas holidays 1994–5

1   *The book that has interested me most so far is* **The Quest for Corvo—An Experiment in Biography** *...* See *The Quest for Corvo—An Experiment in Biography* by A. J. A. Symons, first published by Cassell, 1934, reissued in Penguin Books, 1986 (etc).

2   *I have also read* **The Infanta Adventure and the Lost Manet** *by Andrew W. Brainerd ...* *The Infanta Adventure and the Lost Manet* by Andrew W. Brainerd, Reichl Press, Long Beach, Michigan City, 1988.

3   *Elizabeth Ellis ... had particularly recommended* **The Search for Gainsborough** ... *The Search for Gainsborough* by Adrienne Corri, Jonathan Cape Ltd, London, 1984.

4   ... *three children's books* ... *Uncle Mick's Magic Trick (for getting rid of monsters)* [1995], *Ten Thousand Sheep (get driven home)* [1997], and *King Gilbert (the indolent)* [1998] ... written and illustrated by the author, published by Scholastic.

Wednesday, 1 February, 1995

1   *David agrees with me ... there would be little sense in attempting to date it using scientific methods* ... It would be possible to take a cross-section of paint, the size of a pin and compare it with a similar cross-section from a known Lloyd Rees painting and compare the two using various equipment including a scanning electron microscope. In this way one could analyse the layering of the paint and the composition of the pigments. But this would not be conclusive. Even if the pigments, say, were of the same composition it would not mean that both paintings were by Rees. In the 1920s, most professional artists chose from the same ranges of commercially available products, most often Winsor and Newton. Such scientific analysis is most useful when trying to date paintings which are well over a hundred years old, where precise accuracy is not required. And when artists used pigments that they ground themselves and which may have been unique.

 Infra-red examination would not be helpful in the case of the boatshed painting since the surface has too much depth. Infra-red rays pick up 'hidden' marks, such as pencil lines, where the surface is comparatively flat.

Monday, 6 February

1   **Flowerpiece** *is referred to ... in Heather Johnson's book on de Maistre ... who may have brought the material for the wall hanging back from France ... [or] ... it could have come from Frank Weitzel* ... See *Roy de Maistre—The Australian Years 1894–1930* by Heather Johnson, Craftsman House, 1988, p72.

2   **When I phone Heather Johnson to discuss this, she is most interested** ... In *Roy de Maistre—The English Years 1930–1968* by Heather Johnson, published by Craftsman House, 1995, Heather states that 'Lady de Chair ... commissioned de Maistre to paint murals in the dining room of her flat in Carrington House, Hartford Street, London. The works

(pictured in *Christie's—Impressionist and Modern Australian Paintings* [catalogue] ..., South Kensington, 30 November, 1989, lots 167–173, restored by Frank McDonald and now in the collection of the Art Gallery of New South Wales) are a blend of chinoiserie designs, stylised animals, silver paint, and views of the de Chairs' *Moon Gate Garden* at their Virginia Water home ...'

Saturday, 1 April

1   *It is hard to explain away the anomaly in the sizes/prices* [*of* **The Red House** *and* **The Bay**] *... if the boatshed painting is* **The Bay** *... The Red House* was sold at Sotheby's, Sydney, on 28 November, 1995. It seemed to be in its original framing which was far more amateurish than that of the boatshed painting. Could this be the reason for its lower price?

2.   *... the sticker numbered 22 on the frame ... The Red House,* like the boatshed painting, had no gallery label on the reverse. This indicates that Basil Burdett may have exhibited Rees's paintings at the New Art Salon in 1922 which were not professionally presented.

3   *'Lloyd Rees may yet add lustre to the name of his native city'...* Quoted from *The Later Work of Lloyd Rees* by Basil Burdett published in *The Queensland Magazine,* July 1924, p28.

BIBLIOGRAPHICAL NOTE

During the writing of this book, Jancis and Alan Rees published *Lloyd Rees—a source book* (The Beagle Press, 1995). This contains biographical notes in chronological order and lists Rees's principal solo and joint exhibitions. It also has a very extensive select bibliography. It is an essential book for anyone studying Lloyd Rees.

Lloyd Rees's two autobiographies are *Small Treasures of a Lifetime—Some Early Memories of Australian Art and Artists*, first published in 1969 by Ure Smith Pty Ltd; and *Peaks and Valleys*, first published by William Collins Pty Ltd in 1985.

Renee Free's *Lloyd Rees* was published by Lansdowne Press in 1972. She subsequently collaborated with Lloyd Rees on *Lloyd Rees—The Last Twenty Years* published by Craftsman Press in 1983 and revised in 1990, and *Lloyd Rees—An Artist Remembers* published by Craftsman House in 1987.

For those interested in art in Sydney in the 1920s, Nancy Underhill's *Making Australian Art 1916–49—Sydney Ure Smith, Patron and Publisher* (Oxford University Press, 1991) has a twenty-five-page bibliography.

Since completing my research for this book, a couple of relevant books have been published. These are Chris McAuliffe's *Art and Suburbia* published in 1996 by Craftsman House, which focuses on paintings of suburban scenes by Australian artists, and Heather Johnson's *The Sydney Art Patronage System, 1890–1940*, published by Bungoona Technologies Pty Ltd, 1997.

Other books consulted during my research can be found in the endnotes. Many of these have extensive bibliographies.

INDEX